ELECTRONICS for INDUSTRY

Continuous seams of steel are unerringly welded by electronic tubes controlled by the small impulse of current through the coils (behind the operator's right hand) caused by passing the pins mounted along the periphery of the synchronously rotating disk between poles of the coil structure.

ELECTRONICS
FOR
INDUSTRY

By

W. I. BENDZ

Westinghouse Electric Corporation
Boston, Massachusetts

With the assistance of

C. A. SCARLOTT

Editor
Westinghouse Engineer

NEW YORK: JOHN WILEY & SONS, INC.
LONDON: CHAPMAN & HALL, LIMITED

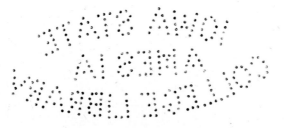

PREFACE

Electronics has come of age. Engineers have rather suddenly come to realize that electronics is not just an associate of the communication arts with minor usefulness in industry. In the late '20's a few nonvital industrial applications were given to electronic devices, with some hesitation and with little faith in the ability of electronic devices to stand up in the rigorous environment of power machinery. To a large extent that uncertainty was justified. But electronic engineers quickly satisfied the demands of industrial service.

With the war came the insatiable requirements for radio devices and the still-astounding radar. Utterly fantastic quantities of magnesium and aluminum were required for aircraft. The light metals for 80 out of every 100 war planes built in the United States were produced by power supplied by electronic rectifiers. With victory in the balance, literally thousands of miles of resistance welding for planes, tanks, jeeps, shells, guns, and other ordnance had to be made quickly. Electronic rectifiers controlled by electronic timers performed this sewing of steel. High-speed production for round-the-clock operation of industry demanded levels of illumination never before known. Fluorescent lamps — electronics again — gave the answer. And so on — electronic regulators of speed, of voltage, of position; electronic eyes that count, sort, grade, inspect, control; electronic oscillators that provide the power to harden steel surfaces, to heat fast-moving tin plate, to cure plastics—these and scores more show that electronics has moved into industry, to stay.

With this stimulus, the interest of engineers whose training has been with power equipment has become directed toward electronic apparatus. These engineers have no necessity or desire to become electronic experts. They need merely to add electronic fundamentals to their present understanding of electric-current principles. They require knowledge of the types of tubes, how they function, the types of circuits, and where these fundamentals are applied.

"Electronics for Industry" is the result of the author's instructing several classes designed according to these principles and presented to practicing engineers already familiar with the fundamentals of electric circuits and for whom the details and mathematics of electronic engineering were not of interest.

v

"Electronics for Industry" is confined as nearly as practicable to the explanation of principles applied to industrial equipment. In many cases these parallel the radio field. In such instances the text is brief with the expectation that a reader desiring more detailed knowledge will refer to any one of the many excellent handbooks devoted to radio engineering.

The text frequently states the principle of important theory without proof, but reference to supplementary reading is given in such cases. Some discussions, particularly those devoted to oscillators and amplitude and frequency modulation, are necessarily confined to basic considerations. It is expected that a reader particularly interested in more than an elementary understanding of these subjects will make use of the references given for further study.

Many of the most frequently employed basic circuits are discussed in Chapter 15. It would be impracticable to include all the circuits found in everyday use. Consequently, throughout the chapters which follow, the circuits employed in several commercial devices are explained in detail. It is hoped that the reader will recognize these as basic functions, useful to an equipment perhaps totally foreign to the specific piece of equipment described by the text. In this respect, chapters 15 to 17, inclusive, are all devoted to the explanation of basic circuits.

"Electronics for Industry" is not the work of the author alone. To the many engineers of the Westinghouse Electric Corporation, for the assistance of the General Electric Company, RCA Manufacturing Company, Weston Electrical Instruments Company, Crystal Products Company and those who offered their valued criticism, the author extends his sincere appreciation.

It is to the engineer already familiar with the fundamentals of electrical devices who wishes to extend his knowledge to include the fundamentals of industrial electronics — not their mathematics — that the author addresses this work.

WALDEMAR I. BENDZ

Weston, Massachusetts
November 1946

CONTENTS

Chapter 1

MEET THE ELECTRON

Mystery still invests electronics. Many engineers not intimately associated with it do not possess a clear concept of what the field of electronics includes and excludes, or on what basis a thing is or is not an electronic device. A brief review of events that led to the present use of the term will aid in a clearer understanding. Electronics obviously has to do with the behavior of electrons, the word electron having been used first by Dr. G. Johnstone Stoney in 1891 as a name for the natural unit of negative electricity. Any such broad definition of electronics, however, is useless, because it covers too much territory — in fact, the whole field of electrical engineering. The electric motor, the incandescent lamp, and every other electric device are but means of controlling the action of electrons for useful purposes. Of necessity, therefore, an arbitrarily restricted definition must be set for the term electronics. This limited meaning has been developed gradually.

The invention of the Fleming valve or vacuum tube in 1905 and the discovery of the possibilities of the control grid by De Forest in 1907 set the stage for radio broadcasting. The vacuum tube was frequently referred to as an electronic tube, because in it electrons departed from the confines of solids and entered the partially evacuated space within the tube. The electric-power industry was firmly established before the electronic theory of matter or the properties of the electron were generally known. Furthermore, the design and operation of electric machines had been in no wise dependent upon the electron concept. In dealing with vacuum tubes, on the other hand, the concept of electrons as discrete particles is important. The science dealing with these vacuum tubes came to be spoken of as electronics.

For many years nearly the only use for electronic tubes was for radio communication. The term electronics became associated with radio. The notion that electronics has to do primarily with communication still persists.

In the middle and late 20's the electronic tube began to find many applications not associated with radio. A tube in a home radio receiver might also be used in a motor-control device. Certain tubes in a broadcasting station are identical with those at work in a tin-plate mill. Obviously, elec-

1

tronics cannot be identified by the job done, but rather by some distinguishing characteristic of the devices themselves. However, to delineate electronics in terms of vacuum tubes alone is inadequate.

The early two-electrode and three-electrode vacuum tubes proved to be only the first of an extraordinarily prolific family. Then came the tubes with four, five, and even more electrodes, various forms of thyratrons, ignitrons, light-sensitive tubes, and others that do not remotely resemble the progenitors of the electronic line. Glass walls gave way in many cases to envelopes of metal. Tubes took every imaginable shape. The degree of vacuum varied with the tubes and their uses, some tubes even using gas under low pressure.

Through all of these variations in the form of the electronic tube, however, a single basic distinguishing feature remains. Electrons by one means or another are induced to leave their normal habitat — the interior of a metal — and move about in the surrounding gas. This gives a simple easily understood test for electronics that anyone can apply. It can be stated thus: *Electronics* deals with those devices in which electrons are emitted from solids or liquids and are caused to move through a vacuum or gas.

With this definition as a criterion, what sorts of things do we find in the electronics family? A surprising array! There are many well-recognized electronic functions, and others are not so apparent. The most conspicuous, because it is oldest, is radio communication, and its younger close relatives, facsimile transmission and television. Also there are the closely related power-line carrier systems and telephone amplifiers or repeaters. Mercury-arc rectifiers are electronic devices, as are X-ray tubes and their power supplies. So also are welding timers, cathode-ray oscillographs, tube-type motor controls, certain voltage and speed regulators, dynamic-balancing machines, tube-type power supplies for induction and dielectric heating, fluorescent lamps, electrostatic air cleaners, and others, some of which the engineer may never have thought of as electronic at all.

Also, the electronic definition includes some really surprising things — arc welding, arc furnaces, circuit breakers, gasoline-engine spark plugs, corona, lightning. Can these be electronic phenomena? The answer is, they are. Since we cannot modify the definition so as to exclude these devices or phenomena, we must accept these familiar things as truly electronic. In fact, a better understanding of "the behavior of electrons in vacuum and gases" facilitates understanding of what devices are electronic and the relationships between them.

The home of the electron is the atom. Just as the family, with its different members is the basic unit of society, so the atom is the basic unit of matter. It, too, has three types of members, *protons*, *neutrons*, and *elec-*

trons. The fact that physicists speak of other kinds of members such as *positrons*, *mesotrons*, and *neutrinos* can be entirely neglected here as they have no bearing on industrial electronics. Like families, atoms come in different sizes, and they differ only in the numbers of protons, neutrons, and electrons present. Conceivably there could be an infinite number of combinations. Actually there are but 92 combinations in nature, that is, 92 elements, starting with hydrogen, the simplest, and ending with uranium, the largest, heaviest, and most complex. (At least four heavier and unstable ones have been created artificially.) All 92 elements have been found except the two corresponding to numbers 85 and 87.

The electron, which is the stock in trade of the electronics engineer, is the fundamental unit of negative electricity. The amount of this charge is incomprehensibly small, but it is a fixed unchanging unalterable quantity.* In electrostatic units it is 1.60203×10^{-19} coulomb. Small though it be, this figure is important. Since an ampere is one coulomb for one second, more than six billion billion (6.24×10^{18}) electrons are required to flow past a point each second to constitute a single ampere.

The mass of the electron is equally beyond conception, 9.1066×10^{-31} kilogram, which means that 31 billion, billion, billion electrons (31×10^{27}) weigh an ounce. The electron is by far the lightest of the atomic trio, and is therefore the particle with smallest mass in all nature. The proton and neutron, which have almost identical weights, are 1849 times as massive as the electron.

The charge of the proton is identical in amount to that of the electron but is opposite in sign. The proton is the positive unit of electricity just as the electron is the negative unit. The neutron† has no charge at all. Being neutral, it is called neutron.

The physical dimensions of electrons, protons, and neutrons cannot be stated with such definiteness. It is known that all atoms are between 5 and 25 billionths of an inch across (that is, 10^{-8} to 5×10^{-8} cm) and that the positive charge is concentrated in a region about $\frac{1}{10000}$ of the diameter of the atom. The electron, in spite of its small mass, is thought to be much larger than the proton. In any event, the sizes of the atomic particles, which are uncertain, are of little importance to the electronics engineer. The important quantities are their mass and electric charge, and these are known to high precision.

With these three fundamental particles all of the 92 kinds of atoms are constructed. Each atom consists of a central core or nucleus surrounded at a great distance by from 1 to 92 electrons, roughly as pictured in Fig. 1.1.

*For a discussion of the methods used to determine this quantity see Millikan, *Electrons (+ and −), Protons, Photons, Neutrons, and Cosmic Rays*, pp 90–124.
†*Ibid*, pp 360–403.

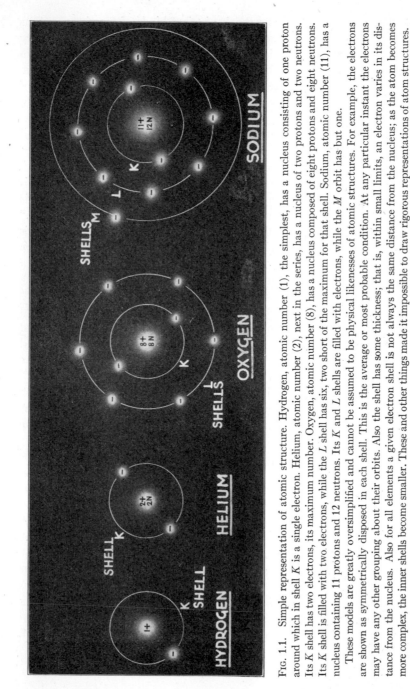

Fig. 1.1. Simple representation of atomic structure. Hydrogen, atomic number (1), the simplest, has a nucleus consisting of one proton around which in shell K is a single electron. Helium, atomic number (2), next in the series, has a nucleus of two protons and two neutrons. Its K shell has two electrons, its maximum number. Oxygen, atomic number (8), has a nucleus composed of eight protons and eight neutrons. Its K shell is filled with two electrons, while the L shell has six, two short of the maximum for that shell. Sodium, atomic number (11), has a nucleus containing 11 protons and 12 neutrons. Its K and L shells are filled with electrons, while the M orbit has but one.

These models are greatly oversimplified and cannot be assumed to be physical likenesses of atomic structures. For example, the electrons are shown as symmetrically disposed in each shell. This is the average or most probable condition. At any particular instant the electrons may have any other grouping about their orbits. Also the shell has some thickness; that is, within small limits, an electron varies in its distance from the nucleus. Also for all elements a given electron shell is not always the same distance from the nucleus; as the atom becomes more complex, the inner shells become smaller. These and other things made it impossible to draw rigorous representations of atom structures.

The nucleus is comprised of all the protons and neutrons that an atom possesses. Because protons and neutrons are heavy compared to an electron, nearly all the mass of any atom is concentrated in the central core or nucleus.

The simplest and lightest atom is hydrogen. It consists of one electron and one proton, separated by a certain distance. Their electric charges are identical but opposite in sign. The electron and proton are moving with respect to each other, and, because the proton is so much heavier, the electron is presumed to be in motion around it in some fashion. For simplicity's sake the electron is said to move in an orbit or shell, although it is not necessarily circular or even elliptical. Physicists are not definite as to the shape of the orbit described by the electron. It doesn't matter fortunately.

Another essential fact about the simple atom is that the distance between the electron and the proton about which it circulates is relatively great. It is thought that the electron does not get closer to the proton than several thousand times the diameter of the proton, or, stated differently, the electron is about two billionths of an inch (0.5×10^{-8} cm) away from the proton. If a hydrogen atom were enlarged so that it was a yard in diameter, the nucleus at the center would still be smaller than a pin point. An atom of hydrogen, and indeed any atom, is relatively empty. All matter, which is seemingly so "solid," is mostly space. If all the atoms that comprise a man's body could be compressed into one solid mass, without any space within or between atoms, it would not cover the head of a pin. If all the buildings of a large city were similarly compacted, the residue would not fill a penny match box. The weight would be so enormous and so concentrated, however, that nothing could support it, and it would immediately sink to the center of the earth. The essential fact is that all matter is dimensionally empty, that vast distances separate the component particles. This has important consequences.

So much for the simplest atom. The next simplest is helium. The core or nucleus is four times heavier than that of hydrogen. It consists of two protons and two neutrons. The nucleus of helium with its two protons has a net positive charge of two. For the helium atom to be neutral requires then two orbital electrons. They move within a common orbit about the nucleus.

The number of orbital electrons, which is also the number of protons in the nucleus, is the atomic number of the element. The combined weights of the protons and neutrons that comprise the core is the atomic weight of the element. Hence hydrogen has an atomic number of one and an atomic weight of about one. (Actually it is 1.0078. The difference has to do with isotopes, a matter outside the scope of this discussion.) Helium, in like manner, has an atomic number of two and an atomic weight of about four (4.002).

Next in the scale of elements after helium is lithium with a nucleus of three protons and three neutrons, and three electrons. Lithium has an atomic number of three. Its atomic weight is 6.940. Climbing the atomic scale, we have beryllium with four electrons, boron with five; carbon, six; nitrogen, seven; oxygen, eight; fluorine, nine; and neon, ten. The top of nature's atomic ladder is reached with uranium, with 92 electrons and an atomic weight of 238.14.

The manner in which the electrons dispose themselves about the nucleus is both important and interesting. It shows the orderliness of nature. The first two electrons of any atom travel about the nucleus in the same orbit or shell. It is designated the K shell. The orbits of the next eight electrons, numbers three to ten inclusive, the last of which is neon, lie in another and more remote shell, called L. This second shell can hold a maximum of eight electrons. Thus neon has two completely filled electron shells, the first and nearest, the K, with two, and the second, or L shell, with eight more — a total of ten. The 11th electron, for the element sodium, starts a third shell, M, still farther removed from the nucleus. The outer shells, beginning with M, do not all have to be filled with the maximum number of electrons before the next more remote shell is begun. Shell M, for example, can contain a maximum of 18 electrons, but electrons start to fill shell N when there are but eight in M. Thus potassium has $2 + 8 + 8 + 1 = 19$ electrons in its K, L, M, and N shells, whereas nickel has $2 + 8 + 16 + 2 = 28$ electrons. However, the structure of the elements tend to follow the general rule that the innermost shells are filled with electrons first.

Atoms are built up in this manner, until a total of seven electron shells are reached. Uranium, with atomic number 92 and atomic weight 238.14, has seven shells containing the following numbers of electrons beginning with K, 2, 8, 18, 32, 18, 12, and 2. These facts for representative elements are given in Table 1.1.‡

An atom with the electrons in their normal positions in the various shells possesses a definite energy characteristic for that atom. Electrons may, however, be displaced from their normal shells into blank positions in more remote shells. The atom is then in an abnormal or excited state and has an energy greater than normal. Thus if an electron moves from one space shell to another the atom either absorbs or radiates a fixed amount of energy. Energy is required to lift an electron from an inner to an outer shell. Likewise, when the electron returns to an inner shell, a specific amount of energy is released, which may be of a frequency in the visible region. This is the source of much of our radiated energy. Indeed this is what is happening in vapor lamps, such as those of mercury and sodium. The atoms of mercury

‡For a complete atomic chart see Dow, *Fundamentals of Engineering Electronics*, p 539.

and sodium are bombarded by the electrons comprising the current. Electrons of these atoms are driven into orbits more distant from their nuclei, and when they fall back into their proper shells the energy is released at the characteristic frequency (color) for that element.

In metals the atoms are closely packed in a crystal arrangement. An electron in the outer shell of a metal atom and hence only weakly attracted by its parent nucleus may be as strongly attracted by the nucleus of the neighboring atom. It then belongs equally to its parent atom and to the adjoining one. This is a *free electron.* Actually, with thermal agitation continually causing constant stirring of the molecules, at any instant in a small bit of metal, billions of these free electrons wander about from atom to atom. For every atom of metal approximately one electron is free to move.§ Thus, in only a cubic inch of metal the free electrons approximate the astronomical number of 16×10^{22} (or 160 000 billion billion).

When an electric field is impressed across a metal, the free electrons start drifting in the direction of increasing positive potential. This, of course, is electric conduction, and, if the drift of electrons is such that 6.24×10^{18} (6.3 billion billion) move past a point each second, the current is, by definition, one ampere.

Those who first established the definitions for electrical terms unfortunately did not know about free electrons; otherwise they would not have surmised that current flows from positive to negative through a voltage drop. Exactly the reverse is true. This unfortunate error cannot be corrected now; hence we must go on remembering that electrons flow from negative to positive, but that, by arbitrary rule, current is considered flowing from positive to negative.

All of electrical engineering, and for that matter electronics, is dependent on the fortunate fact that metals have enormous numbers of electrons free to move through the metal under the influence of an applied electric field. Metals are, by virtue of that fact, conductors. It is equally fortunate that other substances do not have any substantial amounts of free electrons. If air, for example, had large numbers of free electrons, there would be no incentive for electrons urged by an electric potential through a conductor suspended in air to confine themselves to the metal. Instead the electrons would flow through the enveloping air. The air would then be not an insulator but a conductor.

From an electrical point of view almost all substances can be placed in two distinct classes, one in which there are billions upon billions of free electrons (conductors) and those with relatively few free electrons (insulators). Generally speaking, all metals are conductors; most other substances are insulators.

§ MIT staff, *Applied Electronics*, p 63.

Electrons that constitute current do not progress rapidly along the conductor, even when the current is large and the cross section is small. The number of free electrons available is so great that the drift does not have to be speedy even for large currents. The average velocity of the electrons probably does not exceed an inch or two per second, although the effect of the current proceeds with the speed of light. As a matter of fact, the motion given to electrons in a conductor by a strong external field is insignificant compared with the motion they inherently possess. The random current density, that is, the current found by counting the electrons that cross any given plane in one direction and neglecting the same number that cross that plane in the opposite direction, is of the order of 100 trillion amperes per square inch. The exact number depends upon the metal and only slightly upon its temperature. The random velocities of electrons are, therefore, only slightly modified by any drift velocity that can be imparted to them by an applied potential. On this basis man's engineering efforts seem a bit insignificant.

How different the velocities attainable by electrons once they escape solid confines and enter a gas! Even in fields of moderate potential enormously high velocities are attained. If an electron in a vacuum is accelerated by a potential of only ten volts it attains a velocity of 1166 miles per second, as determined by the equation,

$$v = 1.9489 \times 10^6 \sqrt{E} \text{ ft per second}$$

in which E is in volts. This formula holds only for velocities which are small compared to the velocity of light.||

Electrons have been accelerated to velocities of 168 000 miles per second, which is 90 percent of the velocity of light. To reach this speed an electron has fallen through a potential of 206 000 volts.

The *electron volt* is a convenient unit of energy. It is the energy imparted to an electron as it starts from rest and falls through a potential of one volt.

The mass of an electron is given as

$$m_e = 9.1066 \times 10^{-31} \text{ kilogram}$$

or in English units 3.12×10^{28} electrons to the ounce, which is, of course, an incomprehensible figure.

This figure for the mass of an electron is based on an electron at rest or substantially so. As any particle is accelerated it gains in mass. Any particle, even an electron, which is the lightest of all particles, at the speed of light would have, according to the Einsteinian rule, infinite mass. This

|| For a discussion of electron velocity see Millman and Seely, *Electronics*, pp 25–8.

mass, however, does not increase linearly but according to the equation:¶

$$m = \frac{m_0}{\sqrt{1 - (v/c)^2}}$$

This turns out to mean that the mass does not increase rapidly until its velocity nears that of light. In this equation:

m = mass of the particle in motion
m_0 = mass of the particle at rest
v = speed of the particle, meters per second
c = speed of light (2.99776×10^8 meters per second) .

An electron having a velocity 90 percent that of light weighs only a little more than seven times its mass at rest. The speed of an electron must exceed 15 percent of the speed of light for its mass to be affected by more than 1 percent. This is equivalent to 6000 electron volts.

The charge on an electron is also an exceedingly small number.

$$Q_e = 1.602 \times 10^{-19} \text{ coulomb}$$

Said in a different way, the charge on 6.24×10^{18} electrons gives 1 coulomb. From this, by definition comes the usable fact that 6.24×10^{18} electrons moving past a given point per second constitute one ampere.

This charge on an electron, although it seems inconsequentially small, is the basis for all electric forces, some of which are enormous. The reason, of course, is that in numbers there is strength. To picture this a little more graphically, if we were able to separate two one-ounce amounts of electrons by a mile the force of repulsion between them would be 10 billion billion (that is, 10^{19}) tons.

Likewise, if all the electrons and protons in an ordinary lead pencil were dissociated and the two piles separated by the distance between Chicago and New York, the attractive force between them would be 34 000 tons. Interestingly enough, if the electrons were allowed to flow back to the protons at the rate of one ampere, that is, 6.24 billion billion electrons per second, the number of electrons reduced from the pencil would be so large that six weeks would be required for all to make the return trip.

One fact of great importance in connection with the electron is the ratio of the charge of the electron to its mass. Both figures are small, but their ratio is large:

$$\frac{Q_e}{m_e} = 1.7592 \times 10^{11} \text{ coulombs per kilogram}$$

¶ MIT staff, *Applied Electronics*, p 4.

This is a measure of the agility of the electron, just as a grasshopper can jump relatively thousands of times farther than a man because the ratio of the jumping force he can exert to his weight is so much greater than for a man. In this high ratio of the charge to the mass of an electron lies the outstanding characteristic of electronic devices, that is, the rapidity with which they act. In effect, electrons are weightless and hence they can be brought to extremely high velocities, in times measured in fractions of a microsecond, and stopped just as quickly. Nowhere in engineering is such a high ratio of force to weight encountered.

TABLE 1.1. STATISTICS OF SELECTED ELEMENTS

Element	Protons*	Neutrons	Atomic Weight	Electrons in Each Shell						
				K	L	M	N	O	P	Q
Hydrogen	1	0	1.0078	1						
Helium	2	2	4.002	2						
Lithium	3	3	6.940	2	1					
Neon	10	10	20.18	2	8					
Argon	18	20	39.94	2	8	8				
Potassium	19	20	39.10	2	8	8	1			
Copper	29	34	63.57	2	8	18	1			
Gold	79	118	197.2	2	8	18	32	18	1	
Uranium	92	146	238.14	2	8	18	32	18	12	2
Maximum possible number of electrons in shell				2	8	18	32	18	12	2

*Also the atomic number and the number of electrons.

SUMMARY

Electronics is restricted to that branch of electrical phenomena that deals with the actions of electrons in gases. Although electronics employs as its principal device the vacuum tube it is not confined to applications employing tubes. The significant fact of electronics is that in a portion, at least, of its circuit the electrons are not confined to solid or liquid conductors.

The *atom* is the basic unit of all matter. It is made up of one or more electrons moving in orbits around a nucleus, consisting of *protons* and *neutrons*. The electron is the negative unit of electricity. The proton is the positive unit of electricity, equal but opposite in sign to that of the electron, and weighs 1849 times as much as the electron. The neutron has no charge and weighs about the same as the proton. There are 92 kinds of natural elements, comprising the elements having from one to 92 electrons in orbits about the nucleus. These 92 elements range in mass from about one (a single proton) for hydrogen to about 238 for uranium.

The electrons dispose themselves about the nuclei in definite *orbits* or *shells* of which there are a total of six. The shell nearest the nucleus can hold a maximum of two electrons (helium); the next outer orbit, eight electrons, and so on. In general the inner orbits are filled with electrons first.

An electron from an inner orbit can be forced, by the expenditure of energy into a more distant orbit, creating an *excited atom*. When the electron slips back into its normal place the energy is released in the form of radiation, which may or may not be visible.

Both the *charge* and the *mass* of an electron are small definite amounts. The ratio of charge to mass is, however, a large figure; this explains why electronic devices act with such speed.

REFERENCES

MIT ELECTRICAL ENGINEERING STAFF, *Applied Electronics*, John Wiley & Sons, New York, 1943, pp 1–55.

W. G. DOW, *Fundamentals of Engineering Electronics*, John Wiley & Sons, New York, 1937, pp 56–96.

J. BARTON HOAG, *Electron and Nuclear Physics*, D. Van Nostrand Co., New York, 1938, pp 1–66.

R. G. KLOEFFLER, *Principles of Electronics*, John Wiley & Sons, New York, 1942, pp 4–22.

R. A. MILLIKAN, *Electrons (+ and −)*, *Protons, Photons, Neutrons, and Cosmic Rays*, University of Chicago Press, Chicago, 1935, pp 90–124, 182–231, and 360–403.

JACOB MILLMAN and SAMUEL SEELY, *Electronics*, McGraw-Hill Book Co., New York, 1941, pp 111–42.

J. H. MORECROFT, *Electron Tubes and Their Application*, John Wiley & Sons, New York, 1936, pp 1–9.

Chapter 2

ELECTRON ESCAPE FROM SOLIDS — EMISSION

The nature of matter and the movement of electrons in solids are of interest and importance to all electrical engineers, including the electronics engineer. Of special concern to the electronics engineer, however, is the behavior and control of electrons in gases, particularly gases of low pressures. Liberation of electrons from a solid or liquid surface is *emission*. A stream of electrons leaving an emitting surface constitutes emission current.

The fact that emission does not occur under normal conditions indicates that considerable forces within the material prevent the escape of free electrons. If an electron were to depart from an atom at the surface, the atom would be positively charged, reattracting the errant electron to it, so that the net electron escape is normally zero.

For a free electron in a solid to make good its escape to the surrounding space, it must somehow obtain an energy greater than the fixed definite amount of energy that holds it. This work that must be done to enable an electron to leave the surface is called the *work function* and is measured in *electron volts*.

The electron volt, frequently abbreviated to *ev*, used to express work function is a unit of energy just as is foot-pound or kilowatt-hour. It must not be confused with potential. One electron volt is the kinetic energy acquired by an electron while moving through a potential difference of one volt. An electron so accelerated attains a speed of nearly 2 million feet per second (1.9489×10^6), which is about 370 miles per second. The electron volt is a convenient yardstick for measuring energies and is frequently so used by the electronic engineer.

The work function of an element or compound is a fixed unchanging quantity. However, the work functions of various substances differ. The range of work functions for most metals suitable as emitters is from 1 to 7 electron volts. Temperature has only a slight effect on the work function of a substance.

A table of work functions for common metals and substances is given in Table 2.1.* These comparative values give a measure of the relative difficulty of establishing electron emission from these materials.

---

*Work functions of emitter materials as quoted in various reference sources differ, sometimes rather widely. The reason for this is that even minute impurities in the material and small differences in measuring technique have a great influence on the results.

There are five methods of creating electron emission. Of these, four are of practical interest in electronics: thermionic, photoelectric, secondary, and high-field. The fifth type of emission is atomic disintegration which concerns the nuclear physicist with his atom-smashing experiments and those interested in the spontaneous radioactivity of a few elements in nature.

Emission by Boiling

Thermionic emission is, by all odds, the method most frequently used to obtain a flow of electrons from a solid or liquid metal to the surrounding atmosphere. This corresponds quite well to the evaporation of water molecules from hot water. That hot conducting surfaces give off electrons has been known for a long time. In 1725 DuFay discovered the space surrounding a hot body to be a conductor of electricity. Edison in 1883 placed an electrode inside an incandescent lamp and made it positive with respect to the hot filament. He observed a current between the two. This phenomenon became known as the Edison effect, although Edison only noted the effect and made no practical use of it.

When either a solid or liquid metal is heated, the thermal bombardment of the molecules imparts to numerous free electrons an energy greater than the work function of that substance. These electrons are erupted into the surrounding gas, only to fall back into the surface unless a field of positive potential is present of sufficient magnitude to overcome the positive field created by the departure of electrons from the surface. In an incandescent lamp, for example, electrons are continually boiling out from the filament, only to return quickly because no electrode with positive potential is present to attract them. At any instant there are many thousands of free electrons in the space surrounding the filament of an incandescent lamp. The electron population for each filament temperature is in equilibrium, electrons returning to the filament as rapidly as they leave it.

The electrons, on the average, do not travel far from an emitter unless other influences are present. Probably most of them do not go beyond a few ten thousandths of an inch before returning, but a few may fly out as far as $\frac{1}{16}$ of an inch. The initial velocities, however, increase with cathode temperature and may be extremely high. For an electron to escape through the surface of tungsten, it must have a velocity of approximately 620 miles per second†; this is small, however, compared to the velocities attained by electrons under the influence of electric fields.

The ideal thermionic emitter (that is, a hot cathode) would have a low work function. Unfortunately, this is not always possible. Usually metals

†Kloeffler, *Principles of Electronics*, p 33.

having the lowest work function are the most fragile and, therefore, are easily damaged. Consequently, the metals of low work functions are usually employed in relatively small tubes in radio receivers and in the pilot control devices of industrial electronic equipment. When a tube is used for a high-voltage application, the emitter is usually made of a metal with a relatively high work function.

The types of emitters in common use are:

1. Pure metals — tungsten, molybdenum, tantalum, thorium.
2. Atomic film — thoriated tungsten.
3. Oxide coated — barium, strontium-oxide coating.
4. Pool type — mercury.
5. Sintered metals.

The atomic-film emitter, commonly called the thoriated-tungsten cathode, is made of pure tungsten impregnated with about one-half percent of thorium oxide and some carbon. After being mounted in the tube, the cathode is heated to approximately 4200 F for a few minutes. The temperature is then reduced to 2900 F. The first heating reduces some of the thorium oxide to pure thorium. The thorium atoms thus formed slowly come to the surface where they form a skin layer one molecule thick. The emission of electrons comes from the thin layer of thorium atoms, which has a low work function. A high emission current is possible from this cathode.

The oxide-coated type of cathode is indirectly heated by a pure tungsten filament running through the inside of a hollow cylinder. The cylinder is the actual emitter, which in this case, is indirectly heated to approximately 1560 F by the filament. In the preparation of this type of cathode, a cylindrical core of Konel metal (an alloy of nickel, cobalt, iron, and titanium) is coated with a mixture of barium and strontium carbonate. The cathode is then assembled in the tube, and during the evacuation process the coated cathode is heated to 2240 F. At this temperature the barium and strontium carbonates decompose into oxides, and the carbon dioxide gas thus formed is removed by pumps. Barium and strontium oxides are then left on the surface of the cathode. These oxides have low work functions, which make this type of cathode an extremely efficient emitter. Emission curves for common types of hot cathodes are given in Fig. 2.1.

Some years ago one form of the equation expressing thermal-emission relationship was developed by Richardson as

$$I_s + A(0.556\,T + 256)^2\,\epsilon^{-b/0.556T+256}$$

in which I_s is the saturation current in amperes per square inch of emitter surface, T the temperature in degrees Fahrenheit, A and b

constants determined by the emitter material and work function,* of which three are given in Fig. 2.1.

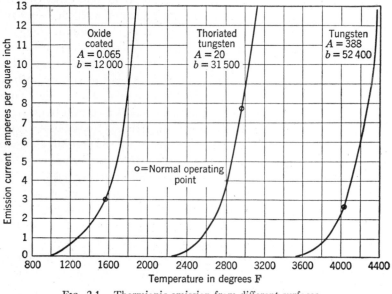

FIG. 2.1.   Thermionic emission from different surfaces.

Emission by Light-Ray Bombardment

Light striking a surface may impart to an electron the energy required for escape. Light behaves as though it travels in discrete units called *quanta.* The energy of a quantum is equal to a fixed number, called *Planck's constant* which is 6.624×10^{-34} joule-second times the frequency of the light. This unit of energy is a *photon.* Thus, when a surface is struck with light, whether it be in the visible spectrum or not, it can be thought of as being pelted with fixed bundles of energy. A quantum of radiant energy in the region of shorter waves, say, the blue and violet, is larger than one in the longer region, that is, toward the red end of the spectrum.

These concepts enable us to visualize the mechanism of photoelectric emission. When a surface is struck at right angles by radiant energy of a single wavelength, it is as though the free electrons at the surface were being dealt fixed blows. If the energy of one of these blows plus any energy the free electron in the surface may itself possess exceeds the work function of that particular surface, the electron may be able to overcome the forces of attraction holding it within the metallic surface and escape into space beyond. If the electron has no energy of its own, that is, the temperature is

*For determination of constants see MIT Staff, *Applied Electronics,* pp 76–83.

absolute zero, all energy for escape must come from the radiant energy. The energy of the photon thereupon must be equal to or greater than the work function for any photoelectric emission to occur. If we remember that the energy contained within a radiation becomes greater with increased frequency (that is, shorter wavelength), and that a minimum energy is required to establish emission, it follows that no emission can occur below a predetermined minimum frequency of illumination. This minimum is called threshold frequency. In other words, for a given kind of surface with its corresponding work function and temperature, no appreciable photoelectric emission results unless the radiation exceeds a certain frequency.

At any temperature above absolute zero, free electrons possess some thermal energy; hence smaller photons of energy are required for emission. This is equivalent to saying that, as the temperature of a surface increases, emission can be caused by radiation of longer and longer wavelengths. For temperatures short of melting of most solids, the number of electrons with high thermally engendered energies is small compared to the total number of electrons. This is the reason why the temperature of the emission surface does not materially affect the quantity of electron emission.

Because radiation of a given frequency is constituted of uniform photons of energy, it follows that the greater the number of light quanta striking a surface in a given time the more electrons that are emitted. The amount of photoelectric emission is directly proportional to the intensity of light, over the entire range of light values from darkness to full sunlight.

The energy or velocity of an electron departing from an emitter surface, on the other hand, does not depend upon the light intensity. The speed achieved by an electron at the time of escape depends on the hardness of the blow, that is, on the size of the photon setting it free. The speed of the emitted electrons does not depend on the amount of light falling on the emitter. Because the energy of the photon is proportional to the frequency of the radiation, the energy and velocity of emitted electrons increase with the frequency or decrease with the wavelength of the incident radiation. Likewise, for most surfaces, a given amount of radiation in the blue end of the spectrum causes more emission than the same amount of radiant energy in the red.

When the threshold wavelengths are known, the maximum work function possible for appreciable emission with light in the visible spectrum — considered to be between 4000 and 7000 Angstroms — can be determined. These work functions are relatively small, of the order of $1\frac{1}{2}$ electron volts.

As with thermionic emitters, the surface with the lowest work function is not a single metal, but one to which "impurities" have been added. Thus, photoelectric emitters are composites, built up to provide a sensitivity-distribution curve to match best the spectrum of the light source with which the phototube is to be used. Sensitivity curves for the more common emitters are given in Fig. 2.2.

Most phototube-emitter surfaces are made up of some light-sensitive surface such as silver as a base, coated with an alkali metal or earth. The alkaline metals and their work functions in electron volts are caesium, 1.36; rubidium, 1.45; potassium, 1.55; sodium, 1.82; and lithium, 2.36. The

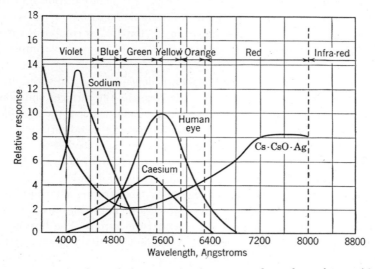

FIG. 2.2. A comparison of the response of common phototube emitters with the response of the eye.

alkaline earths and their work functions are barium, 1.7; strontium, 2.0; and calcium, 2.4. The most widely used emitter is the one marked in Fig. 2.2 as Cs-CsO-Ag, in which a silver surface is well oxidized and a layer of caesium is deposited over the oxide. This type of emitter surface is particularly useful with incandescent lamps as its sensitivity to their light is 10 to 100 times greater than any other known practical emitter surface. The caesium curve is particularly important as it possesses a response closely similar to that of the human eye and hence is useful in color-matching work. The sodium surface is occasionally used when a phototube responsive to ultraviolet is required.

Electrons Knock Out Electrons

Just as electrons can be ejected from a cold cathode by pelting it with photons of radiant energy, so also are electrons emitted when the surface is struck with other missiles, such as fast-moving electrons. An electron striking a metal surface at high speed has considerable kinetic energy, which may be absorbed by the free electrons present, thereby raising their energy beyond the work function and enabling them to escape the surface forces. This is not unlike the splash caused by a single drop of water or object falling into a pool of water. The bombarding electron is spoken of as the *primary electron*. Those caused by the primary electron to erupt from the surface are *secondary electrons*, which gives this type of emission its name. A single primary electron may cause the ejection of only one or two secondary electrons from a pure metal, but from an "impure" or composite surface ten or more secondary electrons may be released by a single impinging electron.

The magnitude of secondary emission is dependent on the speed of the primary electron, the angle at which it strikes, and the surface condition of the electrode. The purer and the cleaner the metal the less the secondary emission. Secondary electrons are created whenever a metal surface is bombarded by primary electrons having energies only slightly in excess of the work function. Generally, however, secondary emission does not become appreciable under 10 electron volts and frequently not under 20.

Secondary emission can also be caused by ions striking a surface in the same way as primary electrons. Ions, which are charged atoms, however, are much less effective in creating secondary electrons. The heavier the ion the fewer the secondary electrons. A helium ion is 100 times more effective than a mercury ion of the same energy, although the ratio of atomic weights are 1 to 50.

Secondary emission has ordinarily been considered a nuisance, requiring means for its prevention. In most electronic tubes the secondary electrons constitute a current opposite in direction to the desired current, and hence they diminish the useful current. This leads to various measures such as special constructions to suppress secondary emission or special coatings on the electrode that discourage secondary electrons. However, secondary emission is not without merit. It is actually made the basis for exceedingly high amplification — up to 100 000 to 1 — in electron-multiplier tubes. (See Chapter 3, p 30.)

Emission Caused by Strong Electric Field

A fourth means by which electrons can acquire sufficient energy to overcome the binding forces of a metallic surface and enter the surrounding gas is by an intense electric field of positive potential. If the potential gradient at the surface is sufficiently high, the electron is literally pulled out of the metal although the metal may be "cold." This is referred to as *field emission* or the *cold-cathode effect*.

Field emission is substantially independent of temperature. The potential required must be high, of the order of several million volts per inch, depending on the work function of the cold cathode. This does not imply that the absolute voltage is necessarily high, but that it is concentrated over an extremely small distance. For example, a high-field is the means of establishing the cathode spot in an ignitron-type mercury-arc rectifier (discussed more in detail in Chapters 6 and 11). This is done by impressing a potential across a high-resistance irregular-shaped igniter dipping into the mercury pool. Although the impressed voltage is only about 100 volts, the concentration of stress at the junction between igniter and mercury pool is probably several thousand volts per inch. Emission by high field is also used in cold-cathode tubes and cathode-ray oscillographs, but plays no useful part in ordinary vacuum tubes.

TABLE 2.1.   THERMIONIC WORK FUNCTIONS OF COMMON EMITTER MATERIALS

	Work Function — Electron Volts		Work Function — Electron Volts
Caesium	1.81	Tungsten	4.54
Calcium	2.24	Iron	4.77
Molybdenum	4.15	Calcium oxide	1.77
Barium	2.11	Strontium oxide	1.27
Thorium	3.38	Barium oxide	0.99
Tantalum	4.12		

SUMMARY

Emission is the liberation of electrons from a solid or liquid conductor into surrounding space. The flow of these emitted electrons is emission current.

Work function is the amount of work done on an electron to enable it to overcome the forces holding it within a liquid on metal surface.

The *electron volt* is a unit of energy and is the kinetic energy acquired by an electron as it is accelerated through a potential difference of one volt.

Emission can be caused in four common ways: by heating the surface (thermionic), by allowing light to fall on certain surfaces (photoelectric), by pelting the surface with electrons or charged atoms (secondary), or by applying sufficiently high positive potential to pull the electrons from the surface (high field).

Thermionic emission is by far the most commonly employed in electronics. There are four common types of thermionic emitters: pure metals, atomic films, oxide coatings, and mercury pools.

REFERENCES

MIT ELECTRICAL ENGINEERING STAFF, *Applied Electronics*, John Wiley & Sons, New York, 1943, pp 62–112.

W. G. DOW, *Fundamentals of Engineering Electronics*, John Wiley & Sons, New York, 1937, pp 148–262.

JACOB MILLMAN and SAMUEL SEELY, *Electronics*, McGraw-Hill Book Co., New York, 1941, pp 143–81 and 182–203.

J. H. MORECROFT, *Electron Tubes and Their Application*, John Wiley & Sons, New York, 1936, pp 10–47.

E. D. MCARTHUR, *Electronics and Electron Tubes*, John Wiley & Sons, New York, 1936, pp 19–40.

E. L. CHAFFEE, *Theory of Thermionic Vacuum Tubes*, McGraw-Hill Book Co., New York, 1933, pp 55–138.

HERBERT J. REICH, *Theory and Applications of Electronic Tubes*, McGraw-Hill Book Co., New York, 1944, pp 19–42.

F. E. TERMAN, *Radio Engineering*, McGraw-Hill Book Co., New York, 1937, pp 103–15.

ROYCE G. KLOEFFLER, *Principles of Electronics*, John Wiley & Sons, New York, 1942, pp 30–43.

Chapter 3

ELECTRICITY FROM LIGHT

Nothing in the electronics engineer's bag of tricks has stirred the popular fancy as that concerned with photoelectricity. Phototubes do things that people can readily grasp, yet which they consider miraculous. Phototubes act as unseen hands to open doors, they count objects, protect against burglars, detect fire or smoke, and turn lights on or off. Inevitably the tubes that do these things were dubbed "electric eyes."

Certain substances when illuminated give off electrons. This *photoelectric effect* was discovered in 1887 by Hertz. In the next year Hallwachs made the corollary observation that a negatively charged body loses its charge rapidly when exposed to ultraviolet radiation. These facts remained little more than scientific curiosities until about 1928 when sound movies skyrocketed into popularity, giving enormous impetus to the development of light-sensitive tubes. Contemporaneously, industry began to employ phototubes for a variety of light-responsive relaying purposes.

Light-sensitive devices fall into two major groups and another, as yet, unimportant and inconspicuous class. Those in which electrons are liberated under the influence of light are termed *photoemissive*. All phototubes are of this class. When the light causes the generation of an electromotive force by chemical or phys cal changes, the action is *photovoltaic*. Cells used in photographic-exposure meters are well-known examples of photovoltaic phenomenon. Finally, the electric conductivity of some substances, such as selenium, increases when they are bathed with light. Relatively little use is made of this principle, known as *photoconductivity*.

Photoemissivity

Phototubes essentially are two-electrode glass-envelope tubes, either vacuum or gas-filled. A typical tube is shown in Fig. 3.1. The cathode is the photosensitive surface of a relatively large area, frequently semicylindrical in shape. The anode is generally a slender straight wire mounted along the axis of the cathode. The anode obviously must be as small as is mechanically feasible so as to cast the least possible shadow on the cathode.

The cathode is usually a steel base that has been silvered to prevent oxi-

Fig. 3.1. In the representative phototube the cathode is a large semicylindrical plate of photoemissive metal with a slender rod-shaped anode at the focus of the cathode. *Courtesy RCA*

dation and deoxidation. Over the silver is laid the photosensitive material selected to give the desired response characteristic.*

Phototubes are made in two general types, vacuum and gas-filled. Their structures may be and usually are identical, the difference being only that in the vacuum type the pressure is of the order of 10^{-3} microns,† whereas the gas-filled tube contains an inert gas such as neon. The pressure is low but several times greater than in the evacuated tube.

The two types of tubes have very unlike responses to light. The current-versus-illumination characteristics of a vacuum phototube are given in Fig. 3.2. When light strikes the photosensitive surface electrons are emitted. If the anode is at some slight positive potential with respect to the cathode, some of the electrons will be drawn to it forming, at most, a small current of a few microamperes, and the remaining electrons will finally return to the cathode. Increasing the

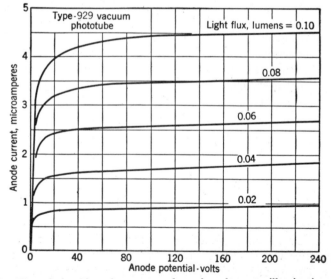

Fig. 3.2. The relationships of current and anode voltage to illumination of a 929 vacuum-type phototube. The response is almost linear up to saturation after which increase in anode voltage results in very slight current increase.

*See Chapter 2, p 17.
†A micron is one thousandth of a millimeter of mercury.

anode potential draws more and more of the emitted electrons to it until at a potential of between 10 and 20 volts all the electrons driven out of the cathode by incoming radiant energy are collected by the anode. Further increase in potential results in almost no increase in current, because no more electrons are available in the interelectrode space. The current of a vacuum phototube can be increased only by increasing the amount of radiation cast onto the cathode. Doubling the amount of radiation doubles the saturation current. The relationship between saturation current and light intensity is linear over a wide range in illuminations.

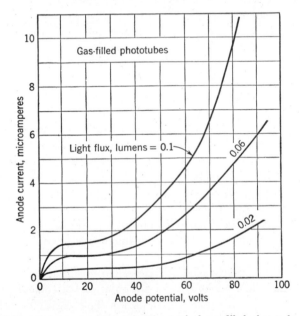

FIG. 3.3. Unlike the vacuum phototube the typical gas-filled phototube responds to light as shown here, the current continuing to rise with voltage because of secondary emission on the anode, ion bombardment of the cathode, and gas-molecule collisions.

The current output of vacuum phototubes is small, being usually of the order of 20 or 30 microamperes with about 100 volts on the anode. The ratio of current to constant visible light intensity is called the *static sensitivity*. Measured in microamperes per lumen, this sensitivity of vacuum phototubes seldom exceeds 25 and is more frequently 15 to 20.

The introduction of gas into a phototube alters its response curves both in shape and magnitude. Representative curves are shown in Fig. 3.3. At low anode potentials the anode currents are about as for the vacuum phototube. However, instead of reaching a saturation point, the anode current continues to rise and in nonlinear fashion. Two reasons underlie this. As an electron is drawn at high speed toward the anode, it collides with one or more of the gas molecules. These collisions may produce free electrons, which proceed with the original electron toward the anode. In effect, these collision electrons increase the tube current. Also the atoms that have lost electrons become positive ions. They begin to wander to the cathode and strike it, although at low velocity, with great force because of their large mass (as compared to electron mass). These blows may have sufficient force to knock more electrons from the surface, constituting secondary emission.‡ Thus in gas-filled phototubes the current results from the initial light-liberated electrons, subsequent gas-molecule-collision electrons, and secondary-emission electrons.

Clearly the effect is cumulative as anode potential is increased, which accounts for the upward sweep of the current curves. In fact, if the anode potential is increased to a certain point a glow discharge takes place. This will, in a short time, damage the photoemissive surface because of the heavy bombardment by positive ions. To save the tube, when this occurs, the anode circuit must be opened. Decreasing or blocking the light does not stop the glow discharge. Once a glow discharge is initiated in a gas-filled tube it is self-perpetuating as long as anode potential is maintained.

The gas-filled phototube is essentially a means of magnifying the photoelectric effect. Although the maximum current ratings for gas-filled phototubes have about the same magnitude as those for vacuum photo-tubes, the amount of light need be only about one fifth as much. The most common range of ratings of gas-filled phototubes are 15 to 30 microamperes at 90 volts. The luminous sensitivities range from about 65 to 125 micro-amperes per lumen.

Gas-filled tubes, because of their high sensitivity, are commonly used in sound reproduction. In such service the light is not constant but varies according to the audio-frequency modulation. The sensitivity at the higher audio frequencies is slightly less than the static sensitivity. It is termed *dynamic sensitivity*.

The decline in sensitivity results from the mass of the gas ions. Because gas ions are heavy and move relatively slowly, a time lag exists between the disruption of a gas atom and the increase in cathode emission caused by the positive ion. As a result of this time lag, fluctuations in the emission caused by positive ions lag behind variations in the primary photoemission. For high frequencies of light change, the lag tends to smooth out the variations in total phototube current and thus, by definition, reduces sensitivity. In well-designed modern tubes, the decline in sensitivity is not manifest under 1000 cycles and amounts to only 20 percent at 10 000 cycles.

Gas-filled phototubes are useful where their high sensitivities are desir-
‡ See Chapter 2, p 18.

able, as in sound reproduction. High-vacuum tubes, on the other hand, have the general merit of linear light response, and a more constant sensitivity through life, and are less likely to be damaged by accidental operation at overvoltage or overcurrent. These features qualify vacuum phototubes for use as light-operated relays and as light-measuring devices.

The response of photoemissive surfaces varies widely with wavelength of the incident radiation. Because various materials respond differently, phototubes are tailored to the light sources for which they are to be used. Phototubes to be used with incandescent-filament lamps, which constitute the most common light-relay application, generally have cathodes coated with caesium and caesium oxide. Those which respond to infrared, as in burglar alarms, also have surfaces coated with caesium oxide, whereas ultraviolet-responsive tubes usually have sodium coatings. For phototubes that must have responses similar to the human eye, the photosensitive area is of specially treated metallic caesium.

The current characteristics of phototubes are substantially independent of temperature. The reason for this is that any energy an electron in the emissive material may have as a result of thermal agitation at ordinary temperatures is exceedingly small as compared to the energies imparted by photons of light. In practice, however, the upper temperature limits set by the tube manufacturer should be observed because of the danger of injuring the cathode by boiling gases out of the photoemissive coating. This limit usually occurs at about 170 F.

One valuable feature of phototubes is their rapidity of response, which for all practical purposes is instantaneous. The time lag has been determined experimentally to be less than one thousandth of a microsecond (10^{-9} second). Thus in practical phototube applications any time delay is produced not by the tubes but by other elements in the circuit.

Phototubes can, in general, be used in three ways: to respond to light presence or absence, to variation in light intensity, or to change in light quality. In industry, that is, excepting sound reproduction, the most common use of phototubes is for relaying. Here the phototube indicates the presence or absence of light, or an amount of light more or less than a specified amount. In a list of such uses of light relays are door openers, burglar alarms, fire detection, printing register, flaw detection, counting, weighing, liquid-level control, and personnel protection as on electrical test floors, and at punch presses.

Phototubes are also extensively used to indicate light intensity. Such services include sound and facsimile reproduction, measurement of smoke density, recording the density of chemicals, and photometry.

Phototubes are useful in color work. Prominent examples are color matching and temperature measurement.

Photovoltaic Devices

Millions of photographers make good use of the photovoltaic principle, although they may not think of it as such. The photographer judges the light on his photographic subjects by a photovoltaic device smaller even

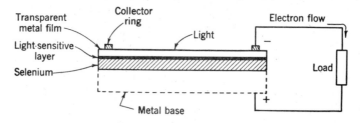

FIG. 3.4. The "sandwich"-type photovoltaic cell consists basically of a light-sensitive surface laid on a semi-conductor, such as selenium supported on an iron base. Some constructions use a copper-oxide semiconductor on a copper base.

than the so-called candid cameras. The device is called an exposure meter.

A *photovoltaic cell* is a device such that when one surface is illuminated a potential appears across its two faces. Thus a photovoltaic cell is a true

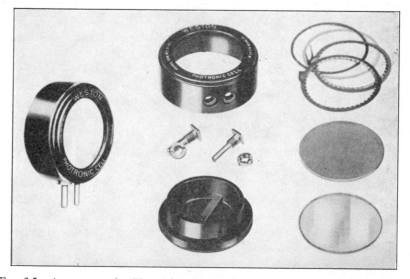

FIG. 3.5. A representative Photronic cell as used in exposure meters. The photosensitive surface is the circular disk at the right above the cover glass.   *Courtesy Weston*

generator of electric potential, which, if the circuit is completed, causes a current flow. It receives light energy and delivers electric energy. In this regard it is quite unlike the phototube, which is more properly termed a light-actuated valve. The phototube requires a battery or other source of energy for current to flow in the circuit in response to the illumination. The photovoltaic cell, on the other hand, requires no source of energy other than the radiation itself. How the cell accomplishes this is not definitely known. Theories have been advanced, some of which are involved, but none has been generally accepted.§

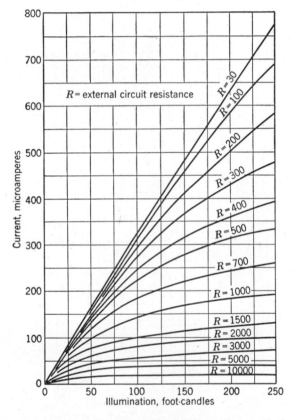

FIG. 3.6. Current output as a function of illumination and external circuit resistance of a typical General Electric photovoltaic cell in which a selenium compound is the photosensitive substance.

The term "sandwich" cells for photovoltaic cells naturally results from their construction. As shown in Fig. 3.4, a cell consists of a metal base over which is laid successively a thick layer of a semiconducting substance, a thin insulating layer, and finally a thin conducting film such as silver on

§See Dow, *Fundamentals of Engineering Electronics*, p 416 ff.

which rests a current-collector ring or electrode. The top or conducting film, which is exposed to the radiant energy, is usually covered with a transparent lacquer simply for protection.

Photovoltaic cells are of two types, similar in construction, appearance, and in performance. The only essential difference is in layer materials. The Photronic cell, Fig. 3.5, employs an iron base and a conducting layer of a compound of selenium. In the copper-oxide cell the base is copper, a layer of cuprous oxide acting as the light-responsive layer.

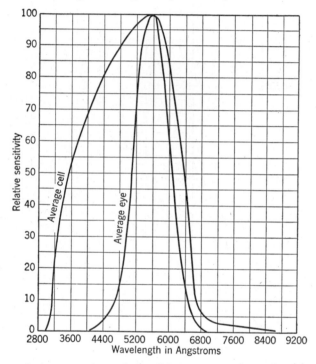

FIG. 3.7. A selenium-type photovoltaic cell is more responsive to the violet end of the spectrum than is the human eye.

The current response to illumination is materially affected by the external circuit resistance as the curves of Fig. 3.6 show. All the curves show a saturation effect, but for the smaller circuit resistances the cells respond almost linearly with illumination. The sensitivity varies considerably with different makes but in general ranges from 150 to 600 microamperes per lumen at an illumination of 100 foot-candles.

Typical photovoltaic cells are considerably more sensitive to the violet end of the spectrum than is the human eye and slightly sensitive to red just beyond the range of the eye. This is indicated in Fig. 3.7. This response to a broader range of wavelengths is generally of no consequence, but, when human-eye response must be matched closely, suitable filters are available.

The performance of a sandwich cell is only slightly affected by changes in temperature, but the cell should not be operated at temperatures beyond about 170 F lest the structure itself be permanently injured. Cells of

FIG. 3.8. A foot-candle meter consists of a photovoltaic cell and a sensitive ammeter.

Courtesy Weston

modern design display but little fatigue effects. The response may decline by as much as 4 percent after exposures of an hour for circuit resistances medium in magnitude. The fatigue effect is less for the lower resistances. Because most of the drop occurs immediately after exposure, for most accurate work readings should be taken after a given length of exposure, say 30 or 60 seconds. This fatigue, however, is temporary. The full response is regained after the illumination has been removed. Cells exposed to strong light for several months may manifest a 10-percent permanent decline in sensitivity.

The most common use of photovoltaic cells is in photographic-exposure meters. Their simplicity, compactness, and acceptable accuracy make them ideal for this purpose. Photovoltaic cells are, however, used for a variety of other purposes, for example, illumination studies (Fig. 3.8) and factory processes such as sorting and grading by color and transparency, as smoke indicators, door controls, and burglar alarms.

The Multiplier Phototube

The conventional phototube produces, at best, weak currents even at fairly high illuminations. The multiplier phototube, Fig. 3.9, offers a way of obtaining much larger currents from low illuminations. With it currents of several milliamperes result from as little as $\frac{1}{1000}$ of a lumen. Its luminous sensitivity under operating conditions is of the order of 2 amperes per lumen (instead of the few hundred microamperes per lumen offered by phototubes).

In the multiplier phototube, under average conditions, current amplifications of 200 000 are reached by capitalizing on secondary emission, an effect considered objectionable in most tubes. The tube contains

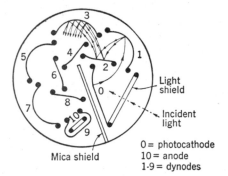

0 = photocathode
10 = anode
1-9 = dynodes

Mica shield

Fig. 3.9. An electron multiplier tube which achieves very high current amplifications by capitalizing on secondary emission. *Courtesy RCA*

Fig. 3.10. Schematic arrangement of a multiplier phototube consisting of a photosensitive cathode, 0; nine dynodes, 1 to 9, inclusive, that utilize secondary emission to achieve electron multiplication; and an anode, 10.

a series of ten electrodes, called dynodes, arranged to encourage secondary emission. The schematic arrangement, shown in Fig. 3.10, somewhat resembles the plan of a golf course. Incident light impinges on the cathode, O, causing the liberation of free electrons, which are drawn to dynode 1 by a positive potential. Here each electron liberates several electrons, which rush against dynode 2 of still higher potential, liberating another swarm of secondary electrons. This process continues with successive dynodes, multiplying electrons at each of the ten dynodes, until electrons are finally collected by anode 10. Average anode characteristics are indicated in Fig. 3.11.

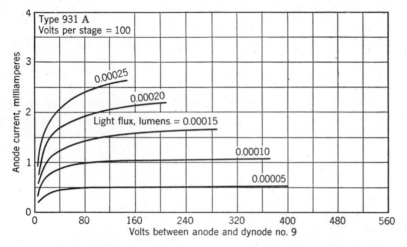

FIG. 3.11. Current output of a multiplier phototube as a function of potential between anode and the last dynode, for different light intensities.

The dynodes are supplied with about 100 volts per stage from taps on the secondary winding of a 115-volt single-phase stepup transformer or an equivalent d-c supply. Thus a fairly high potential exists between the cathode and anode terminals, necessitating some care in the use of the multiplier tube.

Because of its small size, rugged construction, enormous sensitivity, low noise level, extremely small current when not illuminated, and freedom from distortion, the multiplier phototube has practical application in light-operated relays, in sound reproduction from film, in facsimile transmission, and in scientific research, involving low light levels.

SUMMARY

Photoelectric effect is the release of electrons by certain substances when illuminated by electromagnetic radiation in the visible or near-visible region.

The two major useful groups of light-sensitive devices are called *photoemissive* and *photovoltaic*. Photoemissive substances give off electrons when illuminated. Photovoltaic materials, illuminated, give rise to a difference in potential across their faces.

Phototubes are photoemissive devices and require an external source of potential to cause current flow. They are used for a multiplicity of industrial purposes requiring action based on change in light intensity or quality.

The two principal types of phototubes are the *vacuum* and the *gas-filled*. The vacuum phototube produces relatively small currents but they are proportional to voltage across the tubes, up to a saturation point after which increase in potential results in but little current increase. Gas-filled phototubes produce more current per lumen of illumination and the current increases sharply with rising potential because of ion bombardment and secondary emission.

Photovoltaic cells are true electric generators. When they are illuminated a current flows through a circuit connecting the two faces. The best known use of them is as photographic-exposure meters.

In a *multiplier phototube* weak currents resulting from photoemissive effect are amplified by secondary emission from a series of anodes of successively higher potential. The result is a relatively very great increase in photoelectric sensitivity.

REFERENCES

W. G. Dow, *Fundamentals of Engineering Electronics*, John Wiley & Sons, New York, 1937, pp 376–426.

V. K. Zworykin and E. D. Wilson, *Photocells and Their Application*, John Wiley & Sons, New York, 1934.

MIT Electrical Engineering Staff, *Applied Electronics*, John Wiley & Sons, New York, 1943, pp 101–09 also 140–1.

Jacob Millman and Samuel Seely, *Electronics*, McGraw-Hill Book Co., New York, 1941, pp 91–3, also 478–91.

Herbert J. Reich, *Theory and Applications of Electron Tubes*, McGraw-Hill Book Co., New York, 1944, pp 533–63.

J. H. Morecroft, *Electron Tubes and Their Application*, John Wiley & Sons, New York, 1936, pp 165–74.

J. B. Hoag, *Basic Radio*, D. Van Nostrand Co., New York, 1942, pp 136–46.

Royce G. Kloeffler, *Principles of Electronics*, John Wiley & Sons, New York, 1942, pp 136–49.

Chapter 4

ELECTRICITY INTO LIGHT

Patriarch of all present-day electronic devices is the X-ray tube. X radiation was discovered and put to practical use even before the discovery of the electron, two years before the formulation of the electron theory of matter, and long ahead of the first vacuum tube. It was in fact because its discoverer, Wilhelm Konrad von Röentgen, German physicist, did not know the nature of the strange radiation he had discovered that he applied to them the name X rays. Yet so great was the import of Röentgen's discovery in 1895 that three months later X rays were used in surgical operations in Vienna.

X-ray tubes and other electronic devices that convert electric energy into radiation akin to light depend on the establishment of a cathode ray. Sir William Crookes, in his laboratory in England in 1879, discovered that when high voltage is applied to two electrodes in a vacuum a shadow of one of them is formed on the glass envelope. It was as though one electrode, which we now call the anode, was being pelted by particles from the other electrode, the cathode. These particles moved in straight lines from the cathode although Crookes discovered they could be deflected by a magnet. He designated this stream of particles ejected from the cathode as cathode rays, which were later proved to be electrons moving at high speed from the cathode to the anode.

Röentgen in 1895, while experimenting with a Crookes tube, discovered that when a solid chunk of metal was struck with cathode rays of sufficient potential some of the energy was converted into a strange form of radiation. He found that a portion of this radiation passed through thin tube walls and affected a photographic plate. He called it X radiation.

It was subsequently proved that X rays have all the characteristics of light, except they are invisible and of much shorter wavelength. They move in straight lines, can be reflected and refracted as is light, and again like light are not influenced by magnetic or electric fields. Furthermore, these radiations have remarkable powers of penetration of objects opaque to visible light and affect photographic film as does ordinary light. Also when they strike certain substances they are transformed into a radiation within the visible spectrum. This is fluoroscopy.

X radiation, as used both by the medical profession and by industry, is based on the bombardment of a target with a stream of high-voltage electrons (cathode rays) and the resulting transformation of a small part of this energy — less than one percent for medium- and low-voltage tubes — into a radiation capable of penetrating opaque matter.

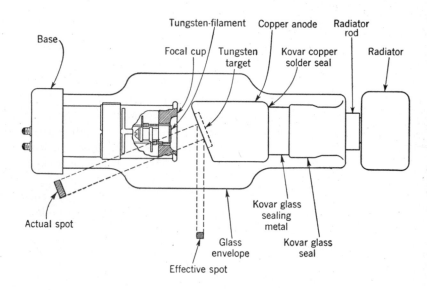

FIG. 4.1. Partial cross section of an 85 000-volt 5-milliampere X-ray tube.

X rays are generated in high-vacuum high-voltage hot-cathode two-electrode tubes.* A partial cross section of an X-ray tube is shown in Fig. 4.1 and a photograph of a modern tube in Fig. 4.2. The filaments are of commercially pure tungsten. By control of the filament temperature the number of electrons emitted is kept low enough that most of them are drawn to the anode so that no space charge (Chapter 5) can form. In this manner the full voltage drop occurs between the electrodes and can be utilized for electron acceleration. The electrons are accelerated to high velocities, producing X rays as they impinge on the anode target face, usually also of tungsten.

The anode is constructed by casting copper around the tungsten target. This construction utilizes the high heat conductivity of copper to provide rapid conduction of heat away from the target. Cooling of the anode is always a major problem in X-ray tube design, because all but a few per-

*A discussion of X-ray tubes is given by Z. J. Atlee, "Design and Application of X-Ray Tubes," *Electronics*, October 1940, p 26.

cent of the energy input to the tube must be removed from its electrodes as heat.

Intensity of X radiation varies inversely as the square of the distance from its source exactly as light, and increases with about the square of the voltage. Also the intensity of the X rays produced at a given voltage is approximately proportional to the current as well as to the atomic number of the target material, because the more massive molecules permit more rapid deceleration of the electrons and hence convert a larger proportion of their kinetic energy into radiation in the X-ray band. This relationship shows one reason why tungsten is a good target material. It has a high atomic number, 74. Furthermore, tungsten has a high melting point, and a fair heat conductivity and can be produced in the necessary shapes and sizes.

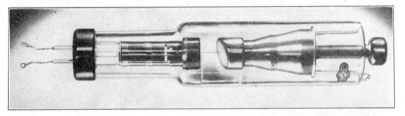

FIG. 4.2. A 220-kv X-ray tube used for therapy purposes. The anode is forced oil cooled.   *Courtesy Westinghouse*

When a target is struck by a high-speed electron the resulting electromagnetic radiation occurs over a fairly wide band of frequencies. The shortest wavelength present in the radiation is inversely proportional to the voltage applied across the tube.

$$\lambda_m = \frac{12\ 350}{\text{volts}} \text{ Angstroms}†$$

Actually but little radiation is produced at this minimum wavelength. The energy distribution is such that the peak of energy occurs at about one and a half times this minimum wavelength.

The shorter the wavelength the greater the penetration of the radiation. Hence the desired penetrating power of X radiation is secured by selection of the proper voltage. This in fact gives a means of classifying X-ray tubes, that is, by voltage rating. Stating the voltage of an X-ray set is one way of stating the shortness of wavelength or penetration of the X radiation produced.

The lowest-voltage X-ray tubes commonly used are those producing

†An Angstrom is one hundred-millionth of a centimeter.

the least penetrating X rays, called Grenz rays. These rays are from about 1 to 10 Angstroms in length and are produced by voltages of from 5 to 15 kv. They are used primarily for radiography of thin objects such as flowers, insects, fabrics, and paper, where low penetration power is adequate.

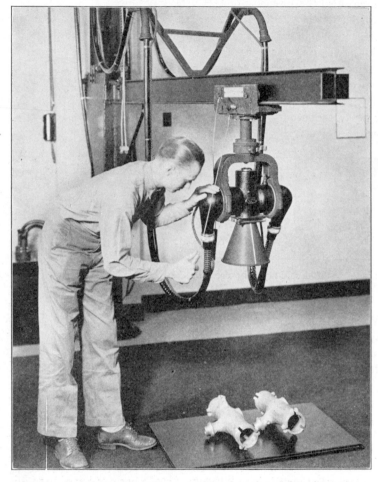

Fig. 4.3.   An industrial-type X ray used for detection of flaws in castings.

Courtesy Westinghouse

Tubes in the 10- to 25-kv range have come into use recently to produce mild X rays for the examination of spot welds of aluminum.

Next in the spectrum order are tubes operating at from about 20 to 50 kv, which produce radiation with minimum wavelengths of about 0.62 to 0.22 Angstrom. These are used extensively for crystallography and

FIG. 4.4. A million-volt X-ray unit being lowered into position preparatory to radio-
graphing a heavy steel casting.   *Courtesy General Electric*

diffraction studies, which provide a means of studying the atomic structure of materials and thereby facilitate prediction of physical and chemical properties of matter. They are also used to some extent in industrial radiography and micro-radiography.

The medical profession uses tubes of a wide voltage range, from about 30 to 100 kv (0.4 to 0.12 Angstrom minimum wavelength) because of the widely varying thicknesses of the human body. Medical and industrial fluoroscopy, in which the X-ray patterns are converted directly into a visible light pattern instead of being allowed to fall upon photographic emulsion, require tubes operating at voltages of 30 kv and upward. Therapy and ordinary industrial X-ray tubes, of which an installation is shown in Fig. 4.3, are in the 50- to 200-kv range. For deep therapy and thick-section industrial radiography operating voltages may be as high as 2000 kv, corresponding to radiation of only 0.006 Angstrom. Such units require special multisection tubes. A high-voltage unit is shown in Fig. 4.4.

FIG. 4.5. The face of an X-ray anode, which is the target for the cathode-ray beam, is tapered to direct the radiation out of the tube for use. The anode is made of some material of high thermal conductivity with the actual target an insert of tungsten, shown in the anode face.

Courtesy Westinghouse

X rays, as pointed out, can be reflected like light rays. The X rays leave the target in all directions. Only a small fraction of them go out through the glass window of its tube. The target is tapered, as Fig. 4.5 shows, so that the projection of the focal spot size in the useful direction is smaller than the actual spot size. This results in an effective concentration of the X-ray beam, because no focusing of X radiation by optical or magnetic methods is possible.

Because most of the energy of the electrons is dissipated at the target as heat, the focal spot becomes very hot for high-current short-time exposures and may be a limiting factor in X-ray production. The heat-dissipation ability of the anode system and its heat capacity are also limiting factors in X-ray production.

One means of increasing the output of the tube is to rotate the anode thereby exposing the target spot to the cathode beam for only a small portion of the time. Each particular spot is allowed a relatively long time to cool during each revolution. This is termed a rotating-anode tube and greatly increases the X-ray output possible without overheating, but of course introduces many mechanical problems, such as internal bearings and perfect balance of rotating anode.

High-speed radiography is the most recent development in the X-ray field. It is possible to make X-ray exposures as short as a millionth of a second, a feat of great value in the study of projectiles, guns, armor, armor-piercing shot, high-speed machine parts, and certain rapid chemical reactions. The equipment required, shown in Fig. 4.6, consists essentially of a

FIG. 4.6. This high-speed X-ray unit permits the taking of shadowgraphs in times as short as a millionth of a second. It consists of a surge generator in the center and X-ray tube standing vertically at the extreme right. The transformer and control units are not shown. The two rectangular members beside the tube are resistors.

Courtesy Westinghouse

surge generator utilizing a modified Marx circuit and an X-ray tube of special design. The bank of capacitors of the surge generator are charged in parallel and then switched to series connection, and their combined charge is suddenly released through the X-ray tube. The discharge — and hence the duration of radiation — is extremely short. No mechanical shutters are needed. The tube embodies a new principle of electron supply to provide the brief flood of current through it. Whereas the currents through ordinary industrial X-ray tubes seldom exceed 20 to 30 milliamperes, the peak current in a high-speed tube is about 2000 amperes.

The Cathode-Ray Oscilloscope‡

In X-ray tubes cathode rays function indirectly to provide the desired radiation. In several electricity-to-light transformation devices the cathode rays are used directly. The cathode-ray oscilloscope is one of them. With this relatively simple and inexpensive device many transient phenomena and steady-state cyclic phenomena of almost any frequency can be viewed and photographed.

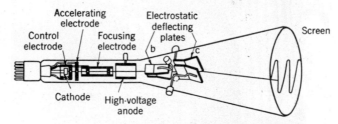

FIG. 4.7.   Diagrammatic view of an electrostatic-type cathode-ray oscilloscope.

A representative cathode-ray oscilloscope is shown in schematic outline in Fig. 4.7. A view of the internal construction of a 5-in. tube is displayed in Fig. 4.8 while a complete portable unit is in Fig. 4.9. The cathode-ray oscilloscope has four basic components sealed in a highly evacuated glass envelope. A thermionic cathode provides a source of electrons. A set of electrodes acts as an electron gun to collect the electrons into a beam, that is, a cathode ray, and to direct it along the central axis of the tube. A means of deflecting the beam in accordance with the phenomenon being studied is in the central portion of the tube. Finally, the inner surface of the enlarged end of the tube is coated with fluorescent material on which the directed cathode beam writes its visible trace.

In Fig. 4.7 the electrons are established by the cathode in the evacuated space. The control electrode controls the beam current. The electrons are accelerated toward the far end of the tube by the next electrode. Two

‡It is becoming commonplace to refer to such instruments as "oscillographs." Clearly such terminology is inaccurate because the device itself does not record although it is possible to photograph the trace with separate equipment. "Oscilloscope" is used here to distinguish such instruments from true oscillographs, discussed on pp 47–8.

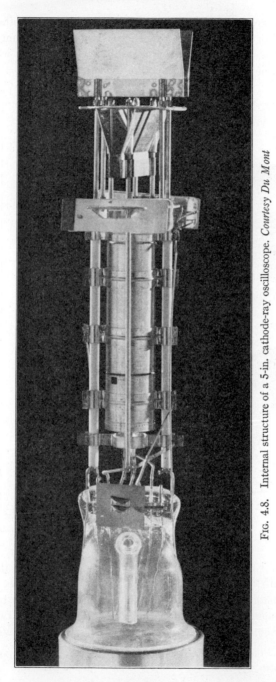

FIG. 4.8. Internal structure of a 5-in. cathode-ray oscilloscope. *Courtesy Du Mont*

anodes are employed. One is a focusing electrode,§ while the other carries a high potential for further accelerating the electrons. These elements simply establish a beam of electrons that, unless subjected to control, would fall at the center spot of the screen at the end of the tube.

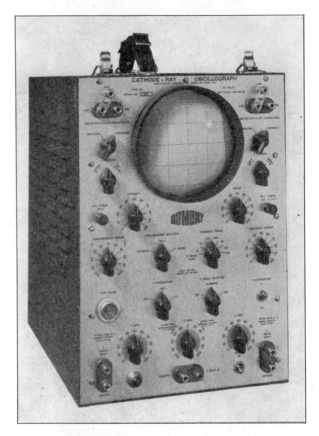

FIG. 4.9. A portable cathode-ray oscilloscope.   *Courtesy Du Mont*

In the central part of the tube is the means of deflecting the beam in accordance with the phenomenon to be "seen" on the scope. A cathode beam, being made up of electrons moving at high speed, can be deflected either by a magnetic or an electric influence. This provides two types of cathode-ray oscilloscopes. The one in Fig. 4.7 is the *electrostatic-deflection*

§For a study of the means by which electrons are focused to a concentrated beam, see Dow, *Fundamentals of Engineering Electronics*, pp 90-3, and MIT staff, *Applied Electronics*, pp 19-55.

type while the *electromagnetic-deflection* type is shown in Fig. 4.10. The system for deflecting the cathode-beam is the only major difference between them. In the electrostatic-deflection system two sets of plates, equivalent to the plates of two capacitors, are placed astride the cathode beam, but turned 90 degrees with respect to each other. If a voltage is placed on

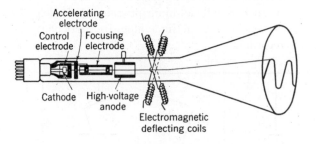

FIG. 4.10. Schematic arrangement of electromagnetic-deflection-type cathode-ray oscilloscope.

the first set of plates b the cathode beam sweeps back and forth in a straight line in accordance with variations in the applied voltage. Another voltage applied to the second set of plates c moves the beam in a line at right angles to the direction of control of the first set of plates. Hence, for example, if some cyclic varying voltage applied to plates b sweeps the beam back and forth at a constant rate,|| and the voltage to be studied is applied to plates c, the resultant action of the two sets of deflection plates causes the beam to trace on the screen the variation of the subject voltage with respect to time. In short, it draws a picture of the wave. If the variation is continuously repeated, the full image of the wave is seen on the screen, due in part to the persistence of vision and in part to the persistence of the fluorescent effect of the phosphor coating.

The action in the electromagnetic-deflection type is the same except that instead of electrostatic plates within the tube, two sets of coils, outside the tube and 90 degrees disposed with respect to each other, achieve the control of the beam in the two dimensions. One field causes the beam to move laterally with time; the other field controls vertical movement in accordance with magnitude of the subject phenomenon.

The electromagnetic tube, as compared to the electrostatic tube has structural simplicity and ruggedness and is slightly shorter. However the electrostatic tube is far more commonly used. Its measuring circuits require exceedingly small amounts of current and power, and are, therefore, simpler.

||Sweep circuits are described in Chapter 15, p 381.

Several natural and synthetic phosphors are available as fluorescent screen material, depending on the characteristics required.¶ Synthetic zinc orthosilicate, which as a natural mineral is known as willemite, is the one most commonly used. When struck by electrons it produces a persistent yellow-green spot, which corresponds closely to the wavelength of maximum eye sensitivity. Hence this phosphor is desirable for visual observation.

Tungstates of calcium and cadmium provide bluish-violet spots of short duration, which, being of high actinic value, are particularly useful for fast photographic recording.

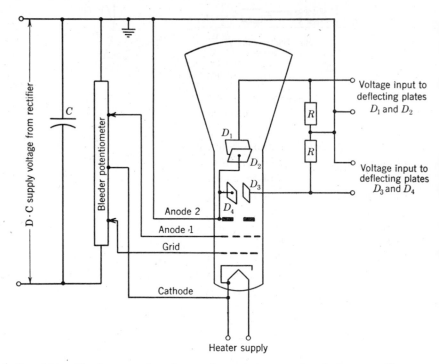

FIG. 4.11. Circuit connections for an electrostatic type of cathode-ray oscilloscope.

Zinc sulphide and zinc cadmium sulphide fluorescence is bluish and has considerable persistence or afterglow, which is a help if photography of low-frequency nonrecurring indications are involved. Zinc phosphate (red fluorescence) has an even longer after-glow, even of several seconds, which permits photography of rapid transients. By using combinations of these and other phosphors and additions of modifiers nearly any combination of screen material, even almost white, can be obtained.

¶ See Millman and Seely, *Electronics*, p 83.

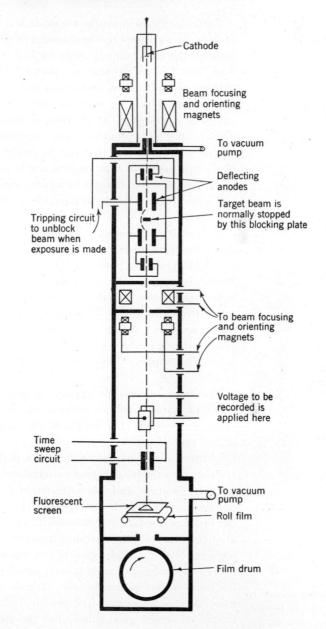

FIG. 4.12.   Schematic view of the electron oscillograph and the main elements of the circuit. Use of the fluorescent screen, roll film, or rotating film drum is optional and any one of these can be selected for operation by a mechanical device from the outside of the instrument, as is shown at the bottom of Fig. 4.14.

FIG. 4.13. The high-voltage cathode-ray beam is formed at the top of this structure and passes between successive anodes and between parallel electrostatic deflecting plates near the bottom, of which one set can be seen edgewise. The recording mechanism is below this beam-forming unit.

Courtesy Westinghouse

Cathode-ray oscilloscopes are made in a variety of sizes. As measured by the diameter of the viewing end, the most common sizes are 1, 2, 3, 5, and 9 in. The 1-in. is too small to permit little more than rough indications and so has rather limited application. The 2-in. scope is used where compactness is essential, as in airborne radar sets. The 3- and 5-in. tubes are most common, being the ones used in sets that can be easily carried like a suit-case. The 9-in. oscilloscope is too large to be portable but has use in laboratories where the more precise results obtainable with it are necessary.

The principal connections for an electrostatic-deflection cathode-ray oscilloscope are given in Fig. 4.11. A high d-c potential of between 1000 and 10 000 is supplied by a vacuum-tube rectifier. Potential for the cathode, grid, and anode 1 are taken from this supply by properly proportioned potentiometers. Anode 2 is connected to the grounded side of the a-c line. The cathode heater is usually supplied from the 115-volt 60-cycle line.

The term oscilloscope applies to sealed glass tubes primarily used for viewing changing electrical happenings. The image on the fluorescent screen can, of course, also be photographed. The brightness and sharpness of the trace depend on the nature of the phosphorous material and on the intensity, voltage, and concentration of the cathode beam. When single nonrepeating transients of the order of one hundred-thousandth of a second are to be observed, the recording limits of even the highest-voltage oscilloscopes is approached. In order to record appreciably greater speed, namely fractions of microseconds, the cathode voltage must be raised to values not practical with grid-controlled sealed glass tubes, and the recording method must be made more efficient. This is most commonly achieved by employing continuously pumped metal-body tubes with the photographic film directly exposed to the cathode ray, as Fig. 4.12 shows; these instruments are normally called cathode-ray oscillographs or electronic oscillographs.

The principle of operation of the oscilloscope and the electronic oscillograph is the same. The construction necessarily differs. The oscillograph, as shown in Figs. 4.12 to 4.14, has, like the electrostatic-deflection oscillo-

FIG. 4.14. The electronic oscillograph is used in laboratories of manufacturers and schools for the recording of electric transients more rapid than can be observed with the magnetic oscillograph or photographed with the cathode-ray oscilloscope.

Courtesy Westinghouse

scope a source of electrons, concentrating coils, anode, and deflection electrodes. The cathode beam, however, instead of falling on fluorescent coating at the bottom of the tube strikes either a film or a movable fluorescent screen, used primarily for adjustment purposes. A major operation difference between the two cathode-ray devices is that the oscillograph must be continuously pumped to maintain the high vacuum (about two microns). This necessity arises from having to place film inside the oscillograph, it being impractical to lead the cathode beam through any window to the film. The oscillograph has an additional set of electrodes and a means of blocking the beam to prevent fogging of the photographic film prior to arrival of the transients. Until a picture is to be taken, the beam falls on a diaphragm that shields the film. The transient to be measured (or a separate source voltage timed simultaneously with the transient), is applied to the electrodes of the beam-blocking section and thereby shifts the beam away from the blocking diagram and allows it to reach the film.

The cathode-ray oscillograph operates on a potential of about 50 000 volts. Use of this high voltage provides a cathode beam of high energy, which is also insensitive to stray fields and other extraneous influences.

Either hot or cold cathodes can be and are used as a source of electrons in electronic oscillographs. A thermionic cathode can provide a given emission at considerably lower voltage than a cold cathode, which depends on high field for electron emission. Hot-cathode electronic oscillographs operating at 25 000 volts have been built. Cold cathodes, on the other hand, have longer life than hot cathodes and, what is very important, provide a more concentrated beam of electrons. High-field emission has the additional merit that it does not require such a high degree of vacuum. For adequate emission, a cold cathode requires some appreciable gas pressure, a pressure that would cause rapid deterioration of a hot cathode by ion bombardment of the emitter surface. The higher gas pressure is desirable from a pumping standpoint and also because it shortens the time required to prepare the unit for operation after it has been opened for a film change or for any other reason.

The Electron Microscope*

Electronics has accomplished at least one "impossible." For many years there was ample and generally accepted proof that the limits of magnifications with microscopes had been reached. The limit is fixed by the wavelength of light. Unless the object is larger than one-half wavelength of the light being used, diffraction effects cause a blurred image according to Abbe's law of refraction. The wavelength of light near the center of the visible spectrum is about 0.000 025 inch, and so the smallest possible dimension for visible observation is about four millionths of an inch. Since the naked eye cannot distinguish differences in dimensions smaller than about 1/250 of an inch, this means the limit of magnifications possible with visible light is about 1000 times. By using light of wavelengths near the violet end of the spectrum and methods of increasing contrast, magnifica-

*Burton and Kohl, *The Electron Microscope.*

tions of about 1500 to 2000 diameters without serious distortion are obtained. No significant increase beyond this figure can be hoped for with the light microscope, if it is assumed that Abbe's law holds. It appeared that man would never be able to see anything smaller than about a few millionths of an inch. Certainly there is no immediate prospect of greater magnifications with ordinary light or even the radiation just below the visible.

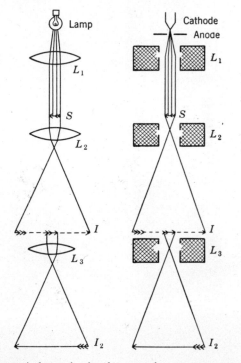

FIG. 4.15. The magnetic lenses in the electron microscope are arranged in the same manner and perform the same functions as the optical lenses in a light microscope. The magnetic lenses, however, are not moved as are the optical lenses; the same effect is more easily obtained simply by varying the current in the coils. This varies the intensity of the field acting on the electron rays and is equivalent to producing a lens with a continuously variable focal length. *Courtesy RCA*

However, with electronics we have a "light" that is not "ordinary." In 1923 Louis de Broglie of Paris put forward the notion that a wave train is associated with a moving electron. Specifically the wavelength of an electron is inversely proportional to the square root of the potential required to accelerate it. The wavelength of electrons, moving with a velocity corresponding to 60 kv have an effective wavelength of 0.05 Angstrom, which is but 1/100 000 that of light. Therefore, theoretically, if wavelength were the only factor, use of the wave motion associated with high-speed electrons should permit magnifications 100 000 times greater than with light. However, in determining the resolving power of any type of microscope another

Fig. 4.16. An electron microscope by which direct magnification in 40 steps from 100 to 20 000 times is possible. With it the eye can see details as small as one-quarter millionth of an inch.
Courtesy RCA

factor called numerical aperture which is a measure of the angle of acceptable incident radiation must be considered. In microscopes with glass lenses this angle can be very large, approaching 180 degrees, but with electron microscopes the angle is small, which decreases the numerical aperture.

In practical electron microscopes the net gain over the best light micro-scopes is at least ten to one; hence magnifications up to 20 000 diameters for direct viewing are readily obtainable. By photographic enlargement of elec-tron-microscope photographs final picture magnifications of 100 000 times have been obtained, compared with the 1000 to 2000 times possible with light microscopes.

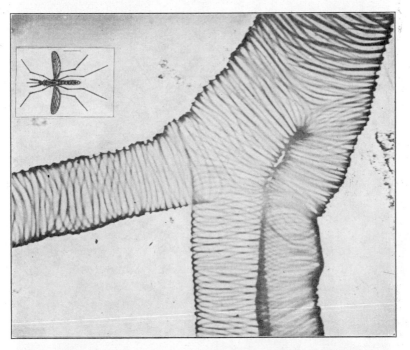

FIG. 4.17. The windpipe of a mosquito as seen tremendously magnified by the electron microscope. The many spiral hoops prevent the collapse of the sheer breathing tube. The smallest structural details are considerably less than one-half millionth of an inch.

Courtesy RCA

Following de Broglie's deduction it has been ascertained that the path of electrons in electric and magnetic fields are equivalent to those of light rays through optical systems. Electrostatic or electromagnetic fields have properties similar to those of optical lenses, and, consequently, electron images or shadowgraphs can be formed of minute particles having variable transparency to the electron beam.

The similarity of the light and the electron microscopes is shown in Fig. 4.15. A hot cathode provides the electrons, which are accelerated to a high velocity by the field between the cathode and the anode made 30 000 to 60 000 volts positive. The electrons speeding through a hole in the center

of the anode are shaped into a parallel beam by a magnetic field in a con-
denser lens and directed onto the specimen. The electron rays pass through
the specimen and are absorbed in varying degrees, depending on the compo-
sition of the subject. Those that pass through are focused and magnified by

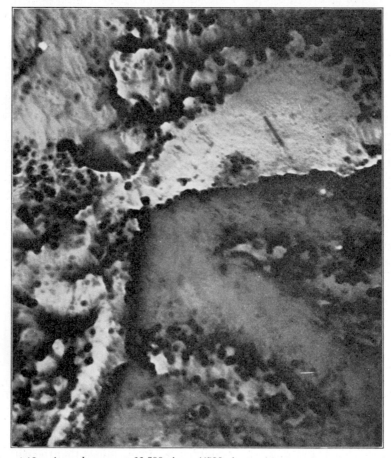

FIG. 4.18.   An enlargement 33 500 times (6700 times with the microscope and 5 by
photographic means) of a polished and etched molybdenum surface.

Courtesy Westinghouse

two or sometimes three successive steps by either electromagnetic or electrostatic fields. Finally the image, many thousand times enlarged, falls
either on a fluorescent screen producing a visible image for viewing, or
directly on a photographic plate if a permanent record is desired.

A high vacuum must be maintained within the housing, as in the cathode-
ray oscillograph, and for the same reason. Because the specimen and the

photographic film must be in the evacuated area a high-vacuum system is an essential auxiliary.

A laboratory version of an electron microscope is shown in Fig. 4.16. Portable models that one man can carry have been developed. The electron microscope is yet young, but already it has proved extremely valuable in the fields of chemistry, bacteriology, and metallurgy. The electron microscope offers some hope of solving the mystery of viruses, which undoubtedly hold clues to knowledge of great importance to man's health. Also extensive research has been done with the electron microscope on thin metallic oxide films that have much bearing on corrosion problems. The fact that the specimen to be magnified must be placed in a vacuum puts one limitation on subject matter. For example, bacteria and other life forms accustomed to pressures roughly atmospheric cannot survive and may be physically distorted under the vacuum conditions of the electron microscope. Also the high vacuum creates a rapid drying action that may affect the results. Because the subject is pelted with high-speed electrons its temperature is quickly raised perhaps enough to injure the specimen before the magnification picture is taken. These are practical limitations to the use of the electron microscope, withal its great resolving power. Thus for many purposes the electron microscope cannot replace the optical microscope. Typical microphotographs taken with the electron microscope are shown in Figs. 4.17 and 4.18.

Electronic Lamps

The passage of electrons through gases can be used to produce light directly. There are many common examples. The omnipresent neon signs are such. These are tubes containing neon, zeon, or other gases. A current discharge is established in the tubes between cold cathodes by potentials across them of several thousand volts. When the gas molecules are bombarded by the electrons in transit they emit a radiation of wavelength (color) characteristics of that gas. Mercury-vapor and sodium-vapor lamps are hot-cathode-discharge light sources. They are in every sense of the word electronic devices.

The most versatile of all electronic light sources is the mercury-vapor discharge. Aside from the well-known light source such as the old Cooper-Hewitt and the more modern high-pressure mercury lamps used widely in industry, the mercury-discharge is variously used as a bactericidal lamp, as a source of "black" light, as a sun lamp, and as the basis for fluorescent lamps. Passage of current through a vapor of mercury produces radiation in several narrow bands, that is, wavelengths; most of them fall outside the visible band, below the ultraviolet, but a few of them are in the visible region. The most important visible ones are the orange-yellow, the yellow-green, and the blue that characterize the mercury-vapor light. The distribution of intensities depends to a large extent on the vapor pressure. At low pressure most of the energy is at 2537 Angstroms which is well within the black-light region and happens to coincide very nearly with the wavelengths destructive to bacteria. As the pressures are increased, the proportion of the radiation occurring at the longer wavelengths increases.

Because at low pressures nearly 90 percent of the radiation from mercury vapor occurs below the violet, that is, invisible, mercury-vapor lamps are simple and economical sources of black light. There are several recognized bands of ultraviolet: the near ultraviolet or fluorescent region (4000 to 3200 Angstroms), the abiotic or bactericidal region (3000 to 1500 Angstroms), and the Shuman region (1500 to 100 Angstroms). Mercury-vapor discharges produce radiations in all of them.

For *black-light* purposes such as for mineralogy, intruder detection, counterfeit detection, and phosphorescent and fluorescent effects in theater and other displays, the mercury-vapor lamp consists of a pair of electrodes and a droplet of mercury. The discharge takes place between the electrodes first through argon, used as a starting gas, which allows the liquid mercury to vaporize. Because the starting voltage required is much higher than the discharge voltage, an auxiliary ballast transformer or reactor is required. The bulb must obviously be a glass that transmits these short radiations, which the ordinary lime and lead glasses used in incandescent lamps do not. Also for black-light lamps the glass envelope may contain pigments that absorb the visible light, or else the lamp fixture must be provided with suitable filters if the visible radiation is to be eliminated.

These same mercury-discharge lamps can also be used as sun lamps, because of the large amount of radiation in the erythemal or "sun-tanning" region. As sun lamps, however, the visible-light filters are not used, because the warmth from the visible and infrared radiations from the heater filament, is desirable.

Instead of producing ultraviolet radiation by a current discharge through mercury, it is possible to use argon, which also gives off these short-wavelength radiations when excited. The argon-glow lamp is built in very small wattages but is useful where low intensities of ultraviolet radiation are required. It has the merit of simplicity as it needs no auxiliaries, and, since its luminous output is small, it can generally be used without a filter.

Radiation of wavelengths from about 3000 to 1500 Angstroms have long been known to be lethal to bacteria. Current through mercury vapor at low pressure produces a particularly intense radiation at 2537 Angstroms, which fortunately coincides nearly with the peak of bactericidal effectiveness. Bactericidal lamps generally take the form of long extremely slender tubes of ultraviolet-transmitting glass in which electrodes are sealed in each end and which contain a small amount of mercury. Emission can be either high field or thermionic, that is, from cold or hot cathodes. Although nearly all types are designed to operate on 110-volt 60-cycle lines, all require starting equipment as explained before.

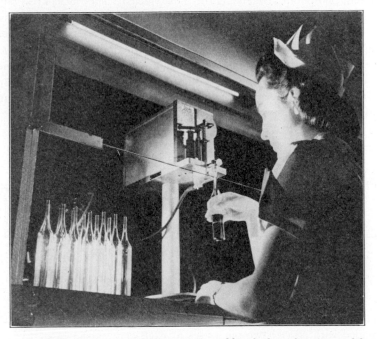

FIG. 4.19. Electronic bactericidal lamps of the cold-cathode variety are used here to purify the air in a serum ampule-filling room. The lamp is mounted horizontally, just above the filling machine. *Courtesy Westinghouse*

Nearly 80 percent of the radiation from this type of bactericidal lamp is in the 2537-Angstrom band, and only a small amount of visible light (bluish) and heat is produced. These lamps are used extensively to provide bacteria-free areas in hospitals and food-processing plants, and in drug preparation and packing plants. They are also used in connection with air-conditioning systems of offices, schools, and public dining places. They aid in the rapid tenderizing of meat by allowing the meat to age at an accelerated rate in warm, bacteria- and mold-free atmospheres. An installation of bactericidal lamps is shown in Fig. 4.19.

The common *fluorescent lamp* is actually a mercury-discharge lamp in which the inner walls of the tubes are coated with phosphors that have the ability to transform into visible light the 2537-Angstrom radiation so plentifully produced by the excitation of mercury vapor. The color of the visible light depends on the phosphor used; for example, zinc silicate fluoresces green; calcium tungstate, blue; and cadmium borate, pink. For daylight and white, combinations of these and other phosphors are used.

The efficiency of the energy transformations varies considerably with different phosphors, green being the most efficient. The efficiency in lumens per watt is, however, high with all fluorescent lamps. In general, they produce from two to four times as much light per watt as do incandescent lamps. Green is the most efficient phosphor with a lumen output of 1300 for the 20-watt lamp. This compares with about 835 for the 60-watt incandescent lamp. Daylight and white fluorescent 20-watt lamps have outputs of 760 and 860 lumens, respectively (which does not include the small amount of energy lost in the ballast).

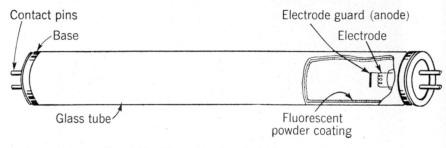

FIG. 4.20.   The mechanism of the fluorescent lamp.

Fluorescent lamps of the hot-cathode variety are tubular in shape and are provided with special two-pin bases at each end, as shown in Fig. 4.20. These pins are connected to the electrodes of the lamps, which are usually preheated before the lamp is started — this accounts for the brief delay in the lighting of a hot-cathode fluorescent lamp after the switch has been closed. A starter and a current limiter are required, although they may be incorporated into one device. In any case the two are connected in series. The starter, which may be a bimetallic thermostat or a neon-glow lamp, allows current to heat each electrode for a brief period and then quickly opens the circuit. This action produces a voltage surge sufficient to establish the arc between the lamp electrodes. The current-limiting device, usually a reactor, reduces the voltage across the terminals after it has started to the discharge voltage, in order to prevent excessive current through the lamp.

The fluorescent lamps with which we are most familiar have hot cathodes. However, the cold-cathode fluorescent lamp is receiving some attention. In this lamp the electron emission is established by a high field. This type of lamp has the merit of instant starting but at a small sacrifice in efficiency and life.

In Conclusion

This does not bring us to the end of the things electrons can do, not even to the edge of the field of usefulness of the versatile cathode ray. The examples chosen are representative and display the basic principles. But there are many more ways in which the principles have been put to work, some that are so new that the extent of their usefulness has not yet been mapped.

The mass spectrometer is one. This device, long known in research laboratories first made its appearance as an industrial tool for performing a sorting operation on gas molecules. Electrons from a thermionic cathode are formed into a beam, which is directed into the gas whose analysis is desired. The fast-moving electrons ionize the gas molecules. The tube in which this action occurs is placed between the faces of a strong curved electromagnet. The ionized molecules under the influence of this strong magnetic field tend to move along the tube in a circular path. The ions, however, have mass; hence the radii of their paths is dependent on the weights of the molecules. The heavier molecules mov e in an arc of larger radius than the lighter ones. At the end of the curved tube are slits through which emerge the molecules, now separated according to their masses. Here they give up their charges, constituting a measurable current that is proportional to the amount of molecules of that mass present in the original sample of gas.

The mass spectrometer, of which a view is shown in Fig. 4.21, is in effect an electronic centrifuge. It probably will have many uses, such as for process control in oil refineries and chemical plants and for leak detection. The mass-spectrometer principle was one of the three used in separation of the uranium isotopes for the first atomic bombs.

Television, of course, rests on the principles of the cathode ray. The iconoscope is a highly developed cousin of the cathode-ray oscilloscope. Facsimile transmission, by which photographs and other information are sent either by wire or by radio, uses electron beams that sweep swiftly across sensitized surfaces varying in intensity in keeping with the image transmitted to produce a faithful likeness of the original.

Indicative of development of the electronics art is that electronics devices are not only simply built as independent tools for specific industrial jobs, but also are being adapted to control other electronic devices. For example, in the making of fluorescent lamps, themselves electronic tubes, the fluorescent powders are now being applied to the inner walls of the tube by the same electrostatic principle used in electronic air cleaning. X-ray exposures are timed automatically by an electronic exposure meter that integrates the amount of radiation falling on the film and shuts off the current when the proper density has been reached.

New and useful electronic devices are appearing with regularity. This would be disconcerting to the student of electronics except for one thing.

Fig. 4.21. Analysis of a mixture of gases is made quickly with the mass spectrometer even if the gases be chemically identical and nearly alike as to mass.

Courtesy Westinghouse

All of them are but variations of the ways the basic principles have been applied. If one has a knowledge of the elementary principles no new electronic device can long be mysterious. It is these principles with which the following pages are concerned.

SUMMARY

X rays have characteristics similar to light, except they are invisible and have a much shorter wavelength. They move in straight lines, can be reflected and refracted, and are not influenced by magnetic or electric fields.

X-ray tubes are broadly classified according to the wavelength of their radiation, indicated by the anode voltage.

Tubes of from 5 to 15 kv are used for the radiography of thin objects where the low penetrating power is adequate.

Tubes of from 20 to 50 kv are used for industrial radiography and crystallography.

Tubes of from 30 to 100 kv are used for medical and industrial fluoroscopy.

Tubes of from 50 to 200 kv are used for industrial radiography.

Voltages as high as 2000 kv are used for thick-section radiography.

Cathode-ray tubes write a visible trace on a fluorescent screen. This is accomplished by deflection of a cathode beam (electrons emitted by the cathode) focused toward the mid-point of the screen. Deflection is either electrostatic (by deflecting plates) or electromagnetic (by deflecting coils).

Cathode-ray oscilloscopes combine the cathode-ray tube with a time-base equipment and a means for deflecting the beam in proportion to the voltage observed.

The electron microscope manifests a magnification at least ten times greater than is possible with the light microscope, largely because of the greater resolving power made possible by the shorter wavelength of an electron beam as compared to a light beam.

Electronic lamps include such common examples as mercury-vapor, sodium-vapor, neon, ultraviolet (sun lamps), black-light, bactericidal and fluorescent lamps. The fluorescent lamp is actually a mercury-discharge lamp in which the inner walls of the tube are coated with phosphors to transform the invisible mercury radiation to light within the visible spectrum.

REFERENCES

W. G. Dow, *Fundamentals of Engineering Electronics*, John Wiley & Sons, New York, 1937, pp 90–3.

MIT Electrical Engineering Staff, *Applied Electronics*, John Wiley & Sons, New York, 1943, pp 19–55.

Jacob Millman and Samuel Seely, *Electronics*, McGraw-Hill Book Co., New York, 1941, pp 83, also 352–8.

Burton and Kohl, *The Electron Microscope*, Reinhold Publishing Co., 1942.

Herbert J. Reich, *Theory and Applications of Electron Tubes*, McGraw-Hill Book Co., New York, 1944, pp 628–48.

R. A. Millikan, *Electrons (+ and −), Protons, Photons, Neutrons, and Cosmic Rays*, Univ. Chicago Press, Chicago, 1935, pp 301–19, also 404–56.

Z. J. Atlee, "Design and Application of X-Ray Tubes," *Electronics*, October 1940, pp 26–30 and 62–64.

Chapter 5

TWO–ELEMENT TUBES

Electronics has to do with the action of electrons in gases. The most simple electronic tube consists of two elements within an envelope containing gas, usually at a low pressure. One of these elements or electrodes is caused to emit electrons by any one of the principles set forth in Chapter 2. Herewith, we are concerned only with the action of a thermionic cathode and its companion electrode, the anode which receives electrons emitted by the cathode. The fundamental laws governing electron emission of a thermionic cathode were made known by Richardson (see Chapter 2, p 14) about the opening of the 20th century and were first introduced in a practical application by Fleming in 1904. So, indeed, began the career of the two-element tube, one of the oldest, most common of the vacuum-tube family, and exceeded by none in range of sizes needed to fill the important role assigned them in present-day electronics.

Classification of Two-Element Tubes

Tubes consisting of two elements, namely, cathode and anode, have been classified by the Radio Manufacturers Association as *kenotrons* if the tube is highly evacuated, or as *phanotrons* if the tube is gas-filled. The RMA classifications of the former types is derived from the Greek "kenos," meaning "empty" and logically applies to vacuum tubes. Phanotrons are derived from the Greek meaning "with light," which applies to gas-filled tubes in which conduction is always associated with a characteristic glow.

In the kenotron the gas pressure is so low that the remaining gas molecules have no appreciable effect upon the operation of the tube. If the cathode and anode are relatively closely spaced, electrons emitted by the thermionic cathode flow to the anode when the anode is more positive than the cathode. When the anode is negative with respect to the cathode there is substantially no current. Hence, the kenotron has a unidirectional conductivity, that is, it is a *rectifier*, the function of which is discussed in detail in Chapter 9.

The cathode of a kenotron is a thermionic emitter of one of the types discussed in the Chapter 2.

The anode is the element functioning as the receiver of all electrons emitted by the cathode. With the exception of a few specialty tubes, the anode is the more positive electrode. In earlier tubes, this element was a rectangular flat electrode and was hence called the "plate." This terminology has been popularly used to date but is not used in this text.

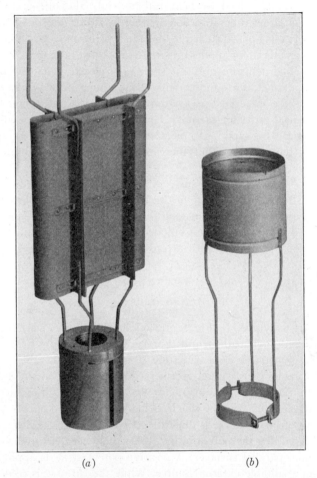

(a) (b)

Fig. 5.1. (a) Kenotron anodes are oblong if the cathode is constructed of several parallel strands supported in a flat plane, or (b) a cylindrical anode is used if the cathode is arranged in a central core. *Courtesy Westinghouse*

Of the two electrodes the anode takes most of the punishment, because physically it is a backstop for fast-moving electrons and must also dispose of much heat picked up from the cathode, resulting from losses within the tube. Heating of the anode is directly proportional to the electron flow in amperes times the voltage between cathode and anode, which varies from a few volts in small tubes to 5 kv in large power tubes. This heat must be radiated by the anode structure as the anode must remain reasonably cool. Therefore, adequate cooling of the anode is one of the important considerations in tube design and operation. The anodes of tubes of 1-kw rating or less are usually cooled by heat radiated into the surrounding space. The anodes of larger tubes are cooled either by water flow or by air forced through ventilating fins attached to the anode structure.

A suitable material for anodes must be a good heat radiator, adaptable to operation at high temperatures, and be a poor electron emitter. The more common anode metals are molybdenum, tantalum, nickel, and zirconium. Sometimes these materials are coated with graphite or carbon black to improve the heat-radiating capacity. Graphite itself sometimes is used as an anode material. It is superior to metals in ability to radiate heat and operate at high temperatures, but increases the difficulty of obtaining and maintaining a high vacuum.

The anode shape must be such as to result in a reasonably uniform current density over the surface of the anode. Kenotron anodes are shaped to obtain a uniform spacing between the cathode and anode surfaces. The two preferred shapes are the flat oblong type represented by Fig. 5.1a, or a cylindrically shaped anode with a centralized straight cathode illustrated by Fig. 5.1b.

Kenotrons

Kenotrons, as typified by Fig. 5.2, are characterized by a variable voltage drop dependent upon load current. Furthermore, the drop is relatively high and may vary between approximately 50 volts for small tubes to several thousand volts for high-voltage rectifiers. This relatively large voltage drop is caused by the *space charge* or dense cloud of electrons that surrounds a heated cathode, the action of which, being negative, is to oppose emission.

The effect of space charge is illustrated by the voltage gradient diagram, Fig. 5.3, illustrating the potential distribution between electrodes assumed to be flat and parallel surfaces. A positive potential P_1 is applied to the anode from a suitable external source. While the cathode is cold, that is, when there is no electron emission, the potential distribution between anode and cathode is uniform and is represented by the straight line 1. If the cathode is heated so as to emit electrons, many electrons surround the cathode in a cloud. Because the electrons produce a negative field, the potential gradient outward from the cathode is modified by the presence of the electron cloud, and the potential distribution curve becomes convex downward as shown by curve 2. If the cathode temperature is increased so as to increase further the density of electrons about the cathode, the poten-

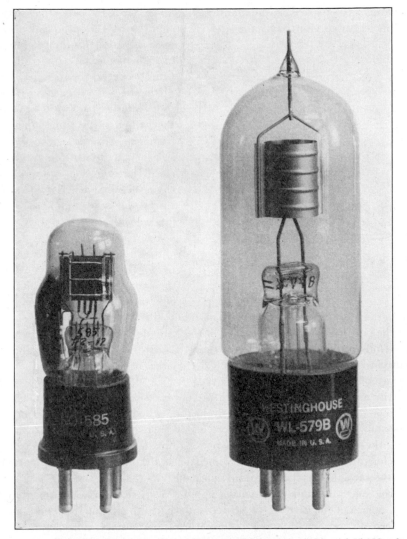

Fig. 5.2. Kenotrons for rectification of 750 volts, 0.01 ampere (left), and 15 000 volts, 0.025 ampere (right). Approximately two-thirds size.   *Courtesy Westinghouse*

tial curve is forced even further downward as shown by curve 3, wherein the slope of the potential line is zero at the cathode surface. As the cathode temperature is further raised the potential dips slightly negative,* curve 4, a short distance in front of the cathode surface.

*For a discussion of this effect see Millman and Seely, *Electronics*, p 223, Dow, *Fundamentals of Engineering Electronics*, pp 188–91 and 242–8.

A density of space charge manifest by either 3 or 4 indicates that some of the electrons emitted by the cathode do not pass to the cathode. This is most apparent by the condition of 4 wherein an electron emitted from the cathode enters a space predominantly negative. It is thereby forced backward, toward the cathode. Electrons emitted from the cathode surface with sufficient speed are able to overcome the repulsion of the electron space charge and do pass to the anode. Others, emitted with less velocity, return to the cathode surface.

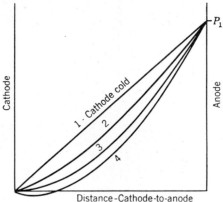

FIG. 5.3. The space charge increases as the cathode temperature is raised to emit more electrons.

Because some electrons emitted by the cathode do not reach the anode, within the conditions illustrated between regions 3 and 4, the anode current is said to be *space-charge-limited*.† Thus, when the slope of the potential line at the surface of the cathode is zero or negative, less electrons reach the anode than are emitted by the cathode and the anode current is limited by the degree of space charge, rather than by the degree of cathode emission.

Any increase in cathode temperature beyond that required to establish a zero or slightly negative gradient from the cathode surface (curve 3 or 4) does not result in appreciably more anode current. The reason for this is that the degree of space charge increases to render the number of electrons reaching the anode approximately unchanged although the number emitted by the cathode may be increased enormously.

The effect of anode potential upon the space charge is shown by Fig. 5.4a. Let the cathode be heated sufficiently to exhibit the large space charge of curve 1 with anode potential P_1 applied. Here, considerably less than the total electrons emitted by the cathode reach the anode because of the strong repelling influence of the negative space charge near the cathode.

†The important role of space charge in electronic tubes is condensed here to illustrate its effect without further explanation. For more detailed account see:
  Dow, *Fundamentals of Engineering Electronics*, pp 97–102 and 188–91.
  MIT staff *Applied Electronics*, pp 115–24 and 155–62.
  Terman, *Radio Engineering*, pp 112–15.
  Terman, *Radio Engineers Handbook*, pp 286–9.
  Millman and Seely, *Electronics*, pp 208–24.

The anode current by these conditions is represented by I_{A1} of Fig. 5.4b. If the anode potential is increased to P_2 without changing the cathode

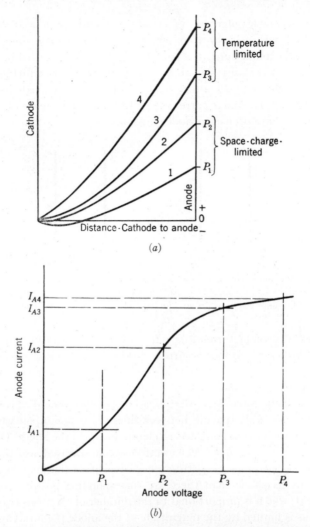

FIG. 5.4. The space charge is reduced (a) by increasing the positive anode potential. This effect upon anode current (b) indicates an appreciable influence at a low potential which diminishes as the potential is raised to attract nearly all electrons emitted by the cathode.

temperature, the negative dip of potential is decreased as curve 2 of Fig. 5.4a shows. More of the electrons emitted by the cathode then pass to the anode. Anode current increases to I_{A2}, Fig. 5.4b. However, for either of these conditions not all electrons emitted by the cathode reach the anode. Some are returned to the cathode surface, and the anode current is space-charge-limited.

Raising the anode potential to P_3 results in a positive slope at the cathode surface, Fig. 5.4a. All electrons emitted by the cathode now reach the anode, and the anode current, I_{A3} of Fig. 5.4b, now is limited by the cathode emission; that is, it is said to be *temperature-limited*. A further increase of anode potential to P_4 alters only slightly the potential distribution, curve 4 of Fig. 5.4a. Anode current, I_{A4}, Fig. 5.4b, is increased but slightly because of the limitation of cathode emission.

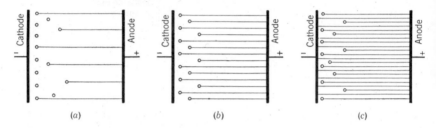

FIG. 5.5. If the anode voltage is low (*a*) few electrons are pulled to the anode; if it is increased (*b*) all electrons emitted by the cathode are pulled to the anode; if it is further increased (*c*) no more electrons are available and the anode current does not increase.

Another way of picturing the effect of space charge is illustrated in Fig. 5.5.‡ At (a) the cathode is surrounded by a space charge of electrons. A relatively small positive potential applied to the anode is represented by a few horizontal lines of force. The magnitude of the potential is indicated by the density of the force lines; that is, a low positive potential corresponds to the relatively wide spacing between lines. Electrons upon which force lines of the positive terminate are accelerated toward the anode. Other electrons remain in the space between electrodes, concentrated near the cathode surface. These electrons constitute a negative space charge. Clearly, more electrons are available than there are corresponding positive force lines. The current, which is proportional to the number of electrons reaching the anode, thus is limited by the magnitude of the anode potential and not by the number of electrons emitted from the cathode. The conditions represented by Fig. 5.5a show that the anode current is space-charge-limited.

If the anode potential is increased, the density of horizontal force lines likewise is increased as in Fig. 5.5b. One positive force line is now available for each electron, and all electrons emitted by the cathode are carried over to the anode. This condition corresponds to curve 3 of Fig. 5.4a. Further

‡For further details of this concept see MIT staff, *Applied Electronics*, pp 166–8.

increase in electron emission by raising the cathode temperature does not result in any appreciable increase of anode current, because the conditions represented by Fig. 5.5a are immediately approached.

If the anode potential is increased as in Fig. 5.5c, more positive force lines are available than electrons, and some positive lines then must terminate directly on the cathode. The magnitude of anode current thus is limited by the number of electrons available, and the anode current is said to be limited by *thermionic emission.*

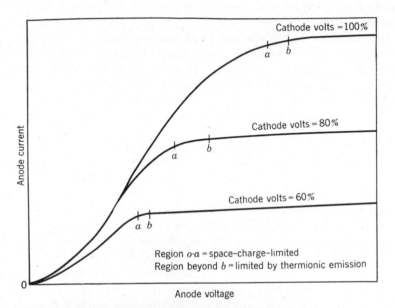

FIG. 5.6. A typical kenotron characteristic illustrates space-charge-limited anode current below the knee of each curve and thermionic-emission-limited above the knee.

The sharpness of the knees of the curves at saturation varies considerably with the type of emitter used. In general, the saturation effect takes place much more gradually with oxide-coated emitters than with those of tungsten or thoriated tungsten.

The characteristics of a typical kenotron are shown in Fig. 5.6 in which characteristic curves are given for three cathode voltages (cathode temperatures). For anode voltages below the knee of each curve (region 0–a), the anode current increases approximately as the three-halves power of the anode voltage. Over this part of the characteristic the anode current is space-charge-limited. As the anode voltage is increased beyond the knee (region beyond b) of each curve, the anode current is practically limited by thermionic emission. The slight rise in anode current throughout this part of the characteristic is caused by the Schottky§ effect and is produced by high-field emission of electrons from the cathode. That is, superimposed upon the dominant thermionic emission is a small amount of emission caused by the increasing positive potential of the anode.

Because of the effect of space charge, kenotrons have a relatively high-voltage drop. If these tubes are to operate at a reasonable efficiency, they must be used in a circuit in which the voltage drop through the tubes is a relatively small percentage of the output voltage. Kenotrons operate at a satisfactory efficiency and have a wide field of usefulness if applied in accord with this principle.

Kenotrons are highly evacuated and have excellent insulating quality when the polarity is reversed, applying a high negative voltage on the anode. Because of this characteristic, these tubes withstand a high inverse voltage and are excellently suited for rectification of high voltages. They are used to supply voltages as high as 100 000 for such services as X ray, radio transmitters, and electrostatic dust precipitators.

Properties of a Gas Discharge

A molecule of gas is structurally no different from a molecule of metal. It consists of a nucleus with its protons and neutrons surrounded by the proper number of electrons to form a neutral atom. These electrons form a configuration about the nucleus and reside in several space shells.

To this point, the description of a gas molecule and one of metal is identical, but the similarity ends here. As discussed, the atoms in a metal are sufficiently close together that free electrons are present in large quantities. In a gas the adjacent atoms are spaced far apart and few free electrons exist. The effective distance that an electron must traverse before colliding with successive atoms in a gas is called the *mean free path* and is inversely proportional to the atomic density.

When one electron is removed from the normal atom of a gas, two particles become the products of the separation. One particle is the removed electron. The other particle is the *ion*, and the process is termed *ionization*. The ion comprises most of the mass; in fact, the electron is so small by comparison that the mass of the ion can be considered the same as the original atom. However, the electric charge on the electron and that on the ion are identical. It is negative for the electron and positive for the ion that has been formed by the removal of an electron from an atom. An atom from which one or more electrons have been removed is said to be positively ionized because it has a deficiency of negative charges. Conversely, an atom with a surplus of electrons is negatively ionized.

§See MIT staff, *Applied Electronics*, p 157.

An electron is removed from a gas atom when sufficient kinetic energy is imparted to one of the outer electrons of the atom by collision with another electron moving at high speed. An electron thus receiving a sufficient amount of added energy is then able to "escape" from its own nucleus. If we remember that the speed of an electron depends upon the electric-field intensity through which the electron moves, it is apparent that a relation exists between electric potential and the speed necessary for one electron to ionize a gas atom. This relationship is called *ionizing potential* and differs widely for different gases. The most commonly encountered figure is 10.39 volts for mercury and 15.69 volts for argon.

The name given to conduction through gases is *gaseous discharge*. Ionization of the gas is necessarily present in all types of gaseous discharge. These can be divided into two classes, non-self-maintaining and self-maintaining depending upon whether or not some external source of ionization is required to maintain the discharge.

TOWNSEND DISCHARGE

The first stage of gaseous conduction in cold-cathode tubes is the *Townsend discharge*‖ with the characteristics illustrated in Fig. 5.7. If voltage is applied between parallel metal electrodes spaced a short distance apart in a

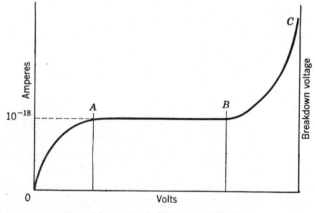

Fig. 5.7. A typical Townsend discharge.

gas, the current increases with small increments of voltage from 0 to A. As the voltage increases from A to B, the current remains constant at a minute value until the voltage reaches B and then increases rapidly as the voltage is increased further to C.

The reason for these three steps lies first in the region 0–A where the

‖See MIT staff *Applied Electronics*, p 138.

relatively few gas molecules present in the space are drawn toward the electrodes by the voltage. Because relatively few ionized particles are present, they are all attracted by a low voltage. Further increase in voltage to value B does not result in a current increase, because no more free electrons are present. The third stage of the characteristic, showing an increase toward C, occurs because the voltage becomes sufficient to accelerate the few electrons already available to velocity sufficient to ionize gas molecules by collision. Additional electrons are then available in the space to contribute to the flow. The current thereupon rises. Toward C a small increase

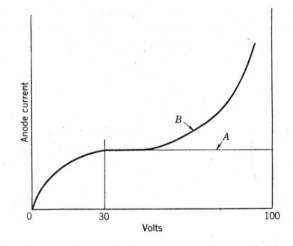

FIG. 5.8.   The anode current of a gas-filled phototube B is several times greater than a vacuum phototube A for the same values of voltage and light intensity.

in voltage tends to increase the current without limit. For all parts of the characteristic from 0 to limit C the discharge is dependent upon a supply of ions from some external source, and the discharge is non-self-maintaining. When the external source is removed, the discharge ceases.

One common device utilizing Townsend-discharge characteristics is the gas-filled phototube. A typical characteristic of a vacuum phototube is represented by curve A of Fig. 5.8. The voltage applied to a vacuum phototube has relatively little effect upon the emission current above about 30 volts. If the tube is filled with an inert gas at the proper pressure, the characteristic changes to curve B. The increase in anode current is a result of ionization caused by the collision of electrons emitted from the light-sensitive cathode with molecules present in the gas space. The current of ionization is usually from three to five times greater than the original emission from the cathode surface. The anode current rises steeply toward 100 volts necessitating the restriction of the voltage across gas-filled photo-tubes to a maximum of 90 volts.

BREAKDOWN

As the voltage across a Townsend discharge is increased, new electrons are liberated from the gas molecules by collision with the electrons. These new electrons also are accelerated by the electric field and further collide with other gas molecules to produce additional new electrons. The process is cumulative. Under these conditions the discharge becomes self-maintaining. It does not depend upon any external source of ionization for its continuance, providing the positive ions so formed release other electrons either from the cathode or the gas itself.

The voltage at which this action takes place is known as the *breakdown voltage*. It depends upon the kind of gas, its pressure and temperature, and upon the material and shape of the electrodes.

GLOW DISCHARGE

A glow discharge is readily recognized by the luminosity in the gas as represented by the familiar neon sign and several common voltage-regulator tubes. The radiation of light is the result of electrons, raised to orbits of high energy in atoms by collision with electrons from the cathode, returning to their normal orbits. As each electron drops into its orbit of lower energy, the surplus energy is released as a quantum of radiation. For many gases, such as neon, the frequency of the radiation is in the visible region.

The electrical characteristic of a *glow discharge* is a voltage drop approximately equal to the minimum breakdown voltage of the gas, which is several times greater than the ionization potential of the gas. The voltage drop between electrodes remains substantially constant as the current is varied over a wide range.

The area of the cathode covered by the glow is proportional to the current of the discharge. The glow area increases linearly with current so as to maintain a constant current density. This characteristic is called a *normal glow*, and the voltage drop remains constant. The maximum current for a normal glow occurs when the entire cathode surface is covered by the glow. A further increase of ·discharge current then increases the current density to an *abnormal glow*, and the voltage drop increases with a rise in current. For this reason, then, glow-type voltage-regulator tubes must operate within the region of normal glow to hold a constant voltage.

ARC DISCHARGE

As the current density at the cathode increases throughout an abnormal glow, the cathode surface becomes heated by positive-ion bombardment.

As the current increases, a transition occurs and the voltage across the discharge suddenly decreases significantly. The discharge then transfers to an *arc* in which the current is observed to concentrate within a small area of the cathode. The current becomes independent of the voltage; in fact, the voltage drops somewhat as arc current increases.

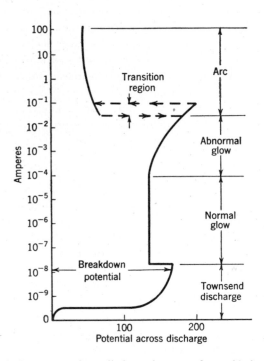

Fig. 5.9. A typical sequence of gas discharge between plane cold electrodes in a gas-filled tube.

The current density in an arc discharge is high. Consequently, the heat generated in the arc core becomes enormous. Arcs are the highest man-created temperatures, reaching 7000 F in carbon arcs or 5000 F in the arc between welding electrodes. For this reason, electrodes used with arc discharges must be able to withstand these high temperatures, such as liquid mercury or carbon pencils. These high temperatures are put to good use in the melting of electrodes for welding and in arc furnaces.

A summary of the various types of gas discharge, showing the change in characteristics as the current is increased is given in Fig. 5.9.¶

¶ See MIT staff, *Applied Electronics*, p 148.

Introduction of Gas in Thermionic Tubes

The previous discussion concerned the characteristic forms of discharge within gas-filled tubes having plane cold metallic electrodes. The behavior of tubes in which the cathode is heated to furnish a source of electrons is quite different.

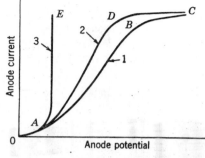

First, consider the effect of introducing a minute quantity of inert gas into a conventional kenotron. With reference to Fig. 5.10, if the tube is highly evacuated and the cathode is heated to normal temperature, the tube characteristics correspond to curve 1. In the region AB the anode current is space-charge-limited and is limited to a maximum value C by thermionic emission.

FIG. 5.10. Introducing a small amount of gas changes a typical kenotron characteristic (1) to a lower-voltage drop (2) and by proper pressure to (3).

If a small amount of gas is admitted to the tube, positive ions immediately become available in copious quantities as a result of collision with them by the electrons moving rapidly toward the anode. The presence of positive ions has two effects. First, being positive charges, they are accelerated toward the cathode and contribute to the current flow. (Remember that current can be considered either as a flow of negative charges from cathode to anode, or a flow of positive charges from anode to cathode.) However, this effect is extremely small in comparison to the electron-current flow and is of little practical importance. The second and more important effect of positive ions is the reduction of negative space charge near the cathode. This is the factor responsible for altering the characteristic of gas-filled tubes. To review the effect of negative space charge in a vacuum tube, the cloud of electrons in the vicinity of the cathode repel those immediately leaving the cathode. Their effect then is to decrease the anode current to something less than the total number of electrons emitted by the cathode. Positive ions appearing close to the cathode, as a result of gas being introduced, partially neutralize the electron space charge clearing the path for a larger portion of the electrons emitted by the cathode to pass unimpeded to the anode.

The partial counteraction of space charge is represented by curve 2, Fig. 5.10, showing that the knee of the characteristic is shifted from B to D. The anode voltage corresponding to the space-charge-limited portion AD of the characteristic is considerably reduced. However, the maximum anode current is still limited to C by thermionic emission as the total number of electrons emitted by the cathode is fixed by its temperature and has not been changed. For a given anode current the voltage drop across the tube is reduced from curve 1 to curve 2.

If the proper amount of gas is admitted to the tube, the characteristic can be further improved to curve 3, corresponding to further neutralization of negative space charge.

The characteristic of curve 3 indicates that anode current is now practically independent of anode voltage. The limit of anode current can be fixed

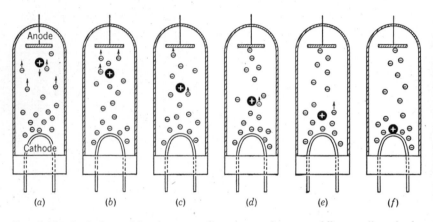

FIG. 5.11. A single positive ion neutralizes many electrons while traveling slowly toward the cathode.

only by the external circuit constants. These must be chosen to restrict the maximum anode current to limit E corresponding to the maximum safe emission from the cathode; otherwise, the gas-filled tube quickly destroys itself.

The effectiveness of the positive ions in neutralizing negative space charge is a result of the relative mass between an electron and a positive ion. The mass of the positive ion is many times greater than that of the electron, but the two are accelerated by the same electric field. Therefore, the relatively heavy ion moves toward the cathode with a velocity equal to only a small fraction of the electron speed (about $1/600$ for mercury or $1/200$ for neon). For this reason, a single positive ion can effectively neutralize many electrons on its flight from anode to cathode.

Neutralization of space charge by positive ions is illustrated in Fig. 5.11. A gas particle is ionized near the anode at (a) and begins moving slowly toward the cathode. An electron moving rapidly toward the anode soon approaches the positive ion, and during the brief interval that this particular electron remains close to the ion the space charge in the vicinity of the pair is effectively neutralized. This original electron is not deterred in its flight toward the anode and soon passes on. A second electron, (b), then approaches the positive ion, and, like the first, a new pair renders the gas space neutral within their sphere of influence.

The process is repeated, (c), (d), and (e), each time the positive ion taking on a new electronic partner until upon its final arrival at the cathode, (e), five different electrons have passed it closely, and with each one a small portion of the gas space has been neutralized. In actuality, the relative speeds between electrons and the slower ions is so greatly different that hundreds rather than five electrons are neutralized for each positive ion. Furthermore, at any instant there are relatively equal numbers of electrons and positive ions present in the gas space, whereas Fig. 5.11 illustrates the presence of only a single ion.

The presence of nearly equal numbers of electrons and positive ions indicates the gas space to be essentially neutral; yet, because of the effect of Fig. 5.11, it is not necessary for them to be produced at equal rates. That they are not is manifest by the proportionally large current carried by electrons with a negligible share assumed by the positive ions.

The characteristic drawn in Fig. 5.10 results if a tube is filled with a small amount of gas. The characteristics typical of practical gas-filled tubes wherein the gas pressure and electrode design are carefully co-ordinated is represented in Fig. 5.12. The voltage drop across the tube remains practically constant and is independent of anode current. In fact, the anode voltage decreases

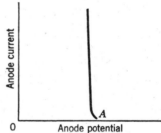

Fig. 5.12.   Positive ions so completely neutralize electron space charges that the tube voltage drop becomes independent of anode current.

slightly with increasing current. The portion from 0 to A, corresponding to the same section of curve 3 of Fig. 5.10, appears at such an infinitesimal anode current that it does not show on the characteristics of commercial tubes.

The effect of gas in a tube is manifested by the potential-distribution diagram of Fig. 5.13. The shape of this curve results from the relative masses of the electrons and positive ions. Electrons emitted from the cathode travel away toward the anode at high velocity while positive ions approach the cathode at low velocity. The result is a denser cloud of positive ions than negative electrons near the surface of the cathode. The effect is a positive space charge called *cathode sheath* near the cathode surface. At the boundary of the cathode sheath, such as point A, the positive space charge raises the potential almost equal to the applied anode voltage and creates a tendency for electrons to collect at this point instead of going to the anode. Each electron neutralizes a positive ion, which diminishes the space charge practically to zero. The zone wherein the space charge is practically zero is called the *plasma* and extends from the extremity of the cathode sheath to within a small distance of the anode surface. Within the plasma region the voltage drop is small. An additional voltage drop appears through a thin layer near the anode surface BC and is called the *anode sheath*.

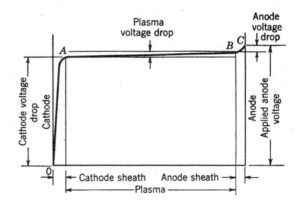

FIG. 5.13. The voltage distribution in a gas-filled tube shows that the anode is virtually moved toward the cathode to the boundary of the cathode sheath.

The voltage drop through the anode sheath and plasma is negligible compared to the drop through the cathode sheath; thus practically all of the voltage drop in gas-filled tubes occurs across the relatively short thickness of the cathode sheath. A comparison of the characteristics of gas-filled tubes, Fig. 5.13, with those of a vacuum tube, Fig. 5.3, helps clarify the principal differences between these two types.

Phanotrons

Phanotrons are gas-filled two-element tubes. Most phanotrons are mercury-filled, although a few special-purpose tubes contain one of the inert gases, such as argon or neon. Phanotrons are characterized by a low potential drop of approximately 15 volts. They usually are employed as rectifiers.

They are used for a wide variety of voltages, from the low voltage required for battery charging to approximately 20 000 volts for high-voltage d-c power supply of broadcast apparatus, industrial radio-frequency generators for high-frequency heating and X-ray equipment.

The gas pressure in phanotrons varies widely depending on the type of tube. In general for low-voltage argon-filled tubes used for battery charging the pressure is about $\frac{3}{4}$ in. of mercury. For mercury-vapor phanotrons the pressures range from 0.001 to 0.004 in. of mercury.

The construction of phanotrons has several features differing from the kenotron features previously illustrated.

PHANOTRON CATHODES

According to the voltage-distribution diagram of Fig. 5.13, practically all of the voltage drop across a phanotron appears through the cathode sheath. The small voltage drop across the plasma is of little consequence. The actual spacing between cathode and anode has little effect on the total tube drop. Therefore, in phanotrons, it is not necessary to maintain a uniform distance between all points on the cathode and the anode as required for all vacuum-filled tubes.

For this reason, phanotron cathodes can be constructed to conserve heat, using novel constructions to minimize heat radiation and conserve the energy consumed in heating the cathode. Oxide-coated ribbon is edge-coiled or corrugated to increase the emission area and yet keeps the effective radiating area small. The efficiency of an edge-coiled ribbon is further increased by enclosing the cathode in a deep cavity so as to lower its radiation losses. One construction is shown in Fig. 5.14.

Cathodes of phanotron tubes must be allowed to attain their normal operating temperature before voltage is applied to the anode. If the cathode is too cold it cannot emit sufficient electrons to result in a current flow required for a normal voltage drop across the load. When this happens nearly the full line voltage then appears across the tube. The voltage is certain to exceed the allowed 22 volts* and causes rapid cathode disintegration.

As Fig. 5.13 indicates, practically all of the anode voltage is applied across a relatively short thickness of the cathode sheath. This steep gradient near the cathode is sufficient to accelerate the positive ions and cause them to strike the cathode at rather high velocity. Because positive ions are heavy, they readily develop sufficient kinetic energy to chip off the cathode coat-

*See MIT staff, *Applied Electronics*, p 213.

ing. This is known as positive-ion bombardment of the cathode and causes rapid deterioration of the cathode. In the average tube the severity of bombardment is negligible if the potential across the tube does not exceed approximately 22 volts.

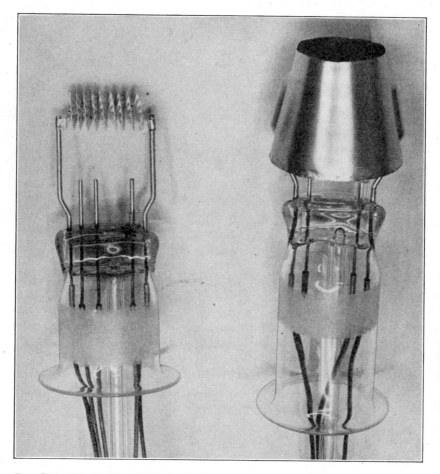

FIG. 5.14. The heating efficiency of phanotron cathodes is improved by edge-coiled ribbon and is sometimes partially enclosed in a hood to reduce further the amount of heat radiated from the cathode.

The heat-conserving shields of efficient phanotron cathodes prolong the time required for the cathode to reach a normal operating temperature, frequently requiring 15 minutes or more. This warm-up period cannot be shortened without possible serious damage to the tube.

PHANOTRON ANODES

Because the space between all points of the cathode and anode need not be uniform, the anode of phanotron tubes can be designed for most efficient radiation of heat. Often it is a flat disk located near the top of the tube. The best anode material is graphite, because it is not injured by high temperature and has little tendency toward secondary emission. Carbonized metal anodes are nearly as good, and frequently are used in smaller phanotron tubes. The structure of a typical large phanotron is that of Fig. 5.15, illustrating an efficient cavity-type cathode and dome-shaped graphite anode.

Gas Pressure and Operating Temperature

The pressure of the gas within the tube has considerable effect upon the characteristics of the tube. If the pressure is high, the voltage drop across the tube is relatively low, and the cathode efficiency can be made high because of the possibility of operating the cathode at a high temperature without abnormal deterioration of the cathode surface. However, high gas pressure has the disadvantage of lowering the ability of the tube to withstand a high inverse voltage (negative voltage applied to anode while the tube is nonconducting). For these reasons, tubes filled at a high gas pressure are restricted to relatively low-voltage applications, such as Rectigons and

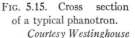

FIG. 5.15. Cross section of a typical phanotron. *Courtesy Westinghouse*

Tungars for charging low-voltage storage batteries. The inverse-voltage rating of a phanotron is increased by reducing the gas pressure. This is done at the sacrifice of the maximum current-carrying capacity of the tube. Therefore, the choice of proper gas pressure depends upon the use of the tube.

The vapor pressure within a mercury-filled phanotron depends upon the tube operating temperature. Mercury-vapor phanotrons are usually designed for a condensed-mercury temperature between 95 and 140 F. These tubes must be operated base downward. Ventilating air should flow vertically upward along the walls of the tube so as to assure the coolest part of the tube wall being near the base. If the top of the tube is allowed to become cooler than the lower part, mercury may condense near the top of the tube and drop upon the anode, with adverse affects upon operation.

The effect of condensed-mercury temperature on the operating characteristics of a typical phanotron is given in Fig. 5.16. If the temperature becomes too low, insufficient mercury ions are available to carry the normal anode current, and, unless the anode current were reduced below normal rating, the cathode would become damaged. For the same reason, the voltage drop across the tube rises as the condensed-mercury temperature is reduced. At high temperature, the mercury-vapor pressure increases and

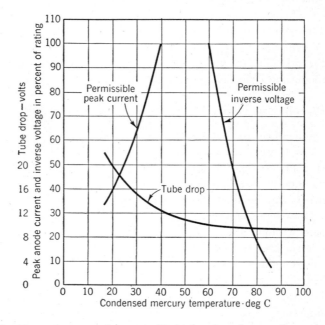

FIG. 5.16. The performance of mercury-filled tubes depends upon the condensed mercury temperature.

the breakdown voltage decreases rapidly, making it necessary to reduce the inverse voltage to prevent reverse current while the anode is negative.

Phanotrons in which an inert gas such as argon or neon is used have an advantage over mercury-vapor tubes in that the gas pressure is not dependent upon the temperature. However, the gas pressure actually does change in such tubes, because some of the gas disappears by being absorbed in the walls and electrodes of the tube. Excess gas must be put into the tube when it is manufactured to make allowance for the decrease in gas throughout the life of the tube.

This method of combating the problem is not satisfactory for high-voltage tubes where the gas pressure must be controlled within narrow limits. For this reason, the use of inert gases is not general except for low-voltage phanotrons. Manufacturing improvements may some day prevent the absorption of gas into the tube parts, and the use of inert gases may then become more general.

The hot-cathode phanotron has high efficiency, good voltage regulation with load, modest cathode power consumption, and low initial cost. On the other hand, it has lower inverse-voltage rating than high-vacuum tubes, has more of a tendency to arc back (that is, carry current in the reverse direction), and its cathode cannot stand high overloads.

SUMMARY

Kenotrons are two-element tubes consisting of a hot cathode and an anode enclosed in a highly evacuated envelope. They are principally applied as rectifiers whereby a source of d-c power is obtained — usually low power at moderate voltage or low current at extremely high voltage.

Space charge is the predominating influence upon the characteristic of kenotrons. Space charge results from a density of electrons close to the cathode surface, which may be sufficient to repel some or all of the emitted electrons back to the cathode surface. Because of this, over the usual range of operation, more electrons are emitted by the cathode than reach the anode.

Anode current of the kenotron increases approximately as the three-halves power of anode voltage over the range limited by the space-charge effect. For an anode current greater than this the value increases but slightly at the higher anode voltages, because anode current is then limited by cathode emission.

Anode-voltage drop of kenotrons is relatively high and varies with load current because of the space-charge influence upon its characteristic.

Phanotrons are two-element tubes consisting of a hot cathode and anode enclosed in a gas-filled envelope. They are principally applied as rectifiers, as low voltage high-current sources for battery charging or high current at moderately high voltage for electronic power sources over the range of sizes of approximately 1 to 100 kw.

Ionization within a gas space takes place as a rapidly moving electron collides with a gas particle, separating it into an *ion* (heavy particle, positive charge) and a new *electron* (light particle, negative charge).

Neutralization of negative space charge is accomplished within phanotrons by positive ions moving slowly toward the cathode where each ion neutralizes many electrons to render the region near the cathode surface free of the negative space charge common to kenotrons.

The *cathode sheath* is an infinitesimally thin layer at the cathode surface. Most of the voltage drop across phanotron tubes occurs across the cathode sheath.

The *anode sheath* is a thin layer at the anode surface. Across this the voltage drop is small although it increases with increase in anode current.

The *plasma* is the space between the cathode and anode sheaths. Through this, the voltage drop is small. Positive ions and electrons reside in approximately equal numbers to render the zone free of space charge.

Anode current of phanotrons is not a function of anode voltage. It is influenced only by constants of the circuit external to the tube.

Anode voltage of phanotrons is much lower than is common to kenotrons and does not change appreciably as the anode current changes.

Cathode bombardment of phanotrons is caused by too rapid movement of positive ions to the cathode surface. For this destruction of the cathode to be avoided, voltage between electrodes must at all times be less than 22 volts — a condition requiring that the cathode be allowed ample time to preheat to normal temperature before closing the anode circuit.

Gas pressure of phanotrons has a marked influence upon the tube characteristics and must be maintained within close limits.

Condensed-mercury temperature of mercury-filled phanotrons must be kept within the limits specified by the manufacturer because of its effect upon the gas pressure within the envelope.

REFERENCES

MIT ELECTRICAL ENGINEERING STAFF, *Applied Electronics*, John Wiley & Sons, New York, 1943, pp 114–65 and 205–18.

W. G. Dow, *Fundamentals of Engineering Electronics*, John Wiley & Sons, New York, 1937, pp 97–102, 188–206 and 208–62.

JACOB MILLMAN and SAMUEL SEELY, *Electronics*, McGraw-Hill Book Co., New York, 1941, pp 15–110, 204–32, 233–87 and 288–323.

E. D. McARTHUR, *Electronics and Electron Tubes*, John Wiley & Sons, New York, 1936, pp 8–18 and 100–20.

F. E. TERMAN, *Radio Engineering*, McGraw-Hill Book Co., New York, 1937, pp 112–15.

F. E. TERMAN, *Radio Engineers Handbook*, McGraw-Hill Book Co., New York, 1943, pp 286–9.

HERBERT J. REICH, *Theory and Applications of Electron Tubes*, McGraw-Hill Book Co., New York, 1944, pp 416–69.

IRVING LANGMUIR, "The Effect of Space Charge and Initial Velocities on Potential Distribution and Thermionic Current between Parallel Plane Electrodes," *Physical Review*, April 1932.

ROYCE G. KLOEFFLER, *Principles of Electronics*, John Wiley & Sons, New York, 1942, pp 23–9 and 44–59.

Chapter 6

THREE–ELEMENT PLIOTRONS

The two phenomena of radio communication and industrial electronics, now grown into giant industries, were really born the day Lee De Forest, in 1907, placed a mesh of wires in a two-element vacuum tube and found he could control the anode current by applying insignificant power to his "grid." Soon even the newspapers carried stories about the astounding vacuum tube that could amplify power millions of times. And true they were! The three-element tube lived up to all its notices and more. It is the foundation stone of all electronics.

Vacuum tubes having three or more elements are classified by the Radio Manufacturers Association as "pliotrons," derived from the Greek "plio," meaning "more." Unfortunately, the RMA classification is not sufficient to describe adequately many types that come under this classification. For this reason, pliotrons are further designated on the basis of the number of elements. Thus triode is a tube having three elements; tetrode, a tube with four elements; and pentode, one with five elements.

The Function of the Triode

The principal function of three-element tubes is amplification, accomplished by the third element or grid. Just as originally done by De Forest, the grid is located between the cathode and anode for the purpose of controlling the anode current. A change in grid voltage is reflected by a much larger change in the anode current. The reason for this is that the grid is physically much closer to the cathode than is the anode; hence a small change in its voltage has enormously greater effect on electron flow than a change in anode-to-cathode potential. Because the grid is almost always maintained negative with respect to the cathode, it "steals" none of the emitted electrons and hence does not consume appreciable power. Amplification is accomplished as manifested by the large ratio of power controlled in the load circuit (supplied by the anode-voltage source) to that required for excitation of the grid.

Grid Control of Space Charge

If the grid is maintained at a negative potential with respect to the cathode, few electrons flow to it and the anode current can be considered

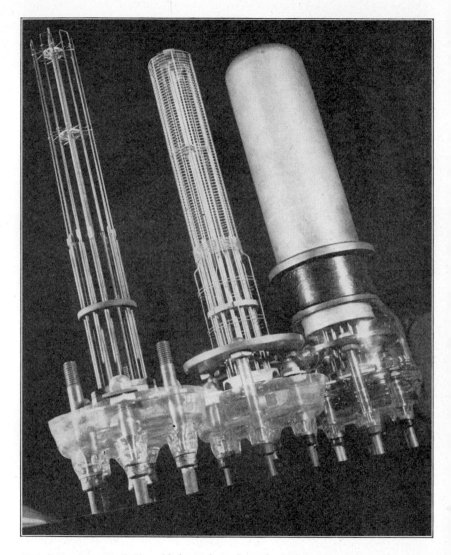

FIG. 6.1. Cathode (left), grid (center), and anode (right), of a large water-cooled triode. Junction between the metal anode and glass is made by a *Housekeeper* seal where the metal is thinned to a feather edge before fusing to the glass. Difference in expansion between metal and glass is taken up by flexing of the thinned metal anode edge. Seals between glass and terminal studs are *Kovar*, a metal having nearly the same expansion as the glass.   *Courtesy Westinghouse*

proportional to the electrons leaving the cathode. Thus, the effect of grid voltage upon the anode current can be determined from the effect of grid voltage on the electrons leaving the cathode. Because the cathode temperature is assumed to be sufficient during all normal operating conditions to prevent limitation of anode current by thermionic emission, all electrons which leave the cathode must be limited by the degree of negative space charge. Grid voltage, by its powerful effect upon space charge, thus controls the current to the anode to an appreciable extent.

Fig. 6.2. Large triodes for commercial broadcasting or heating by high frequency are either water-cooled (center) or forced air-cooled (left or right). A 75-watt lamp indicates the relative size of type GL 889R (left), GL 880 (center), and GL 8002R (right).

Courtesy General Electric

In Chapter 5, the effect of space charge upon the characteristics of kenotron tubes was emphasized. Likewise, neutralization of space charge results in the entirely different characteristics of phanotrons as compared to kenotrons. It is now in order to see how, in pliotrons, negative space charge is increased or decreased by the grid to provide the desired control of anode current.

The effect of space charge on limitation of the anode current is again shown in Fig. 6.3a, wherein the tube elements are assumed as plane parallel surfaces. If a voltage is applied to the anode of a kenotron and the cathode is unheated (that is, there is no electron emission), the potential distribution is a straight line without space charge. If the cathode temperature is raised to cause sufficient emission, the space charge is increased and eventually depresses the potential-distribution curve far enough to make the slope negative at the surface of the cathode.

Assume a triode constructed of parallel flat cathode and anode surfaces, Fig. 6.3b with parallel grid wires interposed between. Because of the mesh construction of the grid the electric field is not the same close to a grid wire as midway between wires. To represent this difference the potential distribution within triodes is usually shown as two curves, one corresponding to a plane passing through a grid wire and the other midway between grid wires.

Such a potential distribution is that of Fig. 6.3c shown for a moderate negative grid voltage and with the cathode cold, that is, no anode current flowing. For this condition the potential gradient is positive at the cathode surface. When the cathode is heated to normal temperature, the negative space charge near the cathode surface alters the potential distribution, Fig. 6.3d, until the slope is slightly negative at the cathode surface.* Many electrons, emitted by the cathode, are then forced to return to the cathode because of the repelling negative space charge. Some electrons within the space charge are drawn to the positive attracting anode, only to be instantly replaced by others freshly emitted from the cathode to keep the magnitude of space charge constant. Viewed in this respect there is a gradual flow of space charge toward the anode. Movement of these electrons constitutes anode current.

As a greater negative potential is applied to the grid, the potential curve for the unheated cathode, Fig. 6.3e, is forced even further downward and may show a negative slope if the grid potential is sufficiently negative. The gradient becomes slightly more negative as the cathode is heated for normal emission, Fig. 6.3f. Here few, if any, electrons are able to pass through the repelling negative gradient between cathode and grid. The anode current is then zero, because all electrons emitted by the cathode return to the cathode surface. The condition resulting in zero or a very small amount of anode current is referred to as *cutoff*, and the least magnitude of negative grid potential required for the condition is called the *cutoff grid voltage*. The actual magnitude of cutoff voltage differs with each value of anode potential, because the potential distribution between electrodes is altered by the magnitude of anode voltage.

The sole purpose of the grid is to permit a variation of the negative space charge just off the cathode surface and thereby control the anode current. If we remember that the degree of space charge increases or decreases to maintain a zero or very slightly negative gradient just off the cathode surface, it is obvious that the magnitude of positive slope with the *cathode unheated* is a measure of the amount of space charge required (at normal emission) for the gradient to be brought to zero. For example, the condi-

*For a detailed account see Dow, *Fundamentals of Engineering Electronics*, pp 2–6, 102–16, 191–4; also MIT staff, *Applied Electronics*, pp 165–74.

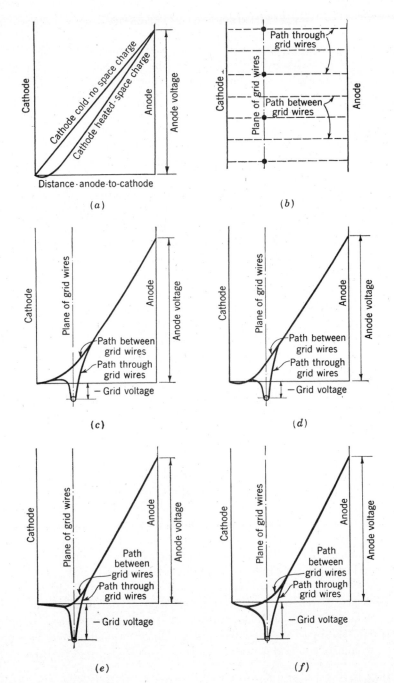

FIG. 6.3. The potential distribution of a kenotron (a) and plan of a parallel plane pliotron (b). Potential distribution for the pliotron is with the cathode cold (c) and (e) and cathode heated normally (d) and (f).

tion of Fig. 6.3c illustrates a moderate positive slope. As the cathode is heated, the space charge increases to make the slope slightly negative, as at (d). Clearly, a negative flexion is required to make the difference (c) to (d). In contrast to this example is that of Fig. 6.3e. For this, a negative slope is shown even with the cathode unheated, and no negative space charge is required to bring about the condition of zero or slightly negative slope with the cathode heated. By comparison, then, the amount of space charge is greater (c) and (d) than when the grid potential is more negative (e) and (f).

The magnitude of anode current is dependent upon the degree of negative space charge. The greater the space charge the greater is the anode current, for it is the flow of space charge, that is, movement of electrons of which the space charge is composed, that constitutes anode current. Once more, by the use of Fig. 6.3, it can be seen that the greater space charge manifest by (c) and (d) also conforms with greater anode current as compared with the example of (e) and (f). Because the potential of the grid is able thus to influence the degree of space charge, it can control the magnitude of anode current.

Triode Characteristics

Triodes are invariably used in a circuit in which the anode current, anode voltage, and grid voltage are continually changing. Although the performance of the tube can be calculated by mathematical equations representing each variable, such a procedure is unnecessarily tedious. In practice, it is convenient to predict the performance of triodes by means of two or, sometimes, three sets of characteristic curves.

One way to illustrate characteristics of a tube is to plot the variation in anode current against changes in grid voltage, as in Fig. 6.4. Because the result is influenced by the magnitude of anode voltage a family of curves covering a wide range of anode voltage is required. These curves are called *transfer characteristics*. The lower end of each curve is referred to as the cutoff end and the upper right is called the saturation end.†

Because the grid is located relatively close to the cathode in the region of space charge, its potential is powerfully effective in controlling the number of electrons reaching the anode, much more so than a like change in anode potential. The ratio of effectiveness of a change in anode potential compared to a change in grid potential to obtain control of the anode current is

---

†Most data, including Fig. 6.4 and 6.5, do not extend to the region where saturation is evident by a marked decrease in slope.

called the *voltage-amplification constant* of the tube, or the *amplification factor*.

Amplification factor is defined as the ratio of a small change in anode voltage to the change in grid voltage required to restore the anode current to the value existing prior to a change in anode voltage. Amplification factor is designated by the Greek letter μ.

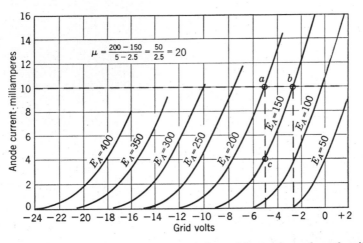

$$\mu = \frac{200 - 150}{5 - 2.5} = \frac{50}{2.5} = 20$$

FIG. 6.4. Transfer characteristics, through their straight sections, show that if the anode voltage is changed 50 volts $a-c$, the grid voltage must be changed $2\frac{1}{2}$ volts $a-b$ in order to hold the anode current constant.

Amplification factor is readily obtained graphically from a transfer characteristic, such as Fig. 6.4. It is usually taken at an anode current approximately equal to the tube rating, which in the case illustrated is 10 ma. If the anode voltage is 200 volts, rated anode current is obtained with a negative potential of 5 volts applied to the grid. If the anode voltage is now changed to 150 volts, the anode current is reduced to 4 ma at point c if the grid voltage remains at -5 volts. By definition, the anode current must be brought back to 10 ma, point b, and, for this to be accomplished, the grid voltage must be changed to -2.5 volts. The amplification factor is the ratio of these voltage changes and results in a factor of 20 for the case illustrated. Another way of looking at it is that the grid is 20 times more influential in controlling anode current than is anode potential.

Tubes are usually applied to operate throughout a region where the curves are reasonably straight and parallel, such that the amplification factor remains essentially constant throughout the normal operating range.

Another form of data plots the anode current against anode voltage for each value of grid voltage. Such curves are called *anode characteristics* and are typically represented by Fig. 6.5. The tube information is exactly the same; it is simply arranged in different form. *Anode resistance* is another

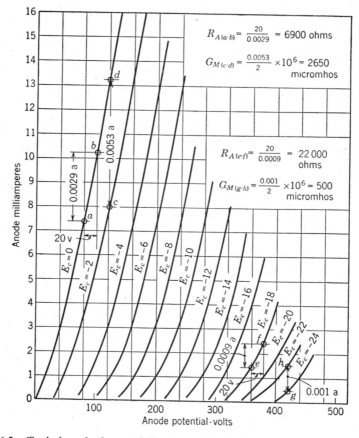

FIG. 6.5. Typical anode characteristics, from which are obtained:

$$\text{Anode resistance} = \frac{\text{change in anode voltage}}{\text{change in anode current}}$$

$$\text{Mutual conductance} = \frac{\text{change in anode current}}{\text{change in grid voltage}}$$

useful tube constant obtained from the anode characteristic. Anode resistance is defined as the ratio of a small change of anode voltage to the change in anode current it causes, the grid voltage remaining constant. Mathematically, it is the reciprocal of the slope of the anode characteristic. Curves of the anode-characteristic family are neither straight nor parallel;

hence the slope does not remain constant, and the anode resistance varies over a wide range under normal operating conditions. This is illustrated in Fig. 6.5 for two extremes. The resistance taken between points a and b is 6900 ohms compared to 22 000 ohms taken between points e and f.

Mutual conductance is defined as the small change in anode current caused by a small change in grid voltage, with the anode voltage unchanged. Mutual conductance is denoted by the symbol G_M and is expressed in micromhos. Mutual conductance varies considerably over the tube operating range. The tube of Fig. 6.5 has a mutual conductance of 2650 micromhos taken between points c and d as compared to 500 micromhos taken between points g and h.

The anode resistances and mutual conductances shown graphically in Fig. 6.5 are only approximate, because true values must be obtained by taking much smaller increments than those illustrated.

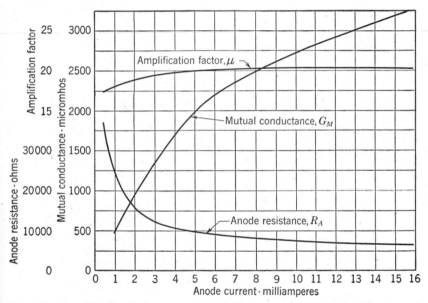

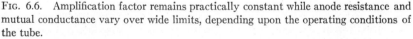

Fig. 6.6. Amplification factor remains practically constant while anode resistance and mutual conductance vary over wide limits, depending upon the operating conditions of the tube.

Amplification factor, anode resistance, and mutual conductance are interrelated, such that $\mu = R_A \times G_M$. If any two are known, the third can be determined. The approximate variation in tube constants over a considerable range of anode current for a typical 6J5 triode, for zero grid voltage, is given by Fig. 6.6. Other curves are obtainable for any other grid voltage.

These three tube constants serve as factors of merit by which one tube can be compared to another. They are not values, which in themselves permit the electronic engineer to design circuit details, although they do illustrate the general characteristics of one tube compared to another.

Inasmuch as the grid affects the anode current by control of the space charge, the relative space between grid and cathode as well as the spacing between grid turns has a strong influence on tube constants. This is shown to some degree in Fig. 6.7a, b, c, and d. High amplification factors can be obtained by using a fine-mesh grid supported close to the cathode. However, mechanical limitations make it impractical to exceed a maximum amplification factor of 150. A figure of 25 is much more common.

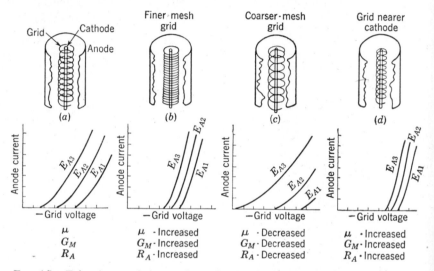

FIG. 6.7. Tube characteristics can be varied by altering the grid structure. Starting with a normal design at (a) the amplification factor can be increased by closer spacing of grid turns (b) or placing the grid nearer the cathode (d). Amplification factor is decreased by wider spacing of grid turns (c) or by placing the grid further away from the cathode.

The basic operation of a triode is conveniently described by reference to a fundamental circuit, Fig. 6.8. The anode voltage is supplied by some suitable source represented by the battery voltage E_{bb}. The load is represented by resistor R_L connected in series between the battery and the anode terminal. The actual voltage applied to the anode is denoted by E_A and is equal to the battery voltage E_{bb} less the voltage drop through the load resistor R_L. A steady negative voltage called the grid bias is applied to the grid by a suitable source of supply such as a battery. A signal voltage is applied to the circuit between the grid terminal and the bias voltage. By

signal voltage is meant the voltage of an incoming a-c wave, a direct voltage from a pilot generator, an impulse voltage from a phototube, or any
other form of voltage input to the tube. The actual grid voltage, E_c is
equal to the bias voltage plus or minus the signal voltage, depending upon
the polarity of the signal voltage.

Operation of the circuit is determined by graphical construction of
parameters upon the tube static characteristics. Citing a specific example
and using a 6J5 tube, for which the performance is given by Fig. 6.5,
assume the anode supply E_{bb} = 400 volts, load resistor R_L = 40 000 ohms,

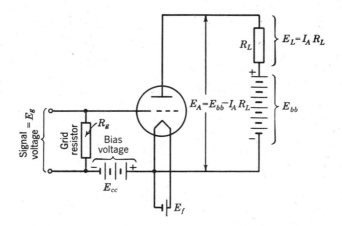

FIG. 6.8.   The fundamental working circuit of a triode consists of the tube, an anode
voltage source E_{bb}, a load device having resistance R_L, a source of bias voltage E_{cc}, and
an input or signal voltage E_g.

and grid bias E_{cc} = 6.0 volts. First step of the graphic solution is the construction of a *load line*. This is readily done by the familiar Ohm's law.
Inspection of the circuit shows the tube cathode-anode and load resistor to
be series connected across the 400-volt anode supply. Momentarily, if we
assume that the tube cathode-anode voltage is zero, the current flowing is
that of circuit voltage through 40 000 ohms or 10 ma. In contrast to this,
when the tube cathode-anode voltage equals that of the supply, no voltage
remains across the load. Hence there is no current. Between these extremes, voltage of the supply is divided between the load resistor and
tube elements. This is represented graphically by the *load line* drawn upon
the tube anode characteristics as Fig. 6.9 shows.

Points where the load line intersects individual curves of the anode
characteristic can be transposed to the transfer characteristic, as in Fig.
6.10. A line drawn through these points of the transfer characteristic then
defines the dynamic response of the circuit with a load resistance of 40 000

ohms. The heavy line of Fig. 6.10 is the *dynamic transfer characteristic* of the tube operating with this particular load resistance. The curves given in manufacturers' literature are static characteristics, because it is impossible to give dynamic characteristics for the wide ranges of loads with which the tubes can be used. However, dynamic curves can be readily constructed from the static curves by the method given here.

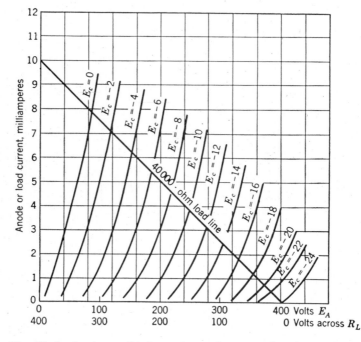

FIG. 6.9. The load-resistance line is superimposed on an anode-resistance characteristic to determine the actual working conditions of the tube.

To illustrate further the circuit operation, assume that the signal voltage is zero. With the bias voltage given, the actual grid voltage is then -6 volts. The circuit then operates at point a on the dynamic characteristic, Fig. 6.10. The anode current is 5.4 ma, the actual anode voltage E_A is 180 volts, read more accurately from Fig. 6.9. The voltage across the load resistance R_L is the battery voltage minus the tube drop or $400 - 180 = 220$, also read from Fig. 6.9.

If a signal voltage of $+4$ volts is now applied, the actual grid voltage becomes -2 volts and the circuit operates at point b of the dynamic characteristic. The anode current is now 7 ma; voltage across E_A is 120 volts and R_L, 280. If the signal voltage changes to -4 volts, the actual grid voltage becomes −10 volts and the circuit operates at point c of the dynamic characteristic. The anode current is then 3.8 ma; volts across R_L is 155; and E_A is 245.

The true operation of the circuit is manifested by the dynamic characteristic of Fig. 6.10 instead of the static transfer characteristics of Fig. 6.5. The *dynamic characteristic* is a co-ordinated result obtained from the tube static characteristic, the load resistance and anode supply voltage. The

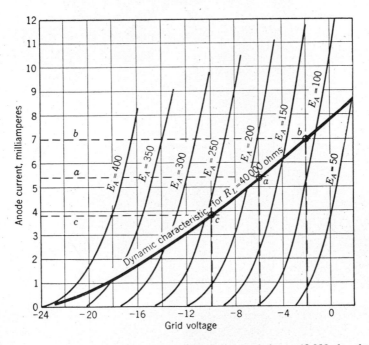

Fig. 6.10. A dynamic-transfer characteristic 0—c—a—b for a 40 000-ohm load is obtained by transposing the points of intersection on Fig. 6.9 upon the static transfer curves. The dynamic characteristics illustrate that the working mutual conductance, that is, change in anode (or load) current for a given change in grid voltage, can never be so great as the static value.

dynamic curve is much straighter than the static characteristic although the slope is considerably reduced. This means that the output of a triode is more linear with grid-voltage variation than is indicated by the static characteristics, although the net change in anode current for a given change in grid voltage can never approach the magnitude indicated by the static characteristics.

If the grid is made positive with respect to the cathode, electrons flow to the grid, being drawn by a positive potential. This means passage of grid current, which usually is undesirable because it represents consumption of power in the grid or input circuit. As discussed in Chapter 12, a flow of grid current can be used to advantage for some special purpose, although in most radio-receiving, communications, and industrial-control equipment,

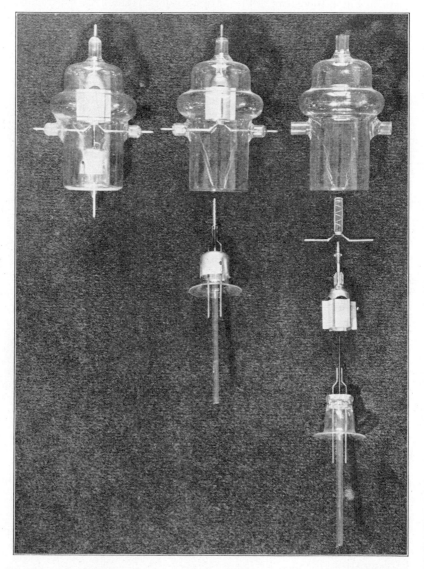

Fig. 6.11.   Construction of a power triode, complete, left. Center, the cathode is removed. Right, the grid structure, anode, and cathode support are below the glass envelope.   *Courtesy Westinghouse*

it is highly desirable to design the equipment so as to consume the least possible power in the grid or input circuit. For this reason, the grid is usually operated at a negative potential. Often the input signal voltage swings the grid toward a positive voltage, although the grid does not actually assume a positive potential with respect to the cathode. This is illustrated at point b of Fig. 6.10, and the electronic engineer frequently uses the expression "less negative" to denote that the grid has been driven toward a positive potential, although the actual polarity is still negative.

Apparatus using triodes for the control of large amounts of power, such as radio transmitters and oscillators often operate with the grid positive. However, in such cases components connected in the grid circuit must be capable of delivering the necessary power to "drive" the grid when its potential becomes positive.

SUMMARY

Three-element pliotrons are popularly known as "vacuum triodes," or more simply, "triodes."

The grid is located between cathode and anode and is closer to the cathode.

Control of space charge near the cathode surface is the predominant function of the grid. As the grid potential becomes highly negative, space charge is reduced and with it anode current is diminished. A grid potential only slightly negative, or sometimes positive, leads to increasing space charge and a larger anode currant.

Cutoff manifests a zero (or extremely small) anode current, brought about by a negative grid potential sufficient to block the passage of all electrons emitted by the cathode toward the anode.

A transfer characteristic plots anode current (ordinates) against grid voltage (abscissas) for a family of anode voltages.

Anode characteristics plot anode current (ordinates) against anode voltage (abscissas) for a family of grid voltage values.

Amplification factor is the ratio of a small change in anode voltage to the grid-voltage change necessary to make the anode current remain a constant. It is reasonably constant over the useful tube operating range.

Mutual conductance or *transconductance* is the ratio of a small change of anode current to the change of grid voltage causing it, the anode voltage remaining constant. Its value changes widely over the useful tube-operating range.

Anode resistance is the ratio of a small change of anode voltage to the anode current causing it, with the grid voltage remaining constant. Its value changes widely over the useful tube-operating range.

Anode supply, designated E_{bb}, is the source of power for the tube anode and load circuit. It frequently is diagrammed as a battery but may be any form of d-c power source.

Grid bias, designated E_{cc}, is the source of potential required to fix the tube-operating grid voltage. It, also, is conveniently diagrammed as a battery.

Signal voltage, designated E_g, is the incoming potential applied to the tube grid circuit.

True anode voltage, designated E_A, is the supply E_{bb} minus voltage lost in the load or circuit external to the tube anode.

True grid voltage, designated E_c, is the bias voltage E_{cc} plus or minus the signal voltage E_g, depending upon polarity of the latter.

Load line is a graphic representation of the voltage expended in the load as anode current through its changes.

A dynamic characteristic is a composite graphic representation tying together the tube performance with load values and circuit voltages. It manifests the characteristic of the tube combined with the device it controls.

REFERENCES

MIT Electrical Engineering Staff, *Applied Electronics*, John Wiley & Sons, New York, 1943, pp 165–84.

W. G. Dow, *Fundamentals of Engineering Electronics*, John Wiley & Sons, New York, 1937, pp 2–18, 102–26 and 263–70.

Jacob Millman and Samuel Seely, *Electronics*, McGraw-Hill Book Co., New York, 1941, pp 501–50.

Herbert J. Reich, *Theory and Applications of Electron Tubes*, McGraw-Hill Book Co., New York, 1944, pp 43–123 and 649–56.

E. L. Chaffee, *Theory of Thermionic Vacuum Tubes*, McGraw-Hill Book Co., New York, 1933, pp 144–241.

F. E. Terman, *Radio Engineering*, McGraw-Hill Book Co., New York, 1937, pp 115–26.

F. E. Terman, *Radio Engineers' Handbook*, McGraw-Hill Book Co., New York, 1943, pp 294–300.

Keith Henney, *Radio Engineering Handbook*, McGraw-Hill Book Co., New York, 1941, pp 239–55.

Royce G. Kloeffler. *Principles of Electronics*, John Wiley & Sons, New York, 1942, pp 60–72.

Chapter 7

MULTIGRID PLIOTRONS

Once the concept of the usefulness of the control grid in a vacuum tube was established, exploration of the possibilities of a second, a third, and even more grids came as a natural result. Although the addition of a screen grid (forming a tetrode), or suppressor grid (in the pentode), or building electrodes of special shape (as in the beam power tube or variable-μ tube) does not have the importance of the original control grid, these devices greatly extend the usefulness of the amplifier family and enormously simplify the circuits using them. In seeking to make the most from these amplifier refinements, designers have brought the vacuum tube to the state of a precision device that is nearly as remarkable as the fineness of control they provide over the tiny electron.

Tetrodes

When, in a typical triode, the anode current increases, the voltage drop across the load increases, it being assumed that the supply voltage E_{bb} remains the same. Hence, less potential is available for anode voltage. This fact is brought out in the discussion in Chapter 6 and shown by the dynamic characteristic Fig. 6.10. The voltage drop across the load resistor thus decreases the actual voltage applied to the anode. As a result, the anode voltage is continually varying with each change of anode current and is always less than the anode source voltage. Thus, the anode current of all triodes is dependent upon *both* the grid voltage and the anode potential. As indicated by the dynamic transfer characteristics, a change in grid potential results in a smaller change of anode current than would be obtained if the anode voltage remained constant.

This is a disadvantage that can be partially overcome by the insertion of an auxiliary grid between the first grid and the anode. A pliotron of this classification is referred to as a *tetrode*, which denotes that it has four principal elements. The grid nearest the cathode is the one to which the signal voltage is applied and is used to control the electron flow. It is the *control grid*. The auxiliary grid, located between the control grid and the anode, is called a *screen grid*. A fixed positive potential is applied to this electrode.

Screen-grid tetrodes were developed about 1924 and were used extensively in radio receivers as radio-frequency amplifiers, but since then have been rendered obsolete by the superior characteristics of pentodes. High-power tetrodes are used as class-B and class-C radio-frequency power amplifiers.

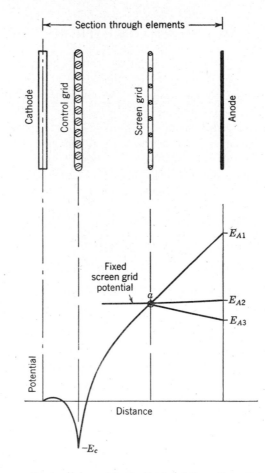

Fig. 7.1. Cross section typifying a tetrode (top) and the voltage distribution (bottom) from cathode to anode shows that the screen grid shields the space-charge region near the cathode from the effects of varying anode voltage.

The relative placement of electrodes about a centralized cathode is indicated in Fig. 7.1. A potential-distribution diagram, shown at the lower part of this figure, illustrates the relative distribution of potential through-out the tube from cathode to anode, the cathode unheated. The function of the screen grid is to attract all electrons accelerated away from the cathode as determined by the potential applied to the control grid. Electrons, attracted toward the screen by its positive potential, pass on through the wire mesh to the anode. A few electrons terminate on the wires of the screen grid and constitute a small screen current. All electrons successful in passing through the screen reach the anode. With this structure, the anode potential can vary over wide limits without appreciable effect on the anode current. Such variation in anode potential is represented between limits E_{A1} and E_{A2}, over which range the anode current remains essentially constant because electrons are drawn away from the cathode by the fixed screen potential at point a. The maximum voltage E_{A1} is fixed by the design of the elements. The screen acts as a barrier to shield the space-charge region near the cathode from any effect of variation in anode potential. Indeed, the screen grid gets its name from its function of screening the control grid from the anode. With the screen grid, the release of electrons away from the cathode (space-charge flow) is but little affected by the anode potential.

The transfer characteristic of a typical tetrode (for a single-grid voltage) is shown in Fig. 7.2. If the anode voltage is maintained equal to, or greater than, the positive potential applied to the screen, the characteristic is approximately a straight and almost horizontal line, indicating that the amplification factor is high. Tetrodes with amplification factors of 1000 are not uncommon.

If the anode voltage is reduced below the screen potential, such as E_{A3} of Fig. 7.1, the characteristic no longer remains a smooth line. Usually it manifests a dip such as point a of Fig. 7.2. As the anode voltage is increased from a low value, the anode current increases 0–d. At some certain anode voltage, as d, electrons are accelerated to the anode and strike it with sufficient velocity to release electrons from the anode surface by secondary emission. These electrons, in turn, are drawn toward a source of positive potential, which is the screen grid, because in this assumed case the screen grid is more positive than the anode. Secondary-emission current from anode to screen grid opposes or neutralizes to that extent the desired flow of current from the cathode to the anode. The effect becomes more pronounced as the anode voltage is raised from d to a, accounting for the negative slope between the points. Below d, the velocity of electrons striking the anode is less than that necessary for appreciable secondary emission. As anode voltage is increased nearly equal to the screen voltage, the difference in potential between anode and screen decreases, thus decreasing the acceleration tendency for the screen to draw to it secondary-emission electrons. Anode current then increases rapidly and nearly in direct proportion to anode voltage, from a to b. For anode voltages above the screen potential, the effect of secondary emission becomes negligible. Beyond b, increase in anode current is slight, which indicates that electron flow is controlled by grid potential and becomes essentially independent of anode voltage. If the effects of the primary electrons, flowing from cathode to anode, and the secondary electrons, flowing from anode to screen grid, could be combined, the relatively smooth dotted curve, Oeb, would result. Thus, the secondary-emission electron flow is the difference between curves Oeb and $Odab$. Maximum secondary-emission current occurs at point a of the characteristic.

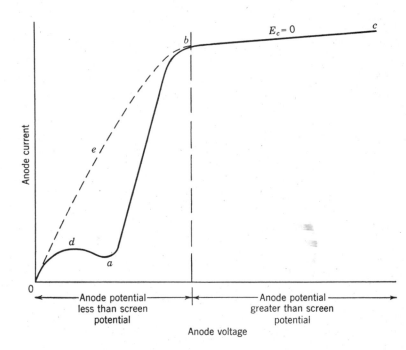

FIG. 7.2.   The anode characteristic of a typical tetrode displays a negative resistance characteristic d–a for anode voltage less than the screen-grid voltage.

The characteristic of a tetrode throughout the range $Odab$ is undesirable because of the unstable operation obtained and distortion introduced.* For this reason, tetrodes normally are operated with anode voltage always slightly greater than the screen potential. This dip in the characteristic curve of a tetrode is equivalent to a region of negative electrical resistance. For some purposes, such as negative-resistance oscillators. this normal disadvantage can be turned to good use.

*This is more clearly understood by reference to Chapter 11.

Interelectrode Capacitance

The elements of a vacuum tube act as plates of a tiny capacitor. Therefore, a small amount of capacitance is present between combination of elements across which exists a varying difference of potential.

The interelectrode capacitance between elements of a triode is illustrated in Fig. 7.3a. Manufacturer's data list the capacitance cathode-to-grid C_{cg}, grid-to-anode C_{ga}, and cathode-to-anode, C_{ca}. The capacitance of particular interest is that between grid and anode, effective in producing a

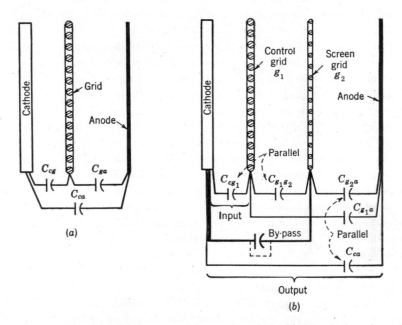

(a)

(b)

Fig. 7.3. (a) The interelectrode capacitances of a triode. (b) The six interelectrode capacitances of a tetrode are effectively reduced to three by the external connection of a by-pass capacitor between cathode and screen, making (1) the input capacitance the parallel of C_{cg1} and C_{g1g2}, (2) the output capacitance the parallel of C_{g2a} and C_{ca} and (3) the control-grid-anode C_{g1a} capacitance very small by the electrostatic shielding of screen grid g_2.

feedback from the output circuit connected to the anode and the input circuit connected to the grid. The reason for this is that the grid becomes one electrode of a capacitor and the anode another, the ensuing capacitance current in the grid is thereby superimposed upon the signal current. If the tube is used for the amplification of a high-frequency signal, the interelectrode capacitance may be large enough to promote sufficient feedback to sustain oscillation of the circuit. This action is explained more fully in

Chapter 12. Thus, the triode has two conspicuous disadvantages: 1, A change in anode voltage affects the flow of electrons toward the anode, and, 2, the grid-to-anode capacitance restricts the use of a triode for high-frequency amplification.†

The screen grid in the tetrode eliminates the first disadvantage of a triode by shielding the space charge in the vicinity of the cathode from the anode. The second disadvantage of the triode is also partially overcome by the screen grid, which forms an effective electrostatic shield between the control grid and the anode to reduce the capacitance between them to approximately 1/1000 of the grid-to-anode capacitance common to an equivalent triode.

The tetrode has six combinations of interelectrode capacitance as Fig. 7.3b indicates. The network of these six capacitors is, fortunately, reduced to three when the tetrode is connected in an actual working circuit. This simplification is made possible by a by-pass capacitor connected externally between the cathode and the screen grid. It is purposely chosen so large in comparison to the interelectrode capacitances that the cathode is effectively connected to the screen grid as indicated by the dotted lines around the by-pass capacitor. With the screen grid effectively connected to the cathode, the capacitance between cathode and control grid, and the capacitance between control grid and screen grid then are paralleled. The average value of these two paralleled interelectrode capacitances is known as the *input capacitance* of the tube. Likewise, the screen-grid-to-anode and cathode-to-anode capacitances are in parallel to form the *average output capacitance*.

Because the screen grid is effectively connected to the cathode, it serves as an electrostatic shield to reduce the control-grid-to-anode capacitance to a small value. This is indicated in Fig. 7.3b. The tetrode then can be used to amplify high-frequency signals without the danger of feedback from the anode to the control-grid circuit.

Pentodes

Although the tetrode can be used over a wider frequency range than the triode, the effect of secondary emission renders this type of tube unsuited for operation with the anode voltage less than the screen voltage. In effect, the available a-c output of a screen-grid tube is limited because of the secondary-emission dip. True amplifier action cannot take place below point *b* on the characteristic curve, Fig. 7.2.

This objection to the tetrode is overcome by the addition of a third grid called the *suppressor*. The tube now has five electrodes and thus is a

†For a discussion of special tubes and considerations at ultrahigh frequencies, see Terman, *Radio Engineers' Handbook*, pp 310–12 with footnotes.

pentode, Fig. 7.4. The suppressor grid, placed next to the anode, is usually connected to the cathode by an external jumper at the terminals of the base.

The potential distribution from cathode to anode is given in Fig. 7.5. The voltage dips sharply in the region of the suppressor grid and then rises to the applied anode potential.

Electrons released from the anode surface by secondary emission return to the anode surface, because the low potential of the suppressor grid (almost equal to the cathode potential) prevents them from being drawn to the screen grid in the manner characteristic of a tetrode. The suppressor grid has little effect on secondary emission but does have a great influence on the secondary electrons once they are produced. The anode potential of a pentode can vary from a maximum such as E_{A1} to a minimum of E_{A3} without affecting the flow of electrons to the anode. The potential E_{A3} is nearly zero (that is, cathode potential being con-

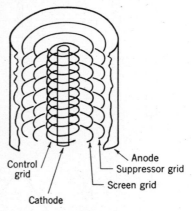

FIG. 7.4. Pentodes have three grids. Nearest to the cathode is the control grid. A suppressor grid is placed near the anode to force secondary electrons to return toward the anode. The screen grid is between control and suppressor grids, unaffected by secondary electrons from the anode.

sidered zero). It is not actually zero, because the suppressor-grid wires are connected to the cathode and are maintained at zero potential, but the space between turns is not at zero potential, thus making the average a small positive potential such as E_{A3}.

Anode characteristics of a typical pentode, given in Fig. 7.6, show the anode current to be practically independent of anode voltage. The undesirable characteristics of a tetrode are eliminated.

The typically flat pentode characteristics indicate both a high amplification factor and large anode resistance. An amplification factor of 1000, and an anode resistance of from 100 000 ohms to 1 megohm are representative of the average pentode. The mutual conductance is approximately the same as an equivalent triode.

The pentode has an advantage that makes it acceptable for inexpensive radio transmitters. Its suppressor grid is brought out to a separate terminal and can be used to modulate‡ the signal. This saves one tube of the transmitting equipment, and, at the same time, modulation is accomplished at a low power level — saving on the power requirements of modulating equipment.

‡The principles of modulation are discussed in Chapter 13.

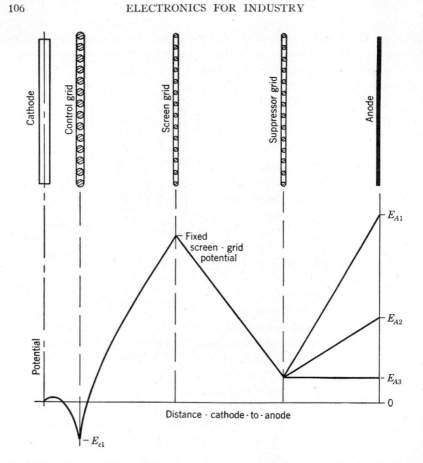

FIG. 7.5. Cross section typifying a pentode (top) and the voltage distribution (bottom) within a pentode shows a low potential through the suppressor grid that prevents secondary-emission electrons released at the anode from reaching the screen grid.

Beam Power Tubes

The effect of the suppressor grid can be obtained by a special design of tetrode known as the beam power tube, Fig. 7.7. The turns of the screen grid are carefully aligned with respect to those of the control grid to obtain effective focusing of the electron stream into flat and parallel sheets. The vertical supports for the grid turns disturb the electron focusing, making it necessary to prevent electron flow toward the supports. This is accomplished by beam-confining electrodes or shields that guide the electron stream between the grid turns and toward the desired area of the anode.

Electrons focused into flat sheets between the grid turns gradually diverge between the screen grid and anode, as indicated in Fig. 7.8. The concentration of electrons in the space near the anode creates a zone of negative space charge in the region between it and the screen grid. The potential distribution from cathode to anode is shown in Fig. 7.9. The zone of negative space charge causes a downward bend of the potential curve, creating a potential minimum between the screen grid and anode. Any

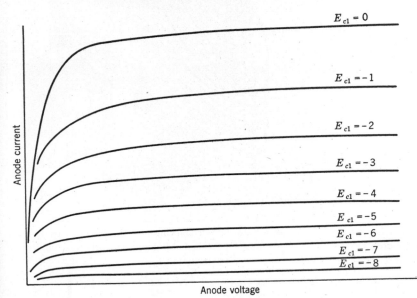

FIG. 7.6. Anode characteristics of a typical pentode extend without appreciable distortion to low values of anode voltage. The small slope indicates a high anode resistance; the small slope together with wide spacing between curves indicates a high amplification factor.

electrons released from the anode surface by secondary emission are prevented from passing the potential minimum, and, therefore, the zone of negative-space charge serves the same purpose as is performed by the suppressor grid of a true pentode. The anode potential can vary over wide limits, and the potential minimum prevents secondary-emission electrons from reaching the screen grid.

Although the beam power tube has only four elements and is a tetrode, its characteristics are essentially the same as a true pentode.

Beam tetrodes do have certain advantages over pentodes. The anode characteristic is a little straighter over a wider range of anode voltage than an equivalent pentode and hence operates over a wider swing of anode voltage than the pentode. The beam tube manifests its greatest advantage for

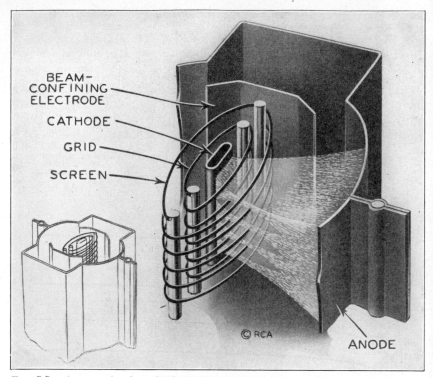

FIG. 7.7. A cut-away view of a beam tetrode showing how the electrons are focused to create a negative space charge near the anode and function similarly to a suppressor, making the beam tetrode equivalent to a pentode. *Courtesy RCA*

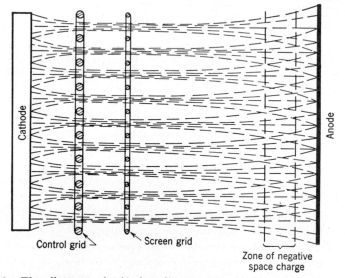

FIG. 7.8. The alignment of grids in a beam tetrode focuses the electrons into flat sheets that diverge beyond the screen grid to create a zone of negative space charge near the anode that is effective in repelling secondary electrons emitted from the anode.

"power" applications where the anode radiates considerable heat. Because the suppressor grid of a pentode is located near the anode, it may get hot enough to emit secondary electrons, defeating its purpose. The beam tetrode does not have this difficulty. However, the beam tube is more

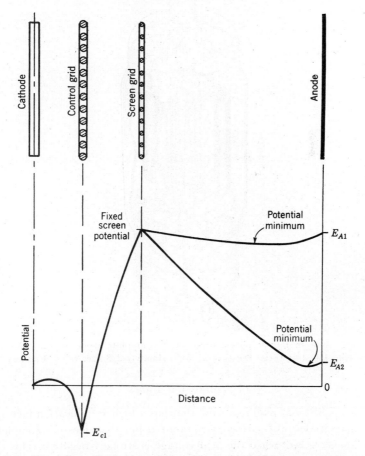

FIG. 7.9. The voltage distribution within a beam tetrode shows a potential minimum between the screen grid and anode (caused by negative space charge near anode) that prevents secondary-emission electrons from the anode passing to the screen grid.

expensive to build and is logically used in preference to the pentode only where necessary, that is, in "power" applications. As a result, pentodes are used as voltage amplifiers where the anode power seldom exceeds 1/4 watt and anode heat is no problem. Beam tetrodes are applied as output tubes where the power may be 10 watts or more. Sometimes beam power tubes,

Fig. 7.10, are used as power amplifiers to drive the grids of large triodes, or as transmitter output tubes by themselves where the anode power dissipation may be approximately 100 watts.

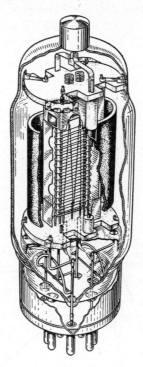

Fig. 7.10.   A beam tetrode power amplifier with graphite anode used for an output of approximately 100 watts. Illustration approximately 2/5 size.   *Courtesy RCA*

Variable-Mu Tubes

Some applications require a tube that has a high amplification factor for small magnitudes of negative grid potential but that does not completely block anode current when the grid voltage is strongly negative. This type of tube is known as the *variable-mu* tube and its construction is shown in Fig. 7.11. The control grid is wound with the turns spaced closely at each extremity of the coil but with a wider spacing at the center, as close inspection of Fig. 7.11 shows. When a small negative potential is applied to the grid, the entire portion of the grid coil controls the flow of electrons approximately the same as if the grid were uniformly spaced. As the grid is made more negative, the closely spaced ends of the grid coil shut off the flow of electrons, but some pass through the center section of the grid to maintain a small current.

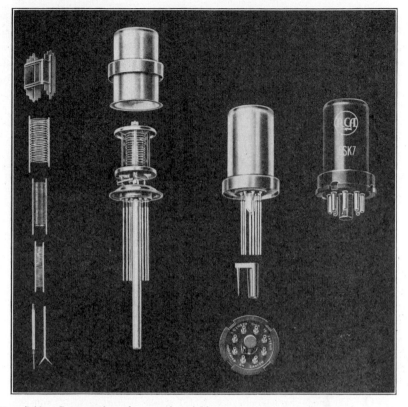

FIG. 7.11. Construction of a metal variable-mu pentode. Left, from bottom to top, cathode (and heater), control grid (showing variable-pitch winding), screen grid, suppressor grid, and anode. Center, tube elements mounted on stem and metal envelope ready for attachment to base. Right, completed metal tube. *Courtesy RCA*

A typical anode characteristic is shown in Fig. 7.12. These characteristics compared to those of a normal pentode, Fig. 7.6, show that for grid voltages between 0 and −3 the control of the tubes is nearly alike. However, with the variable-mu tube the grid voltage must be increased to −20 volts to reduce the anode current to approximately the same value as obtained with −8 volts, using the normal tube.

This fact leads to another distinguishing feature of pentodes. Most tubes of normal design have a *sharp cutoff*, which means that their transfer characteristics are reasonably straight toward the lower end and therefore approach cutoff abruptly. On the other hand variable-mu tubes have a *remote cutoff*. This means that the slope of their transfer characteristic is reduced appreciably at the lower end and requires a larger change in grid potential to attain cutoff of anode current.

Variable-mu tubes are used in radio receivers in the radio-frequency stages before the signal reaches the volume control. Here, the signal voltage can vary over wide limits. A local signal can easily be strong enough to exceed the cutoff point of an equivalent normal pentode, in which case the wave of the amplified signal is badly distorted.§ By the use of a variable-mu

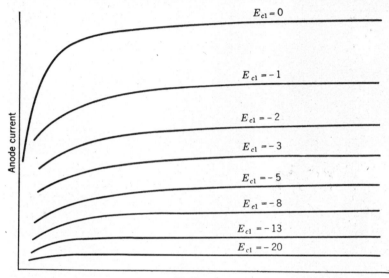

Fig. 7.12. The anode characteristic of variable-mu tube illustrates a high amplification factor (wide spacing per volt of grid voltage) for small negative grid voltages, but a low amplification factor (small spacing per volt) for large negative grid voltage.

pentode strong signals are amplified with considerably less distortion. Variable-mu tubes are used in some industrial-control devices. The distinguishing feature of their application is the necessity of attaining sensitive control over a normal operating range and yet extending operation beyond the normal range at the sacrifice of some sensitivity.

Multielement Tubes

Many tubes combine the function of two independent tubes in a single envelope. The most common example of this practice is the twin diode commonly used for full-wave rectification and voltage doubling. It is equivalent to two kenotrons within one envelope and with a common cathode. A few small phanotrons are also made with two anodes in one

§The principles of amplification are discussed in Chapter 11.

TABLE 7.1. SUMMARY OF TUBES AND THEIR PRINCIPAL CHARACTERISTICS AND USES

Tube Classification	Amplification Factor	Anode Resistance	Maximum Anode Volts	Principal Application
Triodes — low power	5-20	8 000 20 000	300	Audio-frequency amplifiers: industrial-control relay operation.
Triodes — low power, high mu	100	100 000	300	Resistance-coupled audio-frequency amplifiers.
Triodes — medium power	10-50	3 000 20 000	1 500	Audio-frequency power amplifiers and modulators. Industrial control, exciting current for motor or generator fields, etc.
Triodes — high power	10-50	2 000 20 000	20 000	Broadcast and amateur transmitter radio-frequency amplifier and output stages. Industrial radio-frequency generators for induction and dielectric heating.
Tetrodes — low power	500	600 000	250	Resistance-coupled amplifiers for audio and radio frequencies (largely replaced by pentodes).
Tetrodes — high power	200	200 000	3 000	Radio-frequency amplifier stages of broadcast and amateur transmitters.
Pentodes — low power	1200	1 000 000	300	Radio-frequency and resistance-coupled audio-frequency amplifiers. Industrial control amplifiers for photoelectric and sensitive equipment.
Pentodes — low power, variable mu	200/1200	800 000	300	Radio-frequency amplifiers for radio receivers. Industrial control for special purposes.
Pentodes — high power	250	80 000	2 000	Broadcast and amateur audio-frequency, and radio-frequency amplifiers and modulators for transmitters.
Beam tetrodes — *low power	200	40 000	350	Output stage of radio receivers. Industrial control — operating relays, exciting current for motor or generator fields, etc.
Beam tetrodes — *high power	200	40 000	2 000	Radio-frequency amplifiers for broadcast and amateur transmitters.

*"Low power" and "high power" used in this table is only relative. Low-power beam tetrodes are made to handle approximately 25 times as much power as low-power pentodes; 10 times as much as low-power triodes. On the other hand high-power beam tetrodes may handle only 1/200 that of high-power triodes, 1/4 that of tetrodes, the same as pentodes.

envelope. Some tubes combine two independent triodes, a diode and triode, or a diode and a pentode.

The purpose of this practice is to save space and cost and to obtain more effective use of the power expended in cathode heating. Frequently, the two independent elements contained in a single envelope require less cathode-heating energy than these same elements enclosed in separate envelopes, requiring the heating of two cathodes.

Other types of multielectrode tubes contain five grids and are used to convert or mix two signals.‖ Two of the grids are connected to the independent signal circuits, and the electron beam to the anode is controlled by the combined effect of both signals. The anode current thus becomes a mixture of the independent signals applied to the two grids.

SUMMARY

The *screen grid*, of the tetrode, functions to:

(a) Shield space charge near the cathode from the influence of anode potential.

(b) Shield the control grid electrostatically from the anode.

These functions of the screen grid make the tetrode superior to the triode by manifesting a higher amplification factor and lower control-grid-to-anode capacitance.

Secondary emission of electrons striking the anode flow to the screen grid when its potential is more positive than the anode. These nullify the desired flow of electrons to the anode and render the tetrode characteristics undesirable for anode voltage less than screen potential.

Input capacitance is the parallel interelectrode capacitance between cathode and control grid and between control grid and screen grid.

Output capacitance is the parallel interelectrode capacitance between screen grid and anode and between cathode and anode.

The *suppressor grid*, of the pentode functions to arrest the flow of secondary electrons toward the screen grid.

This function of the suppressor grid makes the pentode superior to the tetrode by extending the useful range of operating anode voltage.

Beam power tubes have characteristics similar to pentodes but have only four elements. Secondary electrons from the anode are prevented from reaching the screen grid by focusing the electron beam to form a potential minimum between the screen and anode.

Variable-mu tubes employ a control grid with a variable-pitch winding of the grid coil turns. The amplification factor for these tubes is large for low negative grid potentials and is reduced as the grid potential becomes highly negative.

Multielement tubes combine two or more type elements within a single envelope utilizing a single cathode. A few common arrangements are:

‖See Terman, *Radio Engineers' Handbook*, pp 569–73.

(a) Twin diode — two kenotrons or two phanotrons.
(b) Twin triodes — two three-element pliotrons.
(c) Diode triode — kenotron with three-element pliotron.
(d) Diode-pentode — kenotron with five-element pliotron.
(e) Pentagrid converter — pliotron with five grids.

REFERENCES

MIT Electrical Engineering Staff, *Applied Electronics*, John Wiley & Sons, New York, 1943, pp 184–202.

Jacob Millman and Samuel Seely, *Electronics*, McGraw-Hill Book Co., New York, 1941, pp 551–71.

Herbert J. Reich, *Theory and Applications of Electron Tubes*, McGraw-Hill Book Co., New York, 1944, pp 43–123.

F. E. Terman, *Radio Engineering*, McGraw-Hill Book Co., New York, 1937, pp 126–64.

F. E. Terman, *Radio Engineers' Handbook*, McGraw-Hill Book Co., New York, 1943, pp 298–321.

Royce G. Kloeffler, *Principles of Electronics*, John Wiley & Sons, New York, 1942, pp 70–80.

W. G. Dow, *Fundamentals of Engineering Electronics*, John Wiley & Sons, New York, 1937, pp 125–40.

Keith Henney, *Radio Engineering Handbook*, McGraw-Hill Book Co., New York, 1941, pp 255–68.

J. B. Hoag, *Basic Radio*, D. Van Nostrand Co., New York, 1943, pp 98–105.

Chapter 8

THYRATRONS

The introduction of the cold-cathode grid-glow tube, predecessor of the thyratron, opened the lid of a new electronic tool chest just as De Forest's pliotron had been the means of altering the engineering of communications. In the relatively few years of the thyratron's existence we have come to accept as commonplace such important industrial accomplishments as the perfect welding of metals having a high thermal conductivity and narrow plastic range, the precision register or alignment of multicolor high-speed printing presses, the accurate and rapid machine packaging of most articles displayed for sale in quantity , the accurate velocity measurement of a high-powered bullet in flight, and many other functions upon which engineers have learned to depend. Without the thyratron, none of these things would have come into being, for they all rely upon the outstanding feature of the thyratron. It waits, inert, for a "go" signal, then acts with great suddenness — a few millionths of one second — and is unchecked by the swift passing of its initiating impulse. This characteristic makes the thyratron a natural comapnion to industrial tools in particular, manifested by the fact that practically every electronic device offered for industrial use today contains at least one thyratron among its complement of tubes.

Thyratrons are classified as gas-filled grid-controlled tubes. They may be either triodes, tetrodes, or pentodes, although at the time of this writing it is more common to refer to the triodes as thyratrons while the tetrodes and pentodes are called shield-grid thyratrons.

The function and advantages of gas-filled tubes is discussed in Chapter 5 in connection with phanotrons. It would seem a simple matter to insert a grid into such a tube and obtain the advantages of grid control in a manner similar to the control of anode current by means of a grid common to pliotrons. However, the action of a grid inserted into a gas-filled tube is considerably different from its action in vacuum tubes. An understanding of this difference is essential.

A comparison between the fundamentals of a pliotron and a thyratron are illustrated in Fig. 8.1. A single transfer characteristic of a pliotron gradually approaches the cutoff point of anode current as its grid is made more negative. Starting from a strong negative voltage as the grid potential becomes more positive, no anode current flows until the cutoff point is

116

reached, after which the anode current rises gradually along the curve until saturation of the cathode emission is finally reached. The thyratron behaves quite differently. Starting from a high negative grid potential and gradually making it less and less negative, no anode current flows until a potential is reached corresponding to the cutoff point on the pliotron characteristic.

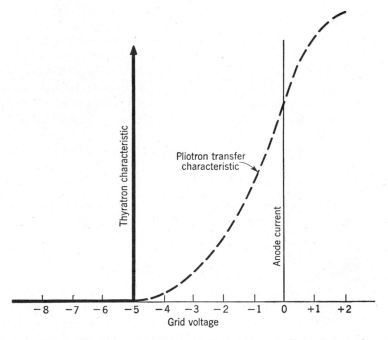

Fig. 8.1. The anode current of a pliotron (dotted) rises gradually as the negative grid voltage is reduced. Thyratron anode current (solid) is zero for all grid potential more negative than the *critical grid voltage* (−5 volts) and rises unlimited at this firing point.

This point on the thyratron characteristic is known as the *firing point* at which the anode current rises abruptly and cannot be controlled by the grid. The value of grid voltage at which the tube becomes conducting is known as the *critical grid voltage*. The magnitude of anode current is limited only by the external circuit constants as previously discussed on p 74.

As explained in Chapter 5, the gas space can be ionized by a relatively few fast-moving electrons. An arc discharge between cathode and anode then rapidly ensues. The grid of a thyratron is instrumental in maintaining control over the establishment of the ionized condition, that is, the firing point, but is powerless to influence the characteristic of the tube once ionization has started. The grid acts like a trigger, because it can initiate conduction but cannot stop the electron flow from cathode to anode. Anode

current of a thyratron can be stopped only by reducing the positive potential of the anode below the arc-drop voltage. In practice this amounts to
opening the anode circuit by some external means such as a switch, or otherwise reducing the anode potential to zero.

Cathodes

The construction of thyratron cathodes is similar to those previously
described for phanotrons, p 77–8. Heat-conserving designs can be used,
because most of the voltage drop is through an infinitesimal thickness of the
cathode sheath. The distance between any part of the cathode and the
anode is not important. Any construction used in phanotrons to conserve
heat is equally adaptable to thyratrons. A typical efficient shielded cathode
is illustrated in Fig. 8.2.

Anodes

Thyratron anodes are similar in design to those used in phanotrons,
p 79, and usually take the form of a flat disk of graphite, or carbonized
metal.

Grids

The action of the grid is to prevent ionization within the gas space and to
hold off conduction. A negative potential on the grid prevents electron
flow away from the cathode surface by control over the negative space
charge near the cathode surface as described in connection with pliotrons on
p 83–8. The grid is thus able to prevent electrons emitted by the cathode
from entering the gas space, arresting ionization that leads to breakdown
within the tube. As the grid potential is made less negative, more electrons
escape into the gas space and begin to increase ionization. Positive ions
within the gas space are then attracted toward the grid surface and begin to
form a positive-ion skin or sheath over the grid surface. The effect is illustrated in Fig. 8.3 wherein it is assumed the grid is constructed of solid wires
represented by the solid circles. The positive-ion sheath forming over the
surface of the grid further decreases the effective negative potential of the
grid, as though the grid potential were made less negative by some external
means. More electrons can then escape from the cathode, further increasing
the degree of ionization and increasing the thickness of the positive-ion
sheath over the grid. Thus the process is cumulative, and the grid becomes
unable to control the avalanche of electron and positive-ion flow that

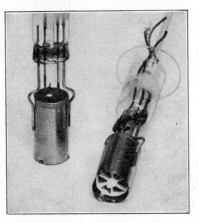

F<small>IG</small>. 8.2.   Thyratron cathodes utilize heat-conserving designs. This type consists of a central core, surrounded by a cylinder and radial fins with all surfaces coated for active emission (light-colored parts). The cathode is enclosed in a deep cylindrical shield to reduce radiant heat loss (dark-colored parts).   *Courtesy Westinghouse*

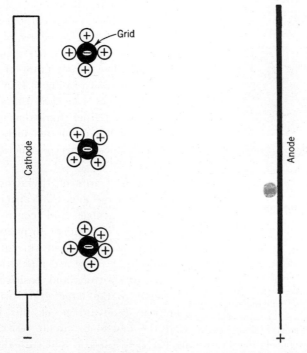

F<small>IG</small>. 8.3.   As the thyratron grid voltage approaches the critical firing point, positive ions begin to form a sheath over the grid and make its effective voltage more positive than the applied potential.

FIG. 8.4. A three-element thyratron with glass envelope removed. The heat shield and a part of the grid are cut away to show (1) the corrugated edge-coiled directly heated cathode. Radiant-heat loss of the cathode is minimized by its being enclosed in the conical heat shield (2). The graphite anode (5) is seen through the cut away window in the cylindrical grid (3). All electrons flowing from the cathode to the anode must pass through a slot (4) seen in the horizontal baffle of the grid (3).

rapidly increases to form an arc discharge from cathode to anode. The time required for this action is known as *ionization time*, usually in the order of five to ten microseconds.

This phenomenon occurs wherever the grid is least able to prevent electrons from entering the gas space. Whereas the grid of a pliotron is designed to obtain an *average* control over the space charge which is in the vicinity of the cathode, thyratron grids must control the space charge in *all directions*, because it would be useless to restrict the majority of electrons but allow a few to escape and start ionization. For this reason, thyratron grids surround the entire cathode and even enclose the anode periphery. This usually takes the form of a solid cylinder with a baffle between the cathode and anode with a small hole in the center of the baffle through which electrons must pass to reach the anode. The construction of a typical thyratron is shown in Fig. 8.4, in which the elements are cut away and the glass envelope omitted. Earlier thyratrons used a grid in the form of a perforated metal cylinder, and many tubes of this construction are still in service.

The surface area of thyratron grids is necessarily large and the capacitance between the cathode and control grid is greater than is common to pliotrons. Also they have a higher grid current prior to breakdown, because a comparatively large number of electrons and positive ions are attracted to the large grid surface. The practical disadvantage of this feature is that the maximum circuit resistance connected between grid and cathode must be much less than in an equivalent pliotron application.

Once the negative grid potential becomes sufficiently low to start conduction, the grid is immediately ineffective in controlling the anode current. As previously explained in Chapter 5, p 76, the space between cathode and anode within a gas tube is composed largely of a *plasma* consisting of equal numbers of electrons and positive ions. The plasma extends to within an extremely short distance of the cathode surface assuring that the grid is located within the plasma boundary. The effect is illustrated in

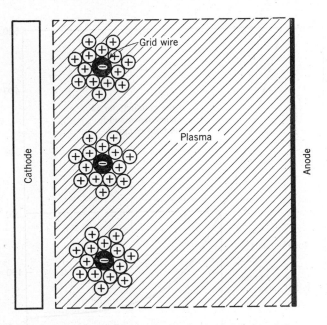

FIG. 8.5. Once conduction starts, the thyratron grid is covered by a positive-ion sheath making its effective potential positive regardless of the applied voltage and rendering the grid ineffective to control the anode current.

Fig. 8.5 wherein, for convenience, the grid is represented as the cross section of a wire helix instead of a cylinder. A negative potential applied to the grid attracts positive ions from the plasma which land on the grid surface. There they form a dense positive-ion sheath, effectively making the grid positive and rendering its negative potential useless in controlling the electron flow. A larger negative potential applied to the grid only results in increasing the thickness of the positive-ion sheath by attracting more positive ions from the plasma. A strong positive potential applied to the grid has the reverse effect: that is, it attracts electrons emitted from the cathode and is likewise ineffective in controlling the anode current.

Because of this loss of control over the anode current at the instant of conduction, current can be stopped only by control of anode voltage external to the tube. Conduction ceases as soon as anode voltage is made less than that required for arc voltage between cathode and anode. The positive ions disappear, and the grid once more regains the control necessary to hold off conduction when anode voltage is reapplied. The time required for the grid to regain this control is known as *deionization time*. It is many times greater than the ionization time, usually 1000 microseconds for most thy-

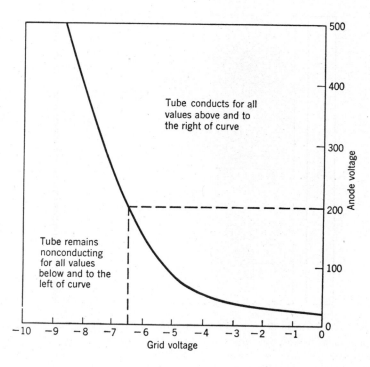

FIG. 8.6(*a*).   Firing curves of a typical negative-control thyratron. For every value of anode voltage there is a corresponding grid voltage at which the thyratron will become conducting.

ratrons. During this interval, anode voltage must be maintained less than the tube arc drop and grid potential more negative than the critical voltage; else the grid is unable to regain control to prevent conduction.

Once conduction has started, the grid current may rise to an abnormal value because of positive ions flowing to the grid if its potential is strongly negative, or by electron flow to a strongly positive grid. Maximum grid current is limited by a resistance connected in series with a thyratron grid to prevent abnormal grid current after conduction starts.

Control Characteristics

Grid construction has an important influence upon the control characteristics. In general the more completely the grid surrounds the cathode the smaller is the negative grid voltage required to prevent conduction. In fact the design can be carried to the point where a positive grid voltage is required to start conduction. This feature classifies thyratrons in two

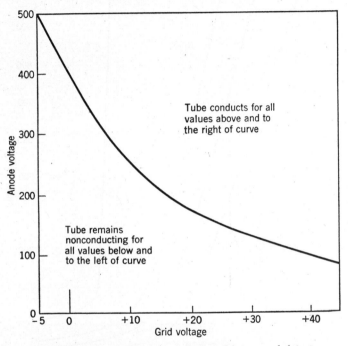

FIG. 8.6(*b*). Firing curves of a typical positive-control thyratron.

groups. One group is referred to as *negative-control* tubes if the grid voltage is predominantly negative in polarity to hold off conduction. The other is spoken of as *positive-control* tubes* if a positive polarity of grid voltage is required to start conduction.

Typical characteristics of these types are shown in Fig. 8.6a and b. These curves represent an entirely different characteristic than previously discussed in regard to all pliotron tubes. These are known as *firing curves*, and they show that for each anode voltage there is a corresponding grid voltage required to hold off conduction. For example, with reference to the negative-control tube (a) if 200 volts is applied to the anode, conduction

*For further details in regard to positive- and negative-control thyratrons, see McArthur, *Electronics and Electron Tubes*, pp 123–7.

cannot start so long as the grid bias is held more negative than the critical grid voltage of −6.5 volts. If the grid voltage is reduced to less than −6.5 volts the tube immediately conducts. The significance of (b) is the same except that the grid voltage is positive in polarity over the greater part of the curve.

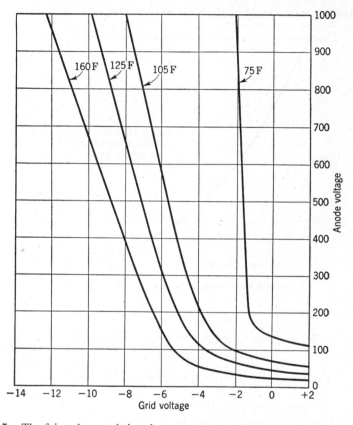

FIG. 8.7. The firing characteristics of a mercury-vapor thyratron are affected by the condensed mercury temperature. Best practice is to operate tubes close to 125 F measured on the glass at the top of the base.

The control characteristics of a mercury-vapor thyratron are considerably affected by the temperature of the tube. The critical grid voltage depends upon the condensed mercury temperature as Fig. 8.7 shows. A higher temperature increases the particle concentration and reduces the mean free path or distance between particles. Therefore, each electron that escapes from the cathode is able to make more collisions resulting in more positive ions. For this reason, a higher negative grid voltage is required at a high tube temperature to hold off conduction. The effect of tube temperature upon the control is varied over wide limits for mercury-vapor thyratrons. The effect is so pronounced that manufacturers usually limit the temperature range to from 75 F minimum to 160 F maximum. This temperature is measured at the bottom of the glass envelope just

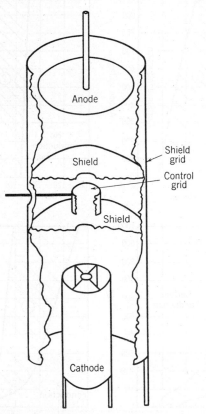

FIG. 8.8. The control grid of shield-grid thyratrons is reduced to a small cylinder (sometimes a ring). The shield protects the control grid from both the cathode and the anode, contributing many advantages.

above the base. In applying thyratrons, one should give careful consideration to ventilation of the equipment to make certain that the air flow is vertically upward along the tubes and that operating conditions will not cause the tube temperature to rise or fall outside these limits.

Shield-Grid Thyratrons

The typical construction of a shield-grid thyratron is illustrated in Fig. 8.8. The shield grid is a metal cylinder completely surrounding the cathode and anode with two parallel baffles between the cathode and anode. Electrons must pass through a small hole in the center of each baffle to reach the anode. The control grid now consists of a small cylinder slightly

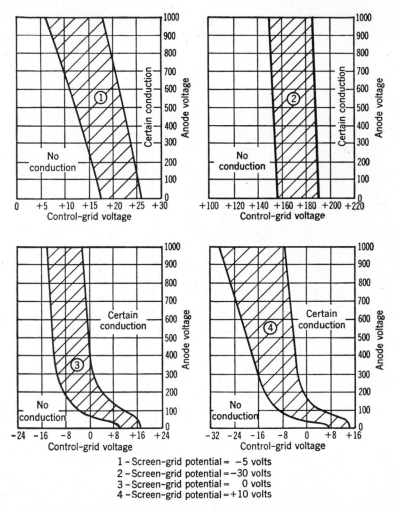

1 – Screen-grid potential = −5 volts
2 – Screen-grid potential = −30 volts
3 – Screen-grid potential =   0 volts
4 – Screen-grid potential = +10 volts

Fig. 8.9.   The characteristics of a shield-grid thyratron can be altered by the voltage applied to the shield. The zone between certain conduction and no conduction represents allowance for the maximum and minimum permissible operating temperature.

larger than the hole in each baffle and is extremely effective in blocking the escape of electrons through the shield grid.

Several important advantages are gained by this modification of the three-electrode thyratron:

1. The area of the control grid is considerably reduced. The grid current and the capacitance between the control grid and cathode are reduced to approximately 1/20th of a comparable three-element thyratron. The reduction in grid current makes it possible to adapt the shield-grid thyratron to control circuits utilizing a much higher grid circuit resistance.

2. The control grid is shielded against radiant heat of the cathode resulting in a lower grid temperature and reducing the possibility of electron emission from the control grid.

3. The control grid is protected against the deposit of material evaporated from the cathode, which further reduces the possibility of secondary grid emission.

4. The control grid is electrostatically shielded from the anode, reducing the tendency for sudden changes in anode potential to affect the instantaneous grid potential.

FIG. 8.10. A small shield-grid thyratron suited to operating control circuit relays. Illustration is actual size. *Courtesy RCA*

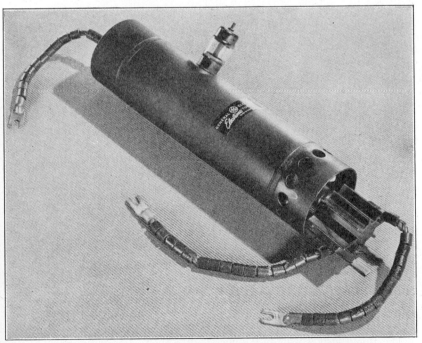

FIG. 8.11. A metal shield-grid thyratron for power applications.
Courtesy General Electric

5. The shield-grid construction more effectively reduces the radiant heat losses of the cathode and contributes to a higher cathode efficiency.

Fig. 8.12. A thyratron rectifier and control equipment for excitation of a synchronous motor field. *Courtesy General Electric*

Shield-grid thyratrons are rapidly replacing the earlier three-element types, for the advantages previously mentioned often have an important bearing upon the operation of a control circuit.

The shield grid is usually connected directly to the cathode where the relatively high current (several milliamperes) collected by the shield returns to the cathode circuit without affecting the control grid. The firing characteristics can be altered if the shield grid is operated at other than the cathode potential. The characteristics of one type of tube when several different bias voltages are being applied to the shield grid are exhibited in Fig. 8.9. These curves also show a method of including an allowance for tube temperature variation by plotting the firing curve as a band. Below this band the tube does not conduct, and above it conduction is assured, over the range of temperature for which the manufacturer guarantees operation. In this case, the recommended condensed mercury temperature is 120 F with a permissible minimum of 105 F and maximum of 175 F.

A small shield-grid thyratron is shown in Fig. 8.10. This thyratron has sufficient capacity to operate the coil of many control-circuit relays and has a wide field of usefulness. A shield-grid power thyratron with metal envelope is shown in Fig. 8.11. Tubes of this classification are suitable for carrying the armature current of d-c motors of several horsepower.

A thyratron rectifier, using metal thyratrons, is shown in Fig. 8.12. This cubicle is the complete field-control equipment for use with a large synchronous motor, the field excitation being supplied by the thyratron rectifier with the usual rotating exciter-generator set eliminated. The rectifier is mounted on the top panel, the lower devices being for the automatic field-control circuits.

Mercury-vapor thyratrons are subject to the disadvantage of being seriously affected by temperature changes as previously illustrated by Fig. 8.7. The zone of temperatures for satisfactory operation can be considerably widened and the effect of temperature variations reduced if the tube is filled with an inert gas. These tubes are subject to the disappearance or "clean-up" of the gas as previously discussed in regard to phanotrons, p 80. In spite of this disadvantage, they are widely used for control circuits where the advantage of their being less affected by temperature changes is more important.

SUMMARY

Thyratrons are grid-controlled gas-filled tubes. They consist of three elements — sometimes of four elements, in which case they are frequently classified as shield-grid thyratrons.

Thyratron cathodes are heat-shielded for high emission efficiency.

Thyratron grids completely surround either the cathode or the anode, frequently both. They are metallic hollow cylinders with a small passage between cathode and anode through which electrons must flow.

Critical grid voltage is the grid potential at which the tube will fire (become conducting); that is, for all values of grid potential more negative (or less positive) than the critical grid voltage the tube remains nonconducting. It is dependent upon anode voltage and tube operating temperature (mercury-vapor tubes).

Anode current of thyratrons (*a*) cannot be adjusted by grid potential, (*b*) is limited only by the anode source voltage and load impedance, and (*c*) once started, can be stopped only by reduction of anode voltage below the arc-drop voltage.

Grid current is relatively greater than is common to pliotrons, is less for shield-grid thyratrons than for three-element tubes, and is greater after conduction than before conduction.

Ionization time is the elapsed time necessary for anode formation of the arc discharge (conduction) after the grid becomes less negative than the critical voltage.

Deionization time is the elapsed time required for deionizing the gas space after anode voltage is reduced below the tube arc-drop voltage. During this interval the grid regains its control to hold off conduction, providing its potential is more negative than the critical grid voltage.

Condensed mercury temperature of mercury-filled thyratrons is measured at the tube envelope just above the base. The temperature affects the tube characteristics to an important degree, and must be maintained within the operating limits specified by the manufacturer.

REFERENCES

W. G. Dow, *Fundamentals of Engineering Electronics*, John Wiley & Sons, New York, 1937, pp 458–78 and 481–500.

MIT Electrical Engineering Staff, *Applied Electronics*, John Wiley & Sons, New York, 1943, pp 228–46.

E. D. McArthur, *Electronics and Electron Tubes*, John Wiley & Sons, New York, 1936, pp 120–34.

Jacob Millman and Samuel Seely, *Electronics*, McGraw-Hill Book Co., New York, 1941, pp 330–7.

F. E. Terman, *Radio Engineering*, McGraw-Hill Book Co., New York, 1937, pp 157–60.

F. E. Terman, *Radio Engineers' Handbook*, McGraw-Hill Book Co., New York, 1943, pp 344–52.

Keith Henney, *Radio Engineering Handbook*, McGraw-Hill Book Co., New York, 1941, pp 269–73.

Royce G. Kloeffler, *Principles of Electronics*, John Wiley & Sons Company, New York, 1942, pp 80–8.

J. B. Hoag, *Basic Radio*, D. Van Nostrand Co., New York, 1943, pp 122–6.

W. D. Cockrell, *Industrial Electronic Control*, McGraw-Hill Book Co., New York, 1944, pp 47–51.

L. W. Livingston and H. T. Maser, "Shield-Grid Thyratrons," *Electronics*, April, 1934, pp 114.

Chapter 9

FROM ALTERNATING TO DIRECT CURRENT

Alternating current by no means has a monopoly over direct current as useful electric power. In spite of the almost universal use of a-c systems for power distribution, modern industry uses more direct current than ever for wide speed-range drives, welding, battery charging, electrolytic deposition, and electrochemical processes. Many rectifier plants are in service in which hundreds of thousands of amperes of direct current are delivered 24 hours a day, 365 days a year, to cells producing aluminum and magnesium. A substantial portion of the electronic engineer's job is to provide direct current not only for use as a product in some industrial process, but also for use in electronic devices themselves.

Many devices and circuits are used to convert alternating to direct current. Some are mechanical, such as the synchronous converter, or mechanical vibrator. Various types of electrolytic rectifiers are used for special purposes. The barrier-layer type of rectifier, such as copper-oxide or selenium, are quasi-electronic and depend on the unilateral conductivity of a surface coating on a base metal. Still others, such as the mercury-pool and the vacuum-tube types, are truly electronic and are our concern here.

To rectify means to allow current to flow unrestricted in one direction and to block completely or effectively impede current in the opposite direction. A two-element electronic tube is well adapted to do this. One element of the tube (cathode) is made an emitter of electrons, while the other (anode) is not. Hence, if alternating voltage is applied between the cathode and anode, electrons emitted from the cathode are drawn to the anode when the potential of the anode is positive. However, when the polarity reverses, no electrons flow because none are emitted by the anode.

By definition, the number of electrons flowing through a circuit per second is a measure of the current. Therefore, a two-element tube allows current to flow whenever its anode is positive but stops current when the anode is negative. Indeed, the English give it the more descriptive name, *valve*, instead of tube. When an alternating potential is applied to such a tube, only a unidirectional current flows through its terminals.

The fundamental principle of rectification is illustrated by the simple circuit shown in Fig. 9.1. When the upper terminal of the a-c generator is positive, the anode of the rectifier tube is positive, and the tube is conducting; that is, electrons flow from the cathode to anode. (Note that the direction of current flow is exactly opposite to the direction of electron flow.) The anode must be positive if the tube is to conduct, and, by the

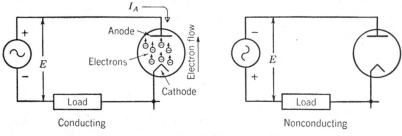

Conducting   Nonconducting

FIG. 9.1. Principle of half-wave rectification.

previously established conventional definition, current flows from positive to negative (through a voltage drop). Yet, it is the flow of electrons from the cathode to the anode that performs the actual conduction of the tube.

Rectifier Circuits

Each of the many rectification circuits is best adapted to some specific set of conditions. The circuits most commonly used for industrial purposes are discussed on the following pages together with the essential comparison of different types.

Rectifier-circuit behavior can be clarified by arbitrarily assigning circuit voltages and tracing the current through a complete conducting path. While the tube is conducting, there is a voltage drop from cathode to anode, arbitrarily assumed as 10 volts in all illustrations. This value bears no resemblance to actual working conditions. Tube drops range from 7 volts to several thousand volts, depending upon the type of rectifier tube and the operating conditions prevailing.

SINGLE-PHASE HALF-WAVE RECTIFIERS*

Present Terms	Proposed Terms
Single-phase half-wave	Half-wave
Single-phase full-wave center-tap	Full-wave
Single-phase full-wave bridge	Single-phase bridge
Three-phase half-wave	Three-phase wye
	Three phase zigzag
Three-phase full-wave bridge	Three-phase bridge
Three-phase diametric	Six-phase diametric
Three-phase double-wye	Double-wye

*The terminology used for rectifier connections is chosen to be descriptive of the circuit and conforms to present use. At the time of this writing a new nomenclature is being considered by the metallic rectifier subcommittee of AIEE.

Consider a simple half-wave rectifier, shown in Figs. 9.2 and 9.3 where a kenotron or phanotron is connected in series with an a-c generator and a pure-resistance load. With the tube conducting, Fig. 9.2, assume that the bottom terminal of the generator is at zero potential and its upper terminal

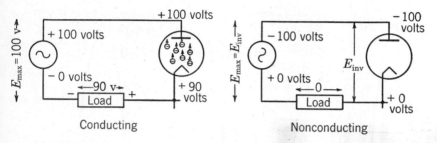

Conducting   Nonconducting

FIG. 9.2. The tube conducts with posi-   FIG. 9.3. The tube is nonconducting
tive polarity to its anode, manifesting a   with negative polarity to its anode. An
forward voltage drop. Load positive   inverse voltage appears across the tube.
terminal is toward the tube cathode.

+100 volts. Because of voltage drop through the tube (assumed as 10 volts), the cathode potential is somewhat lower than the anode potential, thus making the potential of the cathode +90 volts relative to the bottom terminal of the generator. The potential of the cathode relative to the anode is −10 volts. The cathode of the tube is then connected to the positive terminal of the load. The output of the rectifier is 90 volts (peak). The difference between the 100 volts from the generator and 90 volts applied to the load is the *tube voltage drop*, or *forward drop* through the tube.

An important limitation of every rectifier tube is illustrated in Fig. 9.3, which shows the conditions existing when the generator polarity has reversed and the tube blocks the flow of current. An *inverse voltage* is applied across the tube while nonconducting. The inverse-voltage rating signifies the maximum peak voltage that the tube can withstand while blocking reverse current. The 100-volt output of the a-c generator, Fig 9.3, then appears between the anode and cathode of the tube and with negative potential applied to the anode. For the single-phase half-wave rectifier the inverse voltage is the maximum voltage of the a-c source. Obviously, the maximum inverse voltage should not exceed the tube rating as the tube will be injured by current flowing backwards through it. Reverse conduction is called *flashback* or *arc-back*. Clearly this type of rectifier allows current to flow during the positive half-cycles of the applied a-c wave and blocks current during the negative half-cycles. Thus, this circuit earns the name half-wave rectifier.

The wave form of the voltage appearing across the load is shown in Fig. 9.4b. The voltage is always above the zero axis and therefore can properly be called unidirectional, although it is by no means the equivalent of "smooth direct voltage" obtained by battery or d-c generator.

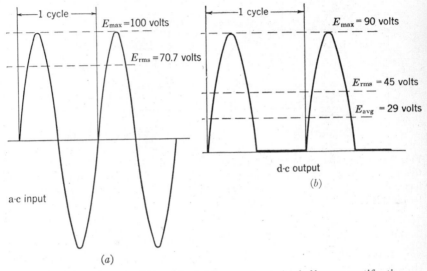

FIG. 9.4. A-c Supply (*a*) and load (*b*) wave forms for half-wave rectification.

Because of the irregular wave form of rectified voltage, it is always necessary to consider three values of the voltage:

The maximum alternating sine voltage applied to the circuit is symbolized as E_{max}, shown in Fig. 9.4a.

The rms value of the d-c wave is E_{rms}, Fig. 9.4b. This is 50 percent of maximum alternating voltage for a single-phase half-wave rectifier.

The average value of the d-c wave is E_{avg}, Fig. 9.4b. For a single-phase half-wave rectifier it is 31.8 percent of the maximum voltage.

The unevenness in the rectified wave is the *ripple*, and the factor that expresses its magnitude is the *ripple factor*. A rectified wave can be considered of two components. One is a steady unvarying d-c component on which is superimposed a fluctuating or alternating component. The ripple factor is the ratio of the alternating component to the direct component. The lower the ripple factor, the closer a rectified wave approaches pure direct current.

Ripple is not always undesirable, but for much electronic work it must be made as small as possible. For a single-phase half-wave rectifier with resistance load the ripple factor is 1.21, indicating that the pulsating component even exceeds the direct component.

The single-phase half-wave rectifier has a relatively low efficiency.†
The maximum theoretically possible is 40.6 percent, and this is attained
only when the tube resistance is small compared to the load resistance.

FIG. 9.5. A phanotron (metal tube) rectifier for single-phase full-wave automatic
charging of a 60-cell lead storage battery; maximum 12.5 amperes.

(*Courtesy General Electric*)

When the two resistances are equal, the efficiency is but 21 percent. In this
type of circuit, only a portion of the power input to the rectifier circuit is
delivered to the load; the power consumed in the rectifier tube is wasted as
heat.

The wave form of current is subject to the same factors as previously
mentioned, and, if the load is solely resistance, the numerical figures are the
same as given for voltages.

The unidirectional current through the rectifier also flows through the
a-c supply because of its series connection. Practical rectifiers usually
employ transformers of which the secondary winding serves as the a-c
supply. For this, the effects of unidirectional current must be considered.
As current through the transformer rises, and then falls to zero, flux within
the core rises also but does not fall to zero, leaving behind a small amount
of residual magnetization of the core. As alternating current flows, the

†For detailed discussion of single-phase half-wave rectifier efficiency see MIT staff,
Applied Electronics, p 258.

residual magnetization is quickly nullified by the reversed direction of current during successive half-cycles. For the half-wave rectifier, current is unidirectional and the residual core magnetization left by a current pulse is not nullified. This leads to magnetic saturation of the transformer core whereby the magnitude of changing flux cannot remain proportional to the changing primary voltage, with detrimental effect upon the transformer function. Transformers designed for the half-wave rectifying circuit must be designed to avoid undue saturation, and therefore must be larger and more expensive than if the unidirectional current were not present. This is one of the disadvantages of the single-phase half-wave rectifier circuit. Another disadvantage is the high ripple factor. Although the ripple can be minimized by a suitable filter, in general a single-phase half-wave rectifier is used only where small power outputs are required.

SINGLE-PHASE FULL-WAVE CENTER-TAP RECTIFIERS

The single-phase full-wave center-tap rectifier is the one most widely used for low-power applications using kenotrons or phanotrons. Such a rectifier is found in many a-c operated radio receivers and the d-c power circuit of many industrial amplifier circuits.

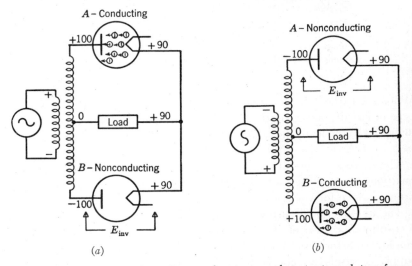

FIG. 9.6. A full-wave rectifier using two kenotrons and center-tapped transformer secondary winding. (a) Tube A conducting and (b) Tube B conducting.

The principle of this type of full-wave rectifier is illustrated in Figs. 9.6a and b. The name of this type of rectifier is derived from the use of a transformer winding provided with a tap in the center. Tube A conducts when the generator polarity is such as to make the anode of tube *A* positive. The operation of the rectifier is the same as previously described for the half-wave rectifier during this part of the cycle. Meanwhile, tube *B* and the lower half of the transformer winding are inactive.

When the applied polarity reverses, the anode of tube *B* becomes positive and tube *B* conducts through the load. During this half of the cycle tube *A* and the upper half of the transformer winding are inactive.

Current is conducted alternately by tubes *A* and *B*, and the rectified output is now continuous throughout both halves of the a-c cycle.

The inverse voltage applied to the nonconducting tube in this case is equal to the full voltage across both transformer secondary windings except for the small voltage drop through one tube. To calculate the inverse voltage, neglect the voltage drop through one tube. Then the inverse voltage across each tube is twice the peak alternating voltage of one-half the transformer secondary. Inasmuch as the inverse voltage is always taken as the peak value, this results in 2.82 times the rms alternating voltage of half of the transformer voltage.

The center-tap rectifier connection affords a means of obtaining a full-wave rectifier with only two kenotron (or phanotron) tubes. Many rectifier tubes are available with these two diode elements sealed within a single envelope.

The popularity of this rectifier connection is explained by the fact that full-wave rectification is thus obtained with the fewest tubes. Also the circuit eliminates d-c saturation of the transformer core, because the d-c components in the two halves of the secondary winding flow in opposite directions to cancel the d-c saturating effect.

Some disadvantages must be weighed against the advantage of simplicity. Each of the diode elements must withstand an inverse voltage of approximately 3.14 times the average d-c output voltage. Also, only one half of the secondary winding is effective at any particular instant in supplying power to the d-c load The transformer materials are not used to the maximum advantage, which makes a transformer for a center-tap circuit more expensive than a comparable unit for use in the bridge circuit, explained in the following.

The direct-voltage wave form of the full-wave rectifier has twice as many loops as has that of the half-wave rectifier, as a comparison of Figs. 9.4 and 9.7 shows. The average direct voltage is twice as great as for the half-wave rectifier or 63.6 percent of the maximum voltage, and the rms voltage is increased to 70.7 percent.

The ripple factor is reduced to 0.48, and the frequency of the ripple is double that for a half-wave rectifier or twice the line frequency (120 cycles for a 60-cycle rectifier). The maximum theoretical efficiency is 81.2 percent.

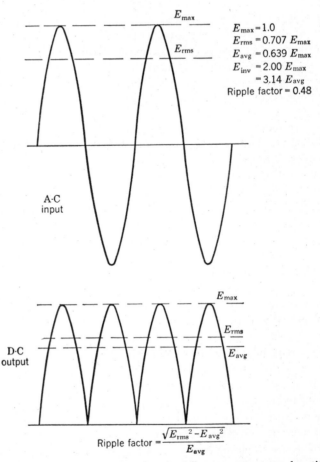

$E_{max} = 1.0$
$E_{rms} = 0.707\ E_{max}$
$E_{avg} = 0.639\ E_{max}$
$E_{inv} = 2.00\ E_{max}$
$= 3.14\ E_{avg}$
Ripple factor = 0.48

A·C input

D·C output

E_{max}

E_{rms}

E_{avg}

Ripple factor $= \dfrac{\sqrt{E_{rms}^2 - E_{avg}^2}}{E_{avg}}$

FIG. 9.7. Wave forms and circuit values for full-wave center tapped rectification.

SINGLE-PHASE FULL-WAVE BRIDGE RECTIFIER

A full-wave bridge-type single-phase rectifier is shown in Figs. 9.8a and b. When the upper end of the transformer secondary winding is positive, current flows through tubes A and B while tubes C and D block reverse current. When the bottom of the transformer secondary winding is positive, tubes C and D are conducting, and tubes A and B are nonconducting. The direction of load current I_L is the same in the two cases.

The inverse voltage is half as great for this type of rectifier as for the full-wave center-tap rectifier, as inspection of the instantaneous voltages show. If the voltage drop through either tube is neglected, the inverse voltage for this connection is 1.41 times the transformer secondary voltage, or 1.00 times E_{max}.

The wave form and voltage ratios with the exception of inverse voltage shown in Fig. 9.9 are the same as for the center-tap rectifier. The ripple factor is 0.48, and the maximum efficiency is 81.2 percent.

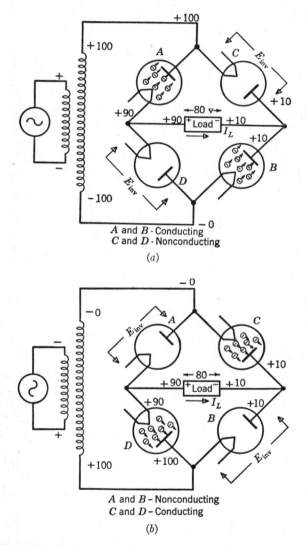

FIG. 9.8.   Four diode elements connected as a single-phase full-wave bridge rectifier. (a) Tubes A and B conducting (b) tubes C and D conducting.

The bridge-type rectifier has two advantages over the center-tap circuit. The inverse voltage across each tube is half as great as for the center-tap connection, and the transformer secondary winding is fully utilized. The transformer cost is, therefore, less than a comparable center-tap design, although four rectifier-tube elements are required for the bridge connection.

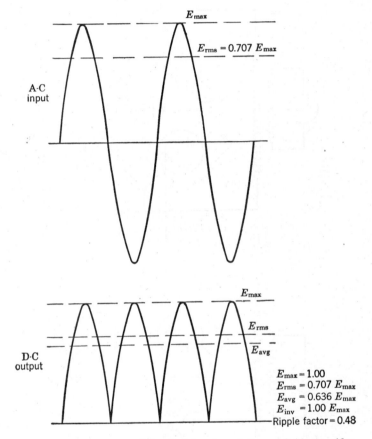

FIG. 9.9.   Wave forms and circuit values for a full-wave bridge rectifier.

Also the cost of tubes enters into the choice of bridge or center-tap circuit. For a given application four tubes each having an inverse-voltage rating satisfactory to the bridge circuit may, in some instances, actually cost less than two tubes each having the higher inverse-voltage rating required for the center-tap connection. Balanced against this possible advantage is the necessity of exciting the cathode of each tube from a separate transformer winding insulated for the maximum potential of the circuit. This is required because the cathodes of tubes within the bridge circuit are not at the same potential as is the case with the center-tap connection.

Rectifiers employing either copper-oxide or selenium rectifying elements are usually built of the bridge-type design, assembled of a large number of rectifying disks, each one by itself having a relatively low inverse-voltage rating, such that several must be connected in series to withstand the full-circuit inverse voltage. The complication of a four-legged connection is no

FIG. 9.10. A selenium-rectifier-stack, single-phase full-wave bridge connection with six disks in series for each leg.　　　(*Courtesy General Electric*)

disadvantage in building a rectifier of either copper-oxide or selenium elements for there are no thermionic cathodes to be excited by insulated transformer windings. Here the more economical transformer design can then be used to its maximum advantage.

THREE-PHASE HALF-WAVE RECTIFIER

A three-phase half-wave rectifier, Fig. 9.11, consists of three tubes connected to a three-phase-wye transformer bank. The alternating voltage applied to the anodes of tube A, B, and C is displaced by 120 electrical degrees, and each tube in turn carries the load one third of the cycle.

The light-face voltages shown in Fig. 9.11 correspond to a 90-degree angle of transformer winding $0–e_1$ at which instant the voltage on the anode of tube A reaches maximum positive. At this instant tube A is conducting while tubes B and C block reverse current. Both tubes B and C are impressed with an inverse voltage of 150 volts, the voltage drop through tube A being neglected.

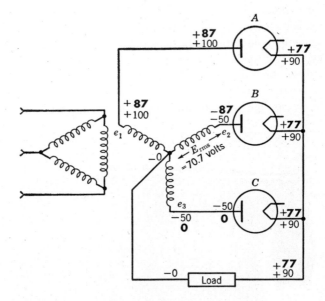

FIG. 9.11. Three-phase half-wave rectifier and instantaneous transformer voltages in 30-degree intervals.

Instantaneous Transformer Voltages

Degrees	e_1	e_2	e_3
0	0	−87	+87
30	+50	−100	+50
60	+87	−87	0
90	+100	−50	−50
120	+87	0	−87
150	+50	+50	−100
180	0	+87	−87
210	−50	+100	−50
240	−87	+87	0
270	−100	+50	+50
300	−87	0	+87
330	−50	−50	+100
360	0	−87	+87

The maximum inverse voltage across any tube occurs in multiples of 60 degrees for which the instantaneous voltages are shown in bold-faced type in Fig. 9.11. If the voltage drop through tube A is neglected, tube B is subjected to a maximum inverse voltage of 173 volts corresponding to 60 degrees of voltage 0–e_1.

The wave form of the output direct voltage is shown in Fig. 9.12 together with the important ratios of maximum, rms, and average voltages.

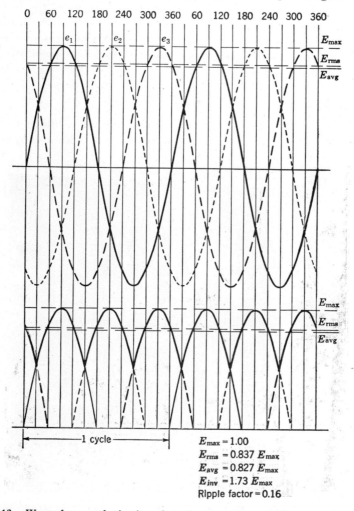

$E_{max} = 1.00$
$E_{rms} = 0.837\ E_{max}$
$E_{avg} = 0.827\ E_{max}$
$E_{inv} = 1.73\ E_{max}$
Ripple factor = 0.16

Fig. 9.12. Wave form and circuit values for three-phase half-wave rectification. A-c supply (top), rectified wave (bottom).

The direct voltage never drops to zero as did the output voltage of the single-phase rectifiers previously discussed. Therefore, the ripple is considerably less for three-phase rectifiers than any single-phase rectifier. The ripple factor for this type of rectifier is 0.16.

The wye-connected transformer secondary winding, Fig. 9.11, is not used in actual practice, because each leg of the winding must carry a d-c component of load current, which results in saturation of the transformer core as previously explained. This can be eliminated by using the so-called zigzag‡ connection or splitting each secondary phase into two windings, each half being placed on a different core and the windings connected so that the d-c component in one winding is diametrically opposed by a like component in another winding.

THREE-PHASE FULL-WAVE BRIDGE RECTIFIER

Six tubes are connected as a three-phase full-wave bridge rectifier, as illustrated in Fig. 9.13 and diagramed in Fig. 9.14, with resulting wave

FIG. 9.13.   The rectifier section (right) of this cubicle supplies approximately 10 000 volts, 3.5 amperes direct current to oscillator tubes (left). Rectifier connection is three-phase full-wave bridge. Three-phase anode transformer, lower right. Cathode-heating transformers, each insulated for anode potential, below each phanotron.

(*Courtesy Westinghouse*)

form shown in Fig. 9.15. The instantaneous transformer secondary voltages are the same as shown in the table with Fig. 9.11. At an instant correspond-

‡MIT staff, *Applied Electronics*, p 355.

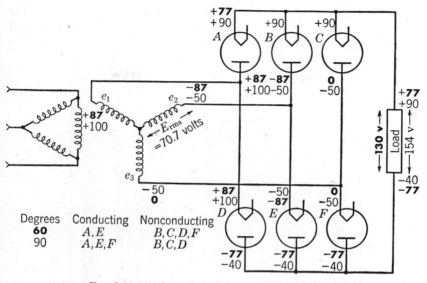

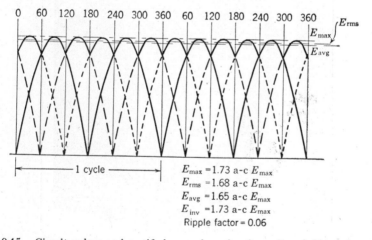

Degrees	Conducting	Nonconducting
60	A, E	B, C, D, F
90	A, E, F	B, C, D

FIG. 9.14. A three-phase full-wave bridge rectifier.

$E_{max} = 1.73$ a-c E_{max}
$E_{rms} = 1.68$ a-c E_{max}
$E_{avg} = 1.65$ a-c E_{max}
$E_{inv} = 1.73$ a-c E_{max}
Ripple factor = 0.06

FIG. 9.15. Circuit values and rectified wave form for three-phase bridge connection.

ing to 90 degrees of voltage $0-e_1$, 100 volts positive is applied to the anode of tube A, and current flows from transformer secondary e_1 through tube A, through the load,§ is equally divided between tubes E and F, and flows

§The analysis given here is descriptive only and is not strictly correct. For an exact behavior of the circuit see Marti and Winograd, *Mercury-Arc Power Rectifiers Theory and Practice*, pp 29–37 and 44–102.

back to transformer secondary windings e_1 and e_3. If the drop through the conducting tubes is neglected, the inverse voltage across tubes B, C, and D is 150 volts.

FIG. 9.16. Illustrating the flexibility of applying copper-oxide elements, this forced-air-cooled rectifier is rated 45 000 volts, 2.1 amperes, three-phase bridge connection.

(Courtesy Westinghouse)

The conditions represented at 60 degrees in the cycle are shown in bold-faced type. At this instant tubes A and E are conducting while the remaining tubes block reverse current. At this instant the inverse voltage across tubes B and D is 173 volts, while the inverse voltage across tubes C and F is

87 volts, tube drop neglected. The conditions at this instant represent both the maximum output voltage across the load and maximum inverse voltage to which any tube is subjected.

The ripple for this rectifier connection is less than for the three-phase half-wave rectifier and the ripple frequency is six times the frequency of the a-c supply.

The three-phase full-wave bridge-type rectifier has the advantage of requiring the least costly transformer design and the lowest tube inverse voltage of any three-phase full-wave rectifier connection. One disadvantage of this connection is that the cathodes are not at the same potential, and the cathode-heating transformer secondary windings must be insulated to withstand the voltage impressed between windings. The bridge connection is frequently used for moderate voltage and power applications using keno-tron or phanotron rectifier tubes, and is universally applied with copper-oxide or selenium rectifying elements. A high-voltage copper-oxide rectifier is illustrated in Fig. 9.16.

THREE-PHASE DIAMETRIC RECTIFIER

This circuit, employing six kenotron or phanotron tubes, Fig. 9.17, is sometimes referred to as a six-phase star or a double three-phase connection. Such a circuit has merit in that all cathodes are connected together

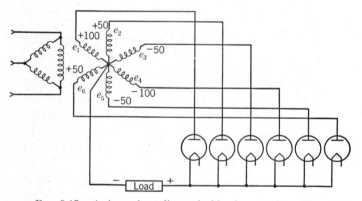

FIG. 9.17.   A three-phase diametric (six-phase star) rectifier.

and supplied from a common source with a common cathode terminal. It is frequently used with kenotron or phanotron tubes for a high-voltage d-c supply, and is also used in conjunction with multianode mercury-arc rectifiers.

The direction of direct current is opposite through halves of the transformer for each phase winding. The d-c components then cancel, leaving no saturation of the transformer core. However, the a-c component of second-ary current is somewhat undesirable|| to the transformer designer.

In comparison with the three-phase full-wave rectifier, each tube is subjected to twice the inverse voltage, but only half the average tube current as required for the bridge connection.

THREE-PHASE DOUBLE-WYE

The three-phase double-wye connection, Fig. 9.18, consists of six tubes with two groups, each a three-phase half-wave rectifier. Each secondary group is displaced 60 electrical degrees from the other. As a result, the output ripple frequency is six times the line frequency, and the same output wave form is obtained as for the bridge circuit.

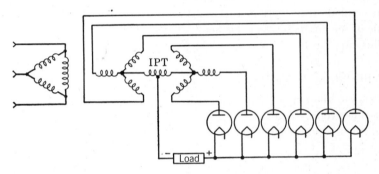

FIG. 9.18. A three-phase double-wye rectifier with interphase transformer.

A reactor, or *interphase transformer*, as it is called (customarily abbreviated IPT) is connected between neutrals of the two secondary groups. Mid-tap of the IPT is connected to the negative load terminal. The purpose of this transformer is to balance the voltage difference between groups, which then makes possible the parallel operation of the two three-phase groups. Load current is divided equally between them, and transformer materials are used to best efficiency.

To determine that balance by the interphase transformer is required refer to Fig. 9.15. Instantaneous voltage of one phase group is here represented by the solid curves, and that of the other group by the dotted lines. For any instant, other than exact multiples of 60 degrees, a voltage difference is found between the groups. This difference voltage appears between ends of the IPT. With respect to its mid-tap it functions to add to the group having a lesser (instantaneous) voltage and subtracts from the group having a greater voltage. Thereby voltage from its mid-tap to the extremity

||See MIT staff, *Applied Electronics*, pp 356–60.

of either group is the same from one instant to another, and parallel operation is made possible.

Voltage across the transformer windings depends upon some current flowing, because it functions as a reactor and magnetizing current is required.¶ Therefore, at extremely light load the IPT is ineffective, and the circuit behaves according to the previously discussed diametric connection. The load current required for the full effect of the IPT is known as the *transition current*, approximately one percent of full-load rating. Below the transition point output voltage is somewhat higher than above this point, because the transformer by its sole purpose divides the instantaneous voltage difference between transformer phase groups.

The double-wye connection is applied principally to mercury-arc or ignitron rectifiers for high current wherein it is desirable to have all cathodes connected to a common positive bus and to take advantage of paralleling two rectifier groups; that is, a greater load current can be carried using tubes of a given rating.

MULTIPHASE CIRCUITS

The development of rectifier circuits, beginning with the single-phase half-wave rectifier and continuing on through the three-phase double-wye circuit, progressively illustrates that as the number of phases is increased the ripple factor is decreased and the nearer the rectifier output approaches what is customarily called pure direct current.

Some rectifier services require a small ripple factor, because ripple is objectionable either directly or indirectly as a cause of telephone interference. Most rectifier services can be satisfied in this respect by one of the three-phase connections as illustrated in Figs. 9.14, 9.17, or 9.18. Twelve-phase rectifier circuits even further reduce the ripple factor and are readily obtained by simple and inexpensive transformer connections.

Occasionally, an application demands a much smaller ripple factor than can be obtained even from a 12-phase connection. The d-c wave form can be considerably improved by employing rectifier connections to obtain more than 12 phases. Connections have been used to build a rectifier of more than 100 phases. Practically, such connections are limited to installations of large power rectifiers wherein the complete rectifier installation consists of a large number of rectifier tubes. In such case, it becomes relatively inexpensive to make use of transformer connections to obtain the result desired.

One scheme of connection to obtain a 36-phase rectifier is that of Fig.

¶For a complete understanding of the IPT see Marti and Winograd, *Mercury-Arc Power Rectifiers*, pp 127–41; also MIT staff, *Applied Electronics*, pp 365–72.

9.19. Six transformer banks are used, each supplying a standard three-phase double-wye rectifier. The winding of each transformer bank is displaced ten electrical degrees with the result that the complete rectifier installation operates as a 36-phase installation.

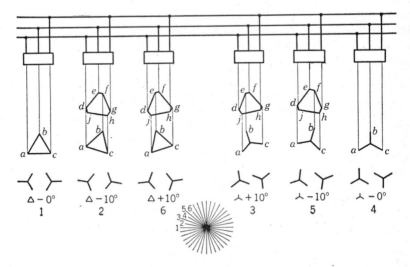

FIG. 9.19. A total of 36 phases are obtained using six three-phase double-wye rectifiers, each shifted 10 degrees by transformer connections.

Transformer bank 1 is delta-connected directly to the three-phase a-c supply and is used as the zero-degree reference. The primary of transformer bank 2 is delta-connected to an auxiliary phase-shifting transformer, such that primary phase a–b is connected between terminals d–f while the corresponding line phase is connected to terminals j–e. The winding d–e is wound on a leg in phase with a–b while the coil e–f is in phase with coil a–c, and d–j is on the leg with coil b–c. By this means, the output of bank 2 lags that of bank 1 by 10 degrees. By the utilization of three delta-connected banks and three wye-connected banks, each rectifier is displaced 10 electrical degrees from any other section.

The number of phases can be further increased by the use of this same scheme of connections to obtain any number of phases desired.

Voltage Doubler

One means of obtaining a direct voltage approximately twice that of the a-c source is by the voltage-doubler circuit, Fig. 9.20. Two kenotron tubes, A and B of the figure alternately charge capacitors C and D, respectively.

As the polarity of the a-c source becomes positive, as shown (a), tube A conducts. Capacitor C is charged during the first half-cycle, as indicated, although the doubled voltage is not established for the load. As the polarity of a-c source reverses, (b), tube B then conducts to charge capacitor D

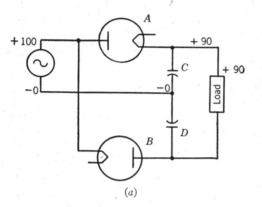

(a)

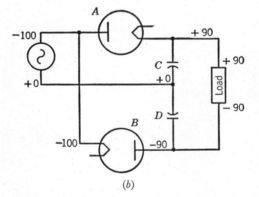

(b)

FIG. 9.20.   Direct-voltage output is nearly twice that of the a-c supply if (a) capacitor C and then (b) capacitor D are alternately charged. Load voltage is the sum of capacitor voltages.

during the following half-cycle. The doubled voltage is then made available across the load for it is connected to the two capacitors in series. Fig. 9.20b shows this.*

The values of C and D are chosen such that neither capacitor is appreciably discharged during the nonconducting portion of the voltage wave.

*In keeping with the previous examples, the tube forward voltage drop is assumed as 10 volts, for illustration only.

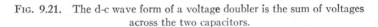

FIG. 9.21.   The d-c wave form of a voltage doubler is the sum of voltages
across the two capacitors.

FIG. 9.22.   Two kenotron tubes connected in a voltage-doubler circuit are used to
obtain 13 000 volts for ionizing potential of the Precipitron electrostatic air cleaner.
Approximately half this voltage (across one tube) is also used for potential to the
collecting plates.   (*Courtesy Westinghouse*)

With reference to Fig. 9.21, capacitor C is charged as the a-c wave rises from zero to a. As the a-c wave declines from its positive peak value at a, passing through zero to negative, tube A remains nonconducting. Capacitor C then discharges some of its stored electrons as current through the load. As it does so, the voltage across its terminals decreases from a to b. Tube A conducts again as the a-c supply rises from 0 to c. The charge lost by capacitor C during the interval $a–b$ is thus replenished as the a-c wave rises from b to c. Similarly, the charge is again partially given up to the load during the nonconducting interval $c–d$.

Capacitor D is charged through tube B as the a-c wave passes from 0 to negative peak e; gives up some electrons $e–f$ that flow through the load; replenishes $f–g$, and again gives up to the load $g–h$.

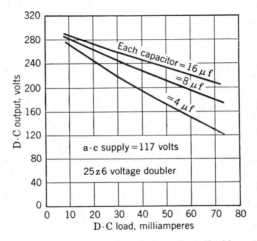

Fig. 9.23. Typical regulation characteristic of a voltage doubler using a twin-diode (two kenotrons in single envelope) RCA 25Z6 tube.

The direct voltage across the load is the sum of the two capacitor voltages. The average load voltage depends upon the relative size of the capacitors, current drawn by the load and tube voltage drop, all of which influence the charge given up during intervals $a–b$, $c–d$, $e–f$, $g–h$, etc. A typical family of performance curves for use with a 25Z6 voltage-doubler tube, Fig. 9.23 shows that the size of capacitors C and D has an important effect upon the d-c output voltage.

This voltage-doubler circuit is not used for any appreciable power, because the output is a function of capacitor values, which become expensive if satisfactory performance is to be had using a large load current. This scheme is used successfully where a few milliamperes direct current at high voltage are ample.

Filters

Most purposes for which rectified d-c power is used require that the wave form be smoother than that forthcoming from any of the tube circuits previously illustrated. The means used for reducing the ripple found in the d-c output wave is by interposing some type of filter between the rectifier and the load.

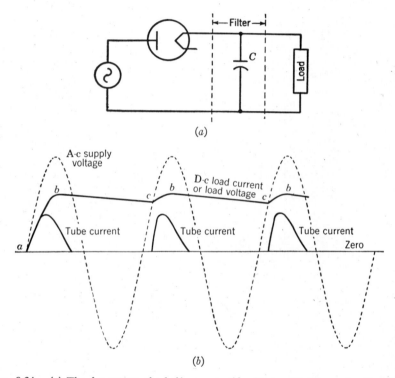

FIG. 9.24. (a) The d-c output of a half-wave rectifier is smoothed by connection of a capacitor across the load. (b) Load voltage is nearly constant while tube current flows in sharp pulses. The scale for tube current is approximately one-third that shown for load current.

Filters operate as an electron reservoir. During instants at which the rectifier output nears its voltage peak, the reservoir absorbs electrons so that, during periods when the rectifier output is less than average load voltage, current to the load is drained from the filter reservoir. Either a filter circuit can store electrons electrostatically, or their flow can be perpetuated electromagnetically. Thus, a filter circuit may consist of a capacitor or a reactor. Frequently, it consists of one or more of each device.

A filter must not be regarded as a source of d-c power. By its reservoir action a filter cannot be effective in smoothing the output wave without requiring that the rectifier tube current or voltage peak exceed the average d-c values. When filter circuits are used, the combined effect of both load and filter upon the rectifier tube must be considered. Both peak and average voltage or current values manifest by the entire circuit must be compared with rated values of the tubes.

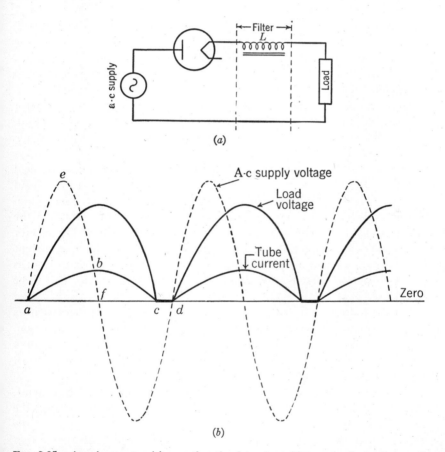

FIG. 9.25.   A series reactor (a) smoothes the d-c output (b) by opposing a change of current through the circuit. Tube current is more nearly continuous (greater than 180 degrees) — compare with Fig. 9.24.

A basic rectifier and filter circuit is shown in Fig. 9.24a in which a capacitor is across the output circuit. The alternating-voltage wave is shown dotted in Fig. 9.24b. Filtering is obtained by charging the capacitor during a half-cycle when current flows through the rectifier tube, for example, *a–b*, Fig. 9.24b. As the alternating voltage decreases below point *b*, the capacitor discharges, although in a properly designed filter the rate of discharge is relatively small such that, during the remaining part of the cycle, the voltage decreases from *b* to *c*. In this way, the voltage across the load is considerably smoothed by the capacitor action.

This type of filter circuit is commonly applied to small loads such as pilot-control circuits of electronic amplifiers, because the method is objectionable when applied to larger loads. The reason for this is the relatively high cost of a suitable capacitor and also that the peak current through the tube is large compared to the average direct current through the load, as inspection of Fig. 9.24b shows. Here, the scale for tube current is reduced to approximately one-third that shown for load direct current.

Another method of smoothing the output wave is by connecting a **reactor** in series with the load circuit as shown in Fig. 9.25a. The a-c wave is dotted, Fig. 9.25b. In this case the energy is stored electromagnetically. While current is increasing through the reactor, energy is used to expand the magnetic field within its core. When the current declines, the magnetic field collapses, returning the energy to the circuit. Without the reactor, the load current would reach a maximum at point *e* corresponding to the maximum of the a-c wave. The reactor opposes any change in current through the circuit such that a maximum of current is shifted to point *b*. The reactor also opposes any reduction of current. By proper design, the load current continues throughout a portion of the rectifier cycle from *a* to *c*. Current is zero from *c* to *d*; that is, the current flow is discontinuous for half-wave rectification.

Practical filters often consist of a combination of one or more capacitors and reactors, which together provide the desired amount of filtering action. The more numerous the stages of filtering, the smoother the resulting wave form.† A few typical filter circuits commonly employed in radio and industrial electronic equipment are shown in Fig. 9.26.

Circuits (a), (b), and (c) are called *capacitor-input* circuits, In general, capacitor-input filters provide a higher d-c output voltage because the input capacitor is charged to a voltage nearly equal to the peak of the rectified voltage. However, filters of this type have the disadvantage that the input capacitor passes a large peak current from the rectifier making

†For further details in regard to filter designs see:

MIT staff, *Applied Electronics*, pp 272–307.

Terman, *Radio Engineers Handbook*, pp 596–614.

P. T. Chin, "Gaseous Rectifier Circuits," *Electronics*, April 1945, p 138, and May 1945, p 132.

A. H. Halloran, "Designing Filters for Specific Jobs," *Electronic Industries*, April 1945, p 76.

the peak current to be carried by the tube considerably greater than the average direct current demanded by the load. For this reason, they can be used only when the rectifier tube can safely carry the peak current passed by the input capacitor.

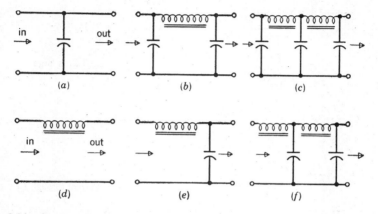

FIG. 9.26. Some common types of filter circuits. (a), (b), and (c) are capacitor-input filters; (d), (e), and (f) are reactor-input filters.

Filters (d), (e), and (f) are called *reactor-input* filters. Although the d-c output voltage obtained with filters of this type is never so high as the capacitor-input type, the filter does not draw high peak current from the rectifier. Reactor-input filters are commonly used in combination with gas-filled phanotron or thyratron rectifier tubes.

Rectifiers usually operate in conjunction with one of the foregoing filter systems as a source of d-c supply. Both the tube anode current and transformer loading are considerably affected by the filter design, and some knowledge of the rectifier operation is required as a background for choosing the rectifier tube and for selecting the power-supply transformer.

Consider the conditions found in a single-phase center-tap full-wave rectifier represented in Fig. 9.27, consisting of tubes A and B, delivering a voltage E_0 to reactor-input filter L_1C_1. At (b), sinusoidal rectified voltage E_0 is smoothed by reactor L_1. If L_1 is large, the voltage across capacitor C_1 and the load is approximately uniform. If L_1 is small, the output voltage contains a ripple shown by the dashed line.

The voltage across reactor L_1 is the difference between the rectifier output E_0 and capacitor voltage E_{dc}. This is represented at (b) by the shaded portion of one-half cycle (L_1 assumed large). The wave form of current through reactor L_1 is shown at (c) for three values of L_1. The solid saw-tooth curves represent a moderately large reactor normally used in a prop-

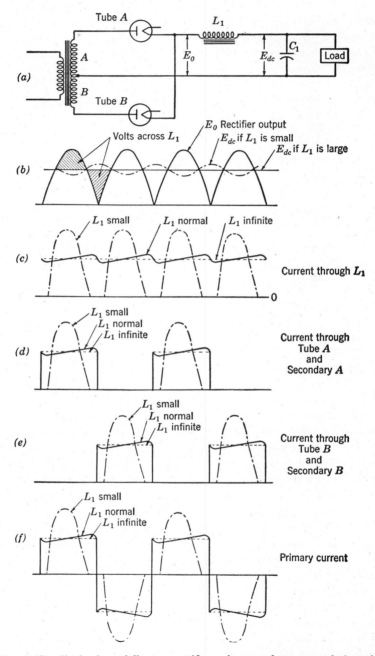

FIG. 9.27. Single-phase full-wave rectifier voltage and current relations for reactor-input filter with wide variation of the inductance value.

erly designed filter. If L_1 is made too small, the current flows in discontinuous pulses. If L_1 were made infinite, the current is without ripple as indicated by the dotted line. The choice of inductance size then becomes a compromise between performance and cost.

The reactors used in rectifier filters must have laminated iron cores with an air gap sufficient to minimize saturation of the core because of the d-c component through the reactor winding. The inductance responsible for attenuating the a-c ripple is decreased by the effect of d-c saturation of the magnetic core, which reduces the efficiency of the filter system.

If the effect of leakage reactance of the transformer is neglected, the current transfers instantly from tube A to tube B, and the tube current is then represented by the rectangular waves at (d) and (e).

The current waves corresponding to three values of L_1 illustrated at (d) and (e) show that the burden on the tube is considerably affected by the size of the filter reactor. If L_1 is infinite, the peak tube current is the same as the load current. If L_1 is chosen moderately large, the peak tube current is only slightly larger than the load current, as shown by the solid curve. If L_1 is small, the peak tube anode current considerably exceeds the average current, and the ratio of tube peak to average current increases. In other words, a rectifier tube, operating into a resistance load or in conjunction with a filter with small input reactance is subjected to a greater peak anode current for a given load current than one feeding into an inductive load or a properly designed filter.

The tube anode current also flows through the transformer secondary windings. According to the curves of (d) and (e), the heating of the transformer windings is greater than for the usual sine wave. Because the transformer capacity is limited by heating, a transformer has less output capacity when supplying a d-c load through a rectifier than when furnishing alternating current to a load in the usual manner. This ratio is called the *utilization factor* of the transformer, and is variable, depending upon the rectifier connections. The transformer primary current is shown at (f) and is a summation of the individual secondary currents. The utilization factor of the transformer primary frequently differs from the secondary factor.

Similar conditions for a three-phase half-wave rectifier, operating with a reactor-input filter, are illustrated in Fig. 9.28, in which the effect of transformer leakage reactance is disregarded.

An entirely different analysis results from the combination of a rectifier feeding into a capacitor-input filter system, as shown in Fig. 9.29. Here, the capacitor C_1 is charged to a peak voltage nearly equal to the maximum of the transformer secondary voltage (any drop through tubes A or B being neglected). The voltage across capacitor C_1 decreases almost linearly during the nonconducting portion of each half-cycle, because the reactor L_1

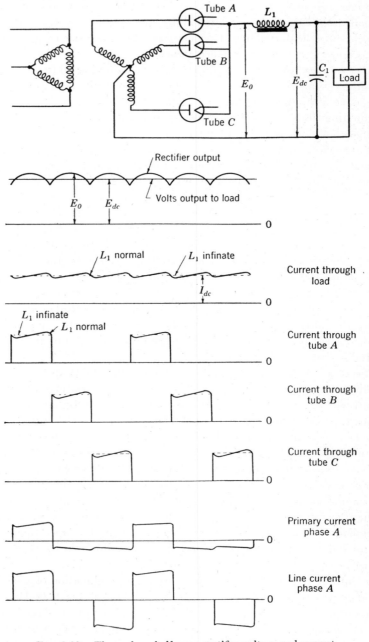

FIG. 9.28.   Three-phase half-wave rectifier voltage and current
relations for reactor-input filter.

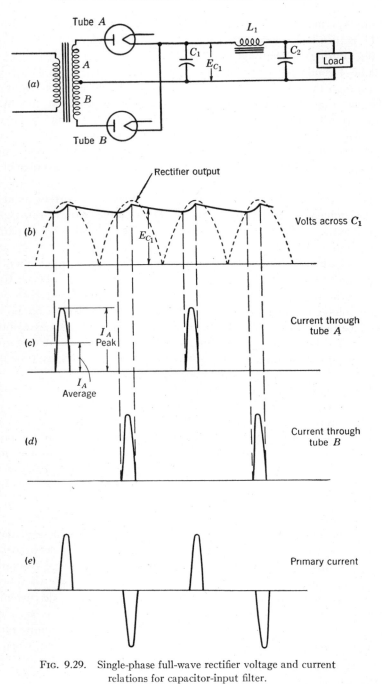

FIG. 9.29.   Single-phase full-wave rectifier voltage and current
relations for capacitor-input filter.

attempts to maintain a constant current through the filter circuit. Capacitor C_1 is then recharged by the amount of charge given up as tubes A or B conduct during each half-cycle.

Tube A conducts only while its anode is more positive than is capacitor C_1, through the relatively short portion of the half-cycle as shown at (c). Likewise, tube B conducts during short current pulses as at (d). Wave shapes at (c) and (d) show that the tube peak anode current is large in comparison to the average current. Hence, when rectifier tubes are used in conjunction with a capacitor-input filter, care must be taken to select tubes having a peak current rating several times greater than the average or d-c output.

The transformer secondary heating and the primary current as at (e) also are influenced by the characteristic current wave shape of this type of filter, making the transformer utilization factor smaller than a comparable reactor-input filter.

In comparison with a capacitor-input filter, a reactor input offers the advantage of a lower ratio of tube peak-to-average current, a better transformer utilization factor, and a better load-regulation characteristic: that is, the voltage of the d-c output does not change appreciably from no load to full load. The capacitor-input filter offers the single advantage of obtaining a higher d-c output voltage from a given set of tubes and transformer. However, this advantage is obtained at the expense of a higher tube peak current.

The capacitor-input filter is usually employed for relatively small power-supply systems, say, 100 watts for radio receivers and industrial amplifiers. Reactor-input filters are universally used with polyphase rectifiers and single-phase rectifiers larger than about 100 watt, because, as the power output becomes larger, the tube peak anode current rating becomes more important, and because the superior load regulation characteristics of this type of filter‡ is often required.

The effect of transformer leakage reactance has been neglected in the foregoing discussion. The load current has been assumed to transfer instantly from one tube anode to another, resulting in the vertical-sided anode-current blocks represented in Figs. 9.27, 9.28, and 9.29. Such idealized cases are not realized in practice, because the transformer leakage reactance§ prevents immediate transfer of load current from one anode to another. With reference to Fig. 9.30, assume tube A is conducting anode current I_A as at (b) and the corresponding instantaneous anode voltage to be e_A as at (c). The effect of transformer leakage reactance prevents the infinite rate of current change represented by rectangular current blocks, and, when the

‡See MIT staff, *Applied Electronics*, pp 288–300.
§*Ibid*, pp 337–43.

phase voltage for tube A crosses line d, the anode current of tube A decreases gradually instead of falling instantly to zero. In the meantime, the anode current of tube B increases gradually from zero to maximum, also retarded by transformer reactance. The elapsed time required for this period of transfer is called the *angle of overlap*, denoted by u. Within the angle of

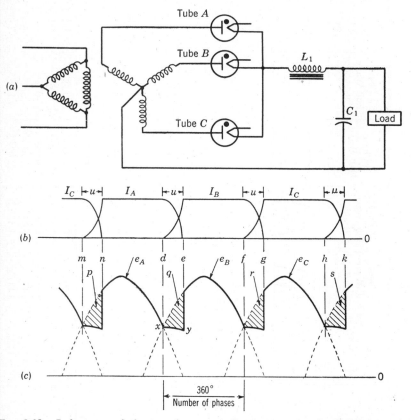

FIG. 9.30. Inductance of the transformer winding prevents an **instantaneous tube** current change and causes overlapping u of the current rectified by **tubes as the voltage** of one phase drops below the rising voltage of the successive phase.

overlap, the anodes of both tubes A and B are conducting the load current, and the instantaneous voltage becomes the average difference between the open-circuit transformer voltage of phases A and B. This is x–y. As soon as the anode current of tube A drops to zero, the instantaneous voltage instantly rises from y to the value e_B as determined by the transformer winding for phase B.

Within the angle of overlap, the instantaneous voltage x–y is decreased

TABLE 9.1. CHARACTERISTICS OF RECTIFIERS AND RECTIFIER CIRCUITS

Rectifier Connection	1-Phase Half-Wave	1-Phase Full-Wave Center-Tap	1-Phase Full-Wave Bridge	3-Phase Half-Wave	3-Phase Full-Wave Bridge	3-Phase Diametric (6-Phase Star)	3-Phase Double-Wye (With IPT)
Typical one-cycle wave of rectifier output voltage — Zero line							
Reference Fig. no.	9.2	9.5	9.8	9.11	9.13	9.15	9.16
No. of tubes required	1	2	4	3	6	6	6
Rectifier Characteristics to Obtain 1.0-Volt 1.0-Ampere D-C Output							
Rectifier Output Characteristics							
Average d-c volts	1.00	1.00	1.00	1.00	1.00	1.00	1.00
Peak d-c volts	3.14	1.57	1.57	1.21	1.05	1.05	1.05
Rms d-c volts	1.57	1.11	1.11	1.01	1.02	1.02	1.02
Ripple factor	1.21	0.48	0.48	0.16	0.06	0.06	0.06
Major ripple frequency	$1F$	$2F$	$2F$	$3F$	$6F$	$6F$	$6F$
Tube Characteristics — Resistance Load Without Filter							
Average anode current (per tube)	1.00	0.50	0.50	0.333	0.333	0.167	0.167
Peak anode current (per tube)	3.14	1.57	1.57	1.21	1.05	1.05	0.525
Rms anode current (per tube)	1.57	0.785	0.785	0.698	0.60	0.428	0.300
Ratio: peak / average anode current	3.14	3.14	3.14	3.63	3.15	6.30	3.15
Inverse peak volts	$3.14E_{dc}$	$3.14E_{dc}$	$1.57E_{dc}$	$2.09E_{dc}$	$1.05E_{dc}$	$2.09E_{dc}$	$2.42E_{dc}$

Tube Characteristics — Large Reactor-Input Filter or Inductive Load

Average anode current (per tube)	0.50	0.50	0.333	0.333	0.167	0.167
Peak anode current (per tube)	1.00	1.00	1.00	1.00	1.00	0.500
Rms anode current (per tube)	0.707	0.707	0.577	0.577	0.408	0.289
Ratio: peak / average anode current	2.00	2.00	3.00	3.00	6.00	3.00
Inverse peak volts	$3.14E_{dc}$	$1.57E_{dc}$	$2.09E_{dc}$	$1.05E_{dc}$	$2.09E_{dc}$	$2.42E_{dc}$‡

Transformer Rating — Large Reactor-Input Filter or Inductive Load

Rms secondary volts per leg	*2.22	1.11	1.11	0.854	0.427	0.740	0.854
Secondary rms amperes	*1.57	0.707	1.00	0.577	†0.820	0.408	0.289
Primary rms amperes	*1.57	1.00	1.00	0.471	0.820	†0.577	0.408
Secondary volt-amperes	*3.49	1.57	1.11	1.48	1.05	1.81	1.48
Primary volt-amperes	*3.49	1.11	1.11	1.21	1.05	†1.28	1.05
Average volt-amperes	*3.49	1.34	1.11	1.35	1.05	†1.55	1.26
Secondary utilization factor	*0.287	0.636	0.90	0.675	0.955	0.551	0.675

A-C Line Input — Large Reactor-Input Filter or Inductive Load

Rms amperes	*1.57	1.00	†0.815	†1.41	†0.815	†0.707
Power factor	*0.29	0.90	0.826	0.955	0.955	0.955
Maximum theoretical efficiency	40.6	81.2	95.5	96.2	96.2	96.2

*Values for Resistance Load Without Filter.
†Values for Delta Connected Primary.
‡Maximum Inverse Peak Volts at Light Load.

somewhat by the transformer leakage reactance. The magnitude of the voltage reduction resulting from this effect is represented by the shaded area q. Thus, the transformer leakage reactance causes a reduction in the rectifier d-c output voltage illustrated by areas p, q, r, and s.

The transformer leakage reactance is also responsible for modifying the anode-current shapes from the idealized rectangular blocks to that shown by Fig. 9.30b. This modified wave shape causes the tube peak anode current to become slightly larger than the d-c output, although the correction factor is usually negligible.‖

Thus, the d-c output voltage of a rectifier decreases slightly as load rises from zero to maximum, because of (1) voltage drop across the rectifier tubes, (2) resistance of the transformer windings, (3) resistance of the filter reactor, and (4) leakage reactance of the transformer which is responsible for overlap.

SUMMARY

Circuits commonly used for rectifier connections are:
 Single-phase
  Half-wave.
  Full-wave center tap.
  Full-wave bridge.
 Three-phase
  Half-wave.
  Full-wave bridge.
  Diametric (star).
  Double-wye.

Single-phase kenotron or phanotron tube rectifiers are usually connected for either half-wave or the full-wave center-tap circuit.

Single-phase copper-oxide or selenium rectifiers usually are connected for either half-wave or the full-wave bridge circuit.

Three-phase kenotron, phanotron, copper-oxide, or selenium rectifiers are usually connected for the full-wave bridge circuit.

Three-phase ignitron, excitron, or mercury-arc rectifiers are usually connected for the double-wye or diametric circuits.

Average direct voltage is measured across the load by a d'Arsonval-type voltmeter.

Average d-c load current is measured through the load by a d'Arsonval-type ammeter.

Peak direct voltage is the maximum instantaneous load voltage.

Ripple factor indicates quantitatively the ratio of varying to uniform components of load voltage.

‖The manner of computing this correction factor is given in Marti and Winograd, *Mercury-Arc Power Rectifier*, pp 175-86.

Average anode current is the average value of current through each tube (or rectifying element).

Peak anode current is the maximum instantaneous value of current through each tube (or rectifying element).

Ratio peak-to-average anode current indicates the ratio by which the maximum instantaneous current through the tube (or rectifying element) exceeds the average value, that is, the direct current.

Inverse voltage is applied across the tube (or rectifying element) with negative polarity at the anode; that is, the tube is nonconducting.

Filters are connected between the rectifier tubes and load for the purpose of reducing the varying component of load voltage.

Capacitor-input filters make available the highest d-c output voltage (for a given a-c input voltage) but manifest a high ratio of peak-to-average anode current. They usually are applied with kenotron rectifying tubes.

Reactor-input filters provide a lower d-c output voltage (than capacitor-input circuits) but manifest a low ratio of peak-to-average anode current and good voltage regulation. They usually are applied with phanotron or thyratron rectifying tubes.

Rectifier tubes and the transformer design required to obtain a given d-c output depend upon co-ordination with the filter and load characteristics. Table 9.1 summarizes many of the required factors by which the tubes and transformer can be chosen.

REFERENCES

MIT ELECTRICAL ENGINEERING STAFF, *Applied Electronics*, John Wiley & Sons, New York, 1943, pp 277–376.

O. K. MARTI and H. WINOGRAD, *Mercury-Arc Power Rectifiers — Theory and Practice*, McGraw-Hill Book Co., New York, 1930, pp 29–209.

F. E. TERMAN, *Radio Engineers' Handbook*, McGraw-Hill Book Co., New York, 1943, pp 589–612.

F. E. TERMAN, *Radio Engineering*, McGraw-Hill Book Co., New York, 1937, pp 471–500.

KEITH HENNEY, *Radio Engineering Handbook*, McGraw-Hill Book Co., New York, 1941, pp 489–513.

JACOB MILLMAN and SAMUEL SEELY, *Electronics*, McGraw-Hill Book Co., New York, 1941, pp 362–418.

HERBERT J. REICH, *Theory and Applications of Electron Tubes*, McGraw-Hill Book Co., New York, 1944, pp 564–90.

Chapter 10

MERCURY–POOL TUBES

The mercury-pool tube far outstrips all other industrial electronic devices in the kilowatt capacity installed for rectification or the control of power equipment. Also it is one of the oldest. Small glass-bulb rectifiers for battery charging were in widespread use before World War I. The number of units of various types now extends into the thousands. The installed capacity totals to several million kilowatts, largely accumulated by the many high-current rectifier installations built during 1941, '42, and '43 for light-metal production.

Mercury, used as a cathode of gas-filled tubes, offers several advantages over solid thermionic cathodes. A mercury-pool cathode serves the dual purpose of supplying electrons and, as the source of the mercury vapor, the gas used for ionic conduction. The mercury cathode is not limited to a peak emission current in the same way as a thermionic cathode, because the pool is capable of electron emission far in excess of any possible requirement. The emission depends only upon the size and number of cathode spots, which in turn are functions of current magnitude. Heavy overload currents can thus be drawn momentarily without danger of cathode disintegration common to thermionic cathodes. The mercury cathode is self-restoring inasmuch as the mercury evaporated from the cathode by the heat of the arc is condensed within the tube and returns to the pool by gravity.

The *cathode spot* formed by termination of the arc at the surface of the mercury pool is a source of abundant electron emission. A current as concentrated as 25 000 amperes per square inch has been observed. Several cathode spots often appear simultaneously, each carrying from 10 to 50 amperes.

The method by which electrons are emitted from the mercury pool is still a matter of scientific conjecture, although it generally is agreed that emission is likely caused by high-field or high-potential gradient at the surface of the mercury pool.

This can be understood by a review of the potential distribution from cathode to anode within a gas tube, as shown in Fig. 10.1, similar to the discussion in Chapter 5. Because the thickness of the cathode sheath is so small as to defy measurement, the potential gradient through the sheath is enormous, perhaps two million volts per inch at the cathode surface. Such a gradient could account for the copious electronic emission from the mercury cathode surface.

The mercury pool cannot by itself initiate emission. An arc must be formed before the high-potential gradient through the cathode sheath

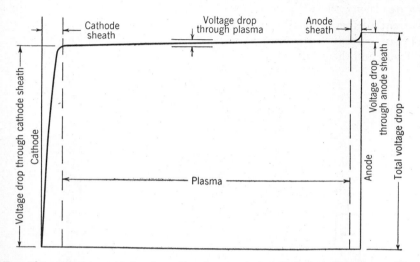

FIG. 10.1. Electron emission from the mercury-pool cathode is believed caused by the extremely high-voltage gradient through the immeasurably thin cathode sheath.

becomes available to cause emission from the cathode pool. Some means of starting the arc is then necessary, of which several methods have been used throughout the development of mercury-pool tubes.

Mercury-Arc Rectifiers

One of the earliest practical mercury-arc rectifiers was a peculiar dome-shaped glass bulb with several arms. When in service it made a weird sight indeed, with the mercury arc dancing about the pool, emitting a characteristic ghastly light, and the vapor condensing inside the dome and running back down into the pool. Although it has now all but disappeared from the industrial scene, it serves well to illustrate the principles of starting of the arc, its maintenance, and the prevention of current reversal or arc-back.

As drawn in Fig. 10.2, for a full-wave rectifier, the mercury-pool with terminal C forms the cathode and arms A_1 and A_2 the anodes. To initiate rectification, the tube is tilted slightly, joining the main pool with the smaller pool containing starting terminal K. Current is passed between C and K and, as the bulb is returned to the vertical, the rupture of the mercury thread between the two pools forms an arc that creates the cathode spot to start emission. Auxiliary or *keep-alive* terminals a_1 and a_2 are continuously maintained about 25 volts more positive than the cathode; hence the arc, started by K, immediately transfers to one or the other. As alternating potential of main anode A_1 becomes more positive than the cathode, or arc plasma, the arc immediately picks up to the main anode, conducting current to the external load circuit. As the positive potential of A_1 decreases, current to the load stops and the arc is maintained by the keep-alive a_2 and then shifts to main anode A_2.

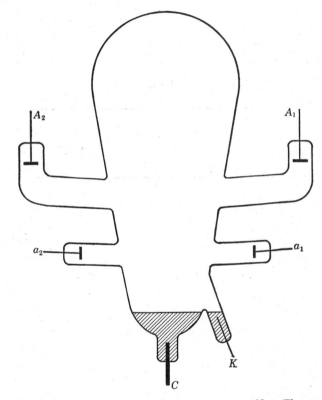

FIG. 10.2. An early design of two-anode mercury-arc rectifier. The arc is started by tipping the bulb to join the cathode pool C with the starting pool K, then returning to the vertical position. Keep-alive anodes a_1 and a_2 maintain the arc which transfers to main anodes A_1 and A_2 for conduction of the load current.

While main anode A_2 carries load current, anode A_1 is subjected to inverse negative voltage. The anodes are located in the horizontal arms to provide some shielding from the ionized space within the central part of the envelope. Without this shielding an anode may be unable to withstand the inverse voltage. It may break down momentarily, allowing current to flow in the reverse direction, known as *arc-back*.

The multiple-anode steel-tank rectifier, appearing soon after World War I, was an outgrowth of the glass-encased rectifier. Instead of having just two anodes, 6 or 12 were more common. With the steel-tank rectifier came refinements and complications,* such as water cooling, anode baffles, grids, and a magnetic-starting electrode to withdraw a starting rod. In these large sizes the tank must be continuously pumped to maintain the required vacuum. Once the arc is started and picked up by one of the main anodes, it is never extinguished and passes rapidly from one anode to another as each adjacent anode becomes more positive throughout the cycle of applied alternating voltage as long as the load requires current.

Elaborate baffling surrounds each anode to prevent undesirable reverse-current conduction or backfire. The introduction of numerous baffles unavoidably increases the voltage drop through the rectifier and contributes to inefficiency. Arc drop in a multianode rectifier is about 20 volts, which is 8 percent of the total on a 250-volt circuit. These disadvantages of the multianode construction led designers to search for a method of separating the anodes, placing only one in each tank, and at the same time to devise a means whereby the arc is extinguished while the anode potential is negative.

This change requires an altogether different method of operation, because the arc to each individual anode must be extinguished and restruck during each cycle instead of being maintained continually as in the multianode rectifier. A mechanical device for initiating the arc during each cycle is obviously impractical. A new method had to be found before the single-anode rectifier could become practical.

Ignitrons

The ignitron is a mercury-pool gas tube containing a third element called an *ignitor*. Its function is to start the arc whenever desired. This may be repetitively at the beginning of each positive half-cycle, at some chosen part of each positive half-cycle, or at a time selected by the action of some circuit. In this regard, the ignitor accomplishes a result similar to the grid of a thyratron in that it triggers the tube after which it plays no further part in tube action until current ceases.

PRINCIPLE OF THE IGNITOR

Ignition by formation of a tiny spot at the cathode surface depends upon the junction of two materials of greatly differing resistivity.

*MIT staff, *Applied Electronics*, pp 222–6. Marti and Winograd, *Mercury-Arc Power Rectifiers, Theory and Practice*, pp 210–41.

Because the ignitor rod, Fig. 10.3, is of relatively high-resistance material, current through it causes a voltage drop vertically along the rod. At the junction between the high-resistance rod material and the low-resistance mercury pool, the current concentrates at a small area, attempting to enter the low-resistance mercury at the nearest possible point of contact.

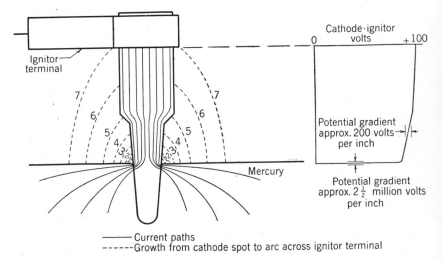

FIG. 10.3. Current through the ignitor rod concentrates at the surface of the mercury cathode producing a high-voltage gradient at the junction between the rod and mercury. Electrons released at the junction form a tiny arc immediately spreading to the ignitor terminal because of the voltage gradient along the ignitor rod.

The phenomenon of ignition† is divided into two distinct functions:

1. The first electrons are drawn from the mercury surface in the form of a tiny spark or spot at the immediate junction between the ignitor rod and the mercury pool. The electronic emission is believed to be caused by high-field or high-voltage gradient at the pool surface. The high-voltage gradient results from the concentration of current at the mercury surface. Indications are that a voltage gradient of $2\frac{1}{2}$ million volts per inch are obtained using the rod material and applied voltage commonly employed. The voltage gradient may even exceed this figure when allowance is made for the rough pointed structure of the ignitor material, which tends to concentrate still more the current at the rod-mercury junction.

2. The initial release of electrons at the rod-mercury junction must be expanded into an arc reaching from the ignitor terminal to the mercury surface, and, eventually, transferred to the main anode. This function

†For a more complete discussion see, Slepian and Ludwig, "A New Method of Initiating the Cathode of an Arc," *AIEE Transactions*, Vol 52, June 1933, p 693.

requires a voltage gradient along the rod to provide an impetus for the upper extremity of the arc to expand in the direction of gradually increasing positive potential. A voltage gradient of approximately 200 volts per inch is sufficient to assure propagation of the initial cathode spot. The resistivity of the rod material must not exceed certain limits, because maintenance and propagation of the arc requires a relatively high current through the rod.

Choice of the rod material is a compromise between the desirability of using an applied ignitor voltage as low as possible, the necessity for a maximum voltage gradient at the rod-mercury junction and of a required voltage gradient along the rod above the pool surface. The material actually used in a modern ignitor is a mixture of boron carbide, boron nitride, and graphite, having an approximate resistivity of 2.5 megohms per inch cube. The choice is not limited to boron carbide and mercury, as the ignitor and pool materials, respectively. Experimental arcs have been started successfully, using a rod of clay and lampblack mixture buried in either a solidified or molten-tin cathode. Likewise, carborundum or galena can be used as ignitor rod materials.

CONSTRUCTION OF IGNITRONS

Ignitrons are most advantageously employed for the conduction of a high current, 50 amperes to more than a thousand. This means that considerable heat must be removed to prevent excessive temperature of the mercury vapor. Therefore, the envelope of ignitrons is made of metal because of the excellent cooling resulting from the good heat conductivity of the metal walls. Usually water jacketing is provided to obtain additional cooling.

The metal used for the tank, as the ignitron envelope is commonly called, must not be attacked by mercury. Stainless steel meets this requirement. Corrosion is intolerable both because of the danger of leaks and because the corrosion process liberates hydrogen, which diffuses through the metal wall and impairs the vacuum. Copper and nickel are not acceptable materials, because they are both active with mercury. Stainless steel, which resists corrosion and is unattacked by mercury, is commonly used for sealed-off tubes. Low carbon steel is used for the tanks of pumped rectifier tubes. When low carbon steel is also used for the water jacket, it is necessary to use a corrosion inhibiter in the recirculated cooling-water system. One manufacturer avoids the corrosion problem by flowing the cooling water through copper tubes welded to the exterior of the tank.

Insulation of the leads entering the tube differs considerably from the practice used in the manufacture of pliotrons. Seals used successfully in vacuum tubes usually consist of a thin copper tube fused to the glass. The slight difference in expansion between copper and glass is compensated by flexing of the thin copper section. However, copper cannot be used with a mercury pool. Various seals are employed by different manufacturers, such as soldering to porcelain, use of Mycalex, or a mercury seal.

IGNITRON CLASSIFICATIONS

Ignitron tubes are classified as being *sealed off* or *pumped*. The first is evacuated and permanently sealed at the factory. The second is continuously pumped by an external vacuum-pumping system and can be disassembled in the field for servicing.

The largest sealed-off tubes, at the time of this writing, have a maximum continuous average current rating of 200 amperes. Larger tubes are of the pumped type. The division of rating between sealed-off and pumped tubes is only an arbitrary economic consideration. Sealed-off tubes will undoubtedly be available in higher ratings as soon as justified by the extension of tube life resulting from manufacturing improvements.

All ignitrons used as rectifiers are built with deionizing baffles. In tubes designed for welding service, 550 volts and below, the baffles are customarily omitted.

SEALED IGNITRONS FOR LOW-VOLTAGE SERVICE

A typical ignitron for 220/600-volt service is pictured in Fig. 10.4 and shown in cross section in Fig. 10.5. Smaller sizes are similar in appearance, except that the cooling radiator is omitted from the anode stud. The ignitor entrance lead is shielded to the top of the ignitor rod to prevent the arc from striking to the lead and damaging the seal. A solid wire is spiraled between the inner tube walls and the outer water jacket to guide the water flow and prevent hot spots. Tubes of this type are commonly applied for resistance-welding duty, of which further details are given in Chapter 16, page 406.

FIG. 10.4. A sealed ignitron for low-voltage service. Approximately one-seventh actual size.

(*Courtesy Westinghouse*)

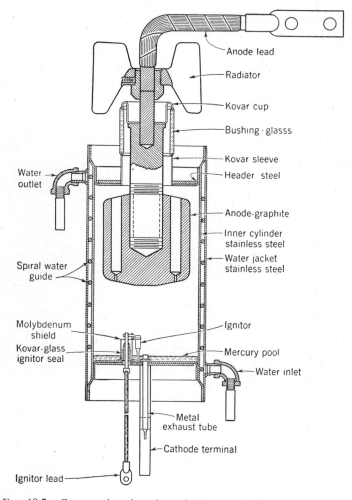

FIG. 10.5. Cross-section view of a sealed ignitron for low-voltage service.

(*Courtesy Westinghouse*)

SEALED IGNITRONS FOR HIGH-VOLTAGE SERVICE

The construction of ignitrons for 2300-volt service and for rectification differs somewhat from that of the preceding classification. A typical cross-sectional view is shown in Fig. 10.6. These contain two complete ignitors, although only one is used at a time. Because rectifiers are often in service continuously, the spare ignitor offers additional assurance of long tube life.

These tubes also contain an auxiliary anode, which is a small element located at the upper extremity of the ignitor rod. This anode holds the arc

during the short interval between formation of the arc by the ignitor and
its transfer to the main anode.

A considerable amount of surging of the mercury pool normally occurs
during conduction, which is further agitated by a high momentary anode

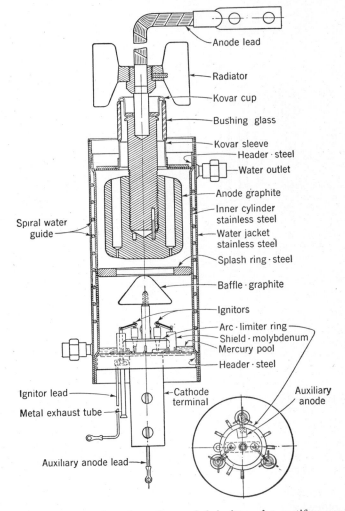

FIG. 10.6.   Cross-section view of a sealed ignitron for rectifier service
containing two ignitors, auxiliary anode, and baffles.   (*Courtesy Westinghouse*)

current. Small globules of mercury, falling on the anode, are harmless for
low-voltage operation. However, as the inverse voltage is raised at higher
service voltages, the globules cause electron emission from the anode during

the negative cycle and may contribute to backfire of a rectifier. Therefore, tubes used as rectifiers invariably include a splash ring and one or more baffles to minimize the possibility of inverse ignition.

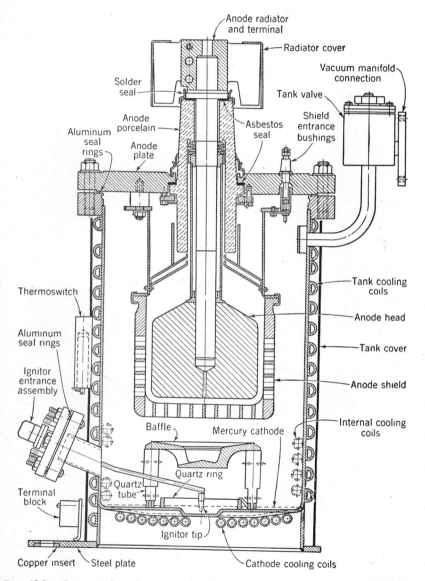

FIG. 10.7.   Cross section of a pumped ignitron for rectifier service. A vacuum-tight seal between the anode insulator and the top plate is made by soldering a sealing ring to the anode insulator.   (*Courtesy Westinghouse*)

PUMPED IGNITRONS FOR RECTIFIER SERVICE

Continuously pumped ignitrons are built in sizes from 8 to 22 inches diameter, having a continuous anode-current rating of from 332 to 1000 amperes. Six of these tubes, used in a six-phase double-wye connection, make a rectifier rated approximately 400 to 1800 kw at 250 volts d-c, or 960 to 3800 kw at 600 volts d-c.

The construction of a pumped ignitron is illustrated in cross section in Fig. 10.7. The principal parts are similar to those of sealed tubes previously described, with modification to permit dismantling the tubes. The ignitor-entrance assembly provides external mechanical adjustment of the depth

FIG. 10.8. Three steps of the anode assembly: (left) top plate, insulator, and anode stud; (center) graphite anode mounted on stud; (right) graphite grid completely surrounds the anode. *(Courtesy Westinghouse)*

to which the ignitor rod dips into the mercury pool. The baffle over the mercury pool protects the anode against a blast of mercury vapor, directs the initial arc stream toward the top of the ignitor rod, and directs the vapor blast toward the tube walls for effective heat removal by the water-cooled walls. The anode stud is insulated from the top plate by a permanent seal between the porcelain insulator and the metal plate. Likewise, the anode-shield terminal is insulated and screwed into the top plate. The entire assembly of the anode, anode shield, and top plate is inserted into the tank and sealed by a vacuum-tight gasket.

Three stages in the assembly of the anode are depicted in Fig. 10.8. The anode stud is at the left, the main anode of solid graphite is in the center, and the anode shield of perforated graphite is shown in place at the right. In Fig. 10.9 the anode, anode shield, and top-plate assembly are being lowered to its tank. Cooling coils around the tank are evident.

FIG. 10.9.   Assembly of upper plate, anode, and grid being lowered into tank. Water-cooling coils surround the outside of the tank. A smooth outer casing is added in final assembly.   (*Courtesy Westinghouse*)

AUXILIARIES FOR PUMPED IGNITRONS

Pumped-type ignitrons require auxiliary equipment for maintaining and indicating the required degree of vacuum. Continuous pumping equipment is required to remove the small amount of gas liberated from parts of the tube itself and to overcome small leaks.

The essential units of a typical vacuum system are shown in Fig. 10.10. The tubes are connected to a common evacuation manifold. A manually operated valve permits the servicing of the pumping equipment without loss of vacuum within the tubes.

Gas pressure of the ignitron must be kept low, to less than 1 micron.

(A micron is the pressure of 0.001 millimeter of mercury and is 1/760 000 of sea-level atmospheric pressure.) This degree of vacuum is obtained by two stages of pumping. A vacuum to about 1/10 millimeter of mercury is provided by a motor-driven rotary pump.

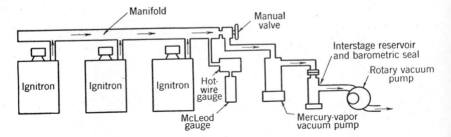

FIG. 10.10. The vacuum pumping system consists of a low-pressure mercury-vapor pump discharging into an interstage reservoir and a rotary pump from the reservoir discharging to the atmosphere. Pressure-indicating equipment consists of a hot-wire gauge for continuous indication and control and a McLeod gauge for accurate calibration.

This is frequently referred to as a backup pump and is of the eccentric rotating type using oil as a sealing medium. This pump, however, cannot carry the vacuum all the way. Hence, in series with it, is a pump of another type. This is a mercury diffusion pump. Although it can achieve the desired low pressure, it cannot operate against a high back pressure; hence, the two types of pumps, in series, are needed.

An interstage reservoir between the two pumping systems allows the motor-driven rotating pump to be removed from service for short periods. Different methods are employed to prevent destruction of the vacuum when for any reason the motor-driven pump is out of service. One type is a barometric seal, which consists of a tube slightly longer than 760 millimeters (about 30 inches), with its lower end immersed in a large mercury pool. The mercury seals the end of the tube so that, if the bottom of the seal be opened to atmospheric pressure because of temporary outage of the rotary pump, mercury rises in the tube to maintain the seal. If a barometric seal is not used, some form of electrically operated valve is employed to operate when the motor-driven pump is out of service.

The three-stage diffusion pump, shown in Fig. 10.11, is capable of discharging against a back pressure of 20 millimeters. Mercury vapor is supplied by an electrically heated boiler at the bottom of the pump and passes up through a feeder tube 1. A portion of the vapor discharges through a diffusion-stage nozzle 2. The blast of vapor from nozzle 2 is directed downward and against the walls of the pump cooled by water

flowing in coils 10. The mercury condenses against the cool walls of the
pump and carries with it any gas that has diffused with the vapor coming
from the ignitrons. A portion of vapor from the feeder tube 1 flows through
the second-stage ejector nozzle 3, taking gas from the first-stage condensing

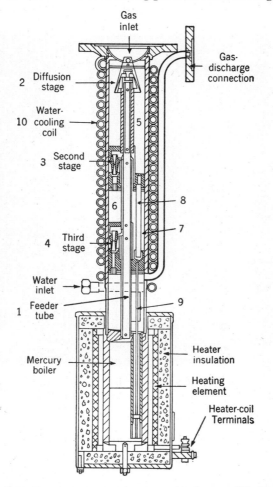

Fig. 10.11. A three-stage mercury-vapor pump absorbs gas diffusing into the top
section, raises the pressure by two ejector-type stages, and exhausts into the discharge
connection. (*Courtesy Westinghouse*)

chamber 5 and discharging into chamber 6 and boosting the discharge
pressure. Vapor from feeder tube 1 flows into the third-stage ejector nozzle
4 taking gas from chamber 6 and discharging into the exhaust chamber 7
and to the discharge connection. The condensed mercury from the first-

stage chamber 5 flows through tube 8 where it is joined by more from chamber 6, and the total volume returns to the mercury boiler through tube 9.

Two vacuum gauges are used for indicating the degree of vacuum. A McLeod gauge is used for an accurate indication of pressure in the manifold. This type of gauge is comparable to the familiar manometer tube,

FIG. 10.12. An ignitron rectifier ready for installation showing (1) mercury-vapor pump, (2) hot-wire vacuum gauge, (3) McLeod vacuum gauge, and (4) rotary vacuum-pump. (*Courtesy Westinghouse*)

except that the scale is considerably expanded to indicate a low pressure accurately to a small fraction of 1 micron. Although the McLeod gauge registers low pressures accurately, it must be manually operated and is not well adapted for a continuous indication or automatic control.

This disadvantage of the McLeod gauge is overcome by a hot-wire vacuum gauge of the Pirani type which, although less accurate, provides a continuous indication of vacuum. Two identical tungsten-filament resistors are connected in opposite arms of a Wheatstone-bridge circuit.‡ One filament is enclosed in a sealed glass tube, highly evacuated. The other is

‡Marti and Winograd, *Mercury-Arc Power Rectifiers, Theory and Practice*, pp 257–66; also, *Ignitron Rectifiers*, Bulletin 3024, Westinghouse Electric Corporation.

enclosed in a duplicate glass envelope, but is connected to the ignitron manifold. A current is passed through the filaments in series. If the pressure in the two envelopes is the same, heat from the filaments is radiated equally, and their resistances, which vary with temperature, remain equal. A change in ignitron manifold pressure alters the thermal conductivity in the open-ended glass envelope, thus changing the temperature of that filament. The bridge is now unbalanced, and current proportionally flows through the milliameter across the bridge. The meter is calibrated in pressure and gives a continuous indication of manifold pressure. Automatic control of the vacuum system is supervised by a contact-making milliameter in series with the indicating instrument.

The hot-wire vacuum gauge is used to obtain a continuous indication of manifold pressure and to obtain automatic control of the vacuum system. The hot-wire gauge acts as a comparator instead of an absolute indication of pressure. Therefore, it must be occasionally checked against the McLeod gauge.

An ignitron unit is shown in Fig. 10.12, illustrating the mercury-vapor vacuum pump, a hot-wire vacuum gauge, a McLeod vacuum gauge and motor-driven vacuum pump.

IGNITRON FIRING CIRCUITS

In the most common class of service the ignitron is in an a-c circuit and must conduct during each positive voltage loop. This requires some means of restriking the arc at the beginning of each positive half-cycle. The equipment used to provide this excitation is known as the ignitron *firing circuit*. Of these, there are several, each having its merits, disadvantages, and proper field of application.

The simplest type of firing circuit,§ Fig. 10.13, is known as *anode firing*, because the ignitor derives its excitation from the ignitron anode circuit. A phanotron is connected in series between the ignitor and the ignitron anode. Frequently, a thyratron is substituted for the phanotron, but the principle of operation is unchanged. As the anode voltage becomes positive, current through the firing tube and ignitor increases from a to b, where it is sufficient to fire the ignitron. The arc immediately transfers to the ignitron anode, effectively short-circuiting the firing tube, and the ignitor current drops almost to zero. Because the firing tube is a rectifier, no ignitor current flows when the ignitor-anode potential is negative. If the load is resistance only, the current rises through the commutating angle at c, corresponding

§For a more complete analysis of ignitron firing circuits see Meyers and Cox, "Excitation Circuits for Ignitron Rectifiers," *Electrical Engineering*, Vol 60, October 1941, p 943.

to the ignitor firing point *b*, and continues sinusoidally for the remainder of the positive half-cycle.

Anode firing has the disadvantage that conduction cannot begin until the anode voltage becomes sufficiently positive to force the required ignition current through the ignitor circuit. That is, portion 0–*c* of the half-cycle cannot be obtained. Another disadvantage is that a variation in ignition

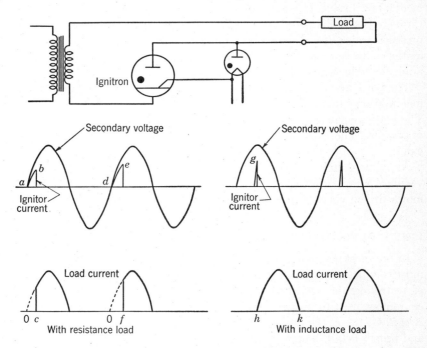

FIG. 10.13.   Anode firing of the ignitor uses a gas tube (phanotron or thyratron) to pass current through the ignitor rod and block the flow of current when the ignitron anode is negative.

characteristics change the conducting portion of the half-cycle. For example, if the current required for ignition should change from *b* to *e*, conduction would be delayed from *c* to *f*. If the load is largely inductive, as for most resistance-welding applications, the load current is more nearly sinusoidal as *h–k* and lags the anode voltage. Here, the firing tube is a thyratron timed to fire and pass ignition current at *g*, approximately at the peak of the anode voltage. Ample voltage is available to assure positive ignition. The anode firing circuit is entirely satisfactory if the load circuit contains sufficient inductance.

Excitation schemes, separate from the ignitron anode, overcome the disadvantages of anode firing. A *thyratron-capacitor* firing circuit is given in

Fig. 10.14. A capacitor C is charged by a rectifier T_3' (a copper-oxide rectifier sometimes is used) from the secondary of transformer TR_3. The capacitor is rapidly discharged by firing thyratron T_2 through the ignitor to start conduction of ignitron T_1. Thyratron T_2 is negatively biased by E_{cc} and is fired by a positive secondary voltage of TR_2. The ignitron can be fired at any desired point throughout the half-cycle by shifting the phase relation between the secondary windings of TR_1 and TR_2. This is conveniently accomplished by one of several phase-shifting methods described in Chapter 15, p 336.

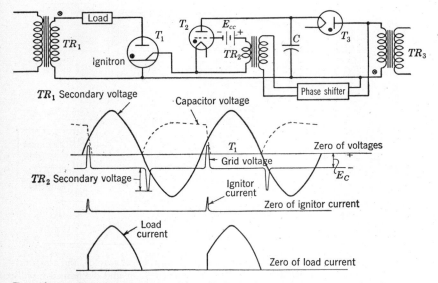

FIG. 10.14. Capacitor-thyratron firing of the ignitor discharges capacitor C through thyratron T_2 and the ignitor to start conduction of ignitron T_1.

The thyratron-capacitor firing circuit has no functional disadvantages, although it is not used extensively at present to fire large ignitrons. The relatively high peak current required for positive ignition of large ignitrons is a severe application for thyratrons. As a result, tube life is impaired, and frequent replacement of the firing tubes is necessary. As the design of thyratrons is improved, this method of firing probably will become better established.

Another firing circuit utilizes a capacitor, a linear reactor, and a saturating reactor connected as shown in Fig. 10.15. Capacitor C is charged from the secondary winding of transformer TR_2 through the linear reactor, so called because it is designed with an air gap and core of proportions to hold constant the relation between flux and reactor current throughout the operating cycle. In contrast to this, the saturating reactor is designed with-out an air gap and employs an alloy steel having a magnetic-saturation characteristic manifesting an extremely sharp knee. Circuit constants are purposely chosen to operate core saturation well above the knee at peak reactor current. Thus, magnetizing current of the saturating reactor is large and rises sharply as voltage across its coil rises above 300 volts, as the characteristic drawn to the right of Fig. 10.15 shows.

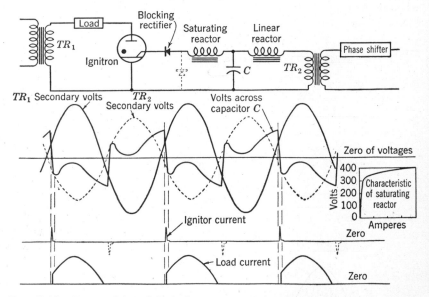

Fig. 10.15. Reactor firing of the ignitor uses a capacitor, linear reactor, and a saturat-ing reactor. Capacitor C is charged through the linear reactor and discharged rapidly through the saturating reactor to provide a pulse of ignitor current to start conduction.

As the charge voltage across the capacitor rises near its maximum, Fig. 10.15, saturation of the reactor increases rapidly with a consequently large magnetizing current. The capacitor is then rapidly discharged through the saturated reactor, the blocking rectifier, and the ignitor. If the saturat-ing reactor is properly designed, the current discharge flows in a sharp peak, the characteristic desired for firing the ignitron. Once fired by the excita-tion circuit, load current is conducted by the anode for the remainder of the half-cycle.

Anode voltage is obtained from the secondary winding of transformer TR_1, while the capacitor-charging voltage comes from the secondary winding of TR_2. The angle of firing the ignitron can be adjusted by any of several convenient devices for shifting the voltage of TR_2 with respect to anode voltage TR_1.

The blocking rectifier, usually copper-oxide, is connected in series with the ignitor circuit to prevent reverse ignitor current during the negative loop of anode voltage, because the saturating reactor and capacitor circuit provide a pulse of current discharging the capacitor during each alternate half-cycle, as noted by the dotted ignitor current peaks and rectifier showing current flow in the opposite direction.

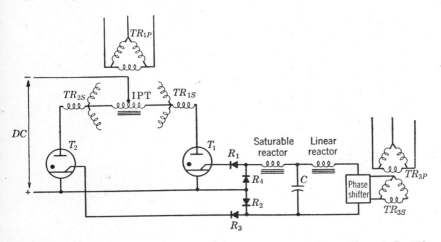

FIG. 10.16. One set of reactor firing equipment operates ignitrons T_1 and T_2, 180 degrees out of phase by using directional copper-oxide rectifiers to direct the ignitor current.

This excitation circuit is used to advantage to fire two ignitrons using a single firing circuit, providing the pair of ignitrons are connected so as to conduct 180 degrees apart. The manner of doing this in a three-phase double-wye rectifier is indicated in Fig. 10.16, in which only the two opposite ignitrons T_1 and T_2 are shown. Two more duplicate firing circuits, the same as previously described, are used in conjunction with the four remaining ignitrons for phases 2 and 3. Ignitron T_1 is fired by discharge of capacitor C through directional blocking rectifiers R_1 and R_2. Ignitron T_2 is fired by the opposite flow of discharging capacitor current through rectifiers R_3 and R_4.

Excitrons

The excitron is a continuously pumped type of mercury-pool gas tube consisting of one anode in a single tank and having an auxiliary or *excitation anode* for holding the arc during intervals when the main anode is nonconducting. In ignitrons the arc is extinguished at the end of each conduction period and is re-established at the beginning of the next conducting

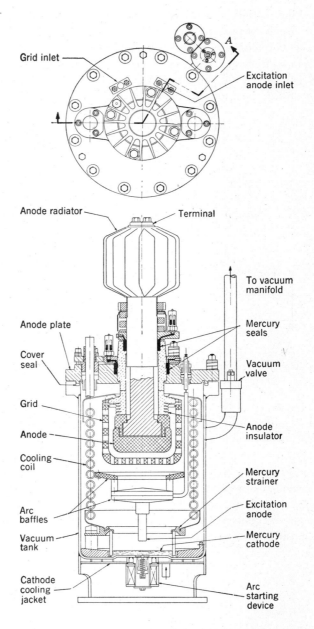

FIG. 10.17.   Cross-sectional view of an excitron.

(*Courtesy Allis-Chalmers*)

period. Excitrons differ in the following respects: 1. The initial arc is started by a mechanical device, essentially the same as in multianode rectifiers. 2. At the end of conducting period, the arc is maintained by a current to the excitation anode and is not completely extinguished. 3. A grid completely surrounds the main anode, and, as long as the grid potential is negative, the excitation arc does not pass through the grid to reach the anode. 4. The beginning of the next conducting cycle is started by applying a positive potential to the grid, which causes the arc to pick up to the main anode.

Construction of the excitron is shown in Fig. 10.17. The mercury-pool cathode is confined within a steel ring lying on the bottom of the tank and enclosed by a quartz ring around the outside of the pool. The excitation anode is a graphite rod suspended above the center of the cathode. The

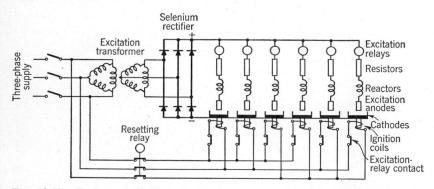

Fig. 10.18. Excitron excitation system. Arc current, started by the ignition coils, flowing through each excitation relay coil opens a contact to de-energize each magnetic ignition coil. (*Courtesy Allis-Chalmers*)

magnetic arc-starting device is below the center of the pool. Energizing the coil of the starting device directs a mercury jet to the excitation anode, effectively short-circuiting it to the cathode. As the mercury thread is broken, an arc starts between the excitation anode and the mercury cathode.

A water-cooling coil is installed inside the tank and insulated from the tank walls. This design is effective in preventing the arc from striking to the tank, a problem of importance to excitrons because the arc is continuous. The cooling coil is fabricated from tubing into a rigid helix and supported by the insulating-entrance bushings in the top anode plate.

Graphite arc baffles divide the tank into two regions: the anode space and the cathode space. The anode is shielded from the mercury vapor generated at the cathode, and the cathode is shielded from the heat of radiation of the anode. The anode is enclosed in a perforated grid supported by the anode insulator and is similar in appearance to the ignitron grid. Unlike the ignitron, however, the grid in the excitron functions as a control grid and governs transfer of the arc from the excitation anode to the main anode.

The auxiliary pumping equipment used with excitrons is the same in principle as that used with ignitrons.

The excitation system of a six-tank excitron rectifier is shown in Fig. 10.18. The excitation anodes are connected to a bus supplying direct current at approximately 35 volts, obtained from a selenium rectifier. A reactor, resistor, and the series coil of the current-operated relay are connected in each anode circuit. Coils operating the magnetic-ignition device are operated from alternating current with the normally closed contact of each series current relay connected in the a-c coil circuits. The initial arcs are formed by closing the a-c switch and operating the magnetic-ignition devices to strike an arc to each excitation anode. A normal arc current of approximately 7 amperes picks up each relay to de-energize each magnetic-ignition device.

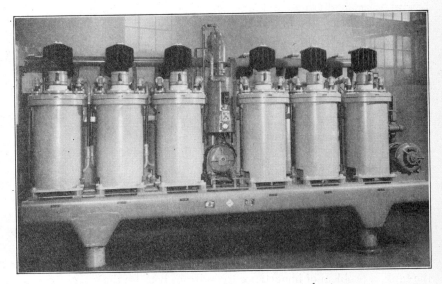

FIG. 10.19. A 12-tank excitron rectifier. Mercury-vapor and rotary vacuum pumps, center with vacuum manifold visible behind anode radiators. (*Courtesy Allis-Chalmers*)

The reactor in each anode circuit aids in maintaining the excitation arc, should there be a momentary dip in the a-c supply voltage. A 12-tank excitron rectifier is shown in Fig. 10.19.

Fig. 10.20. A battery of 5000-ampere 12-tank ignitron rectifiers supplying direct current for aluminum reduction. Power comes in through the anode breakers at the right. The cathode breakers and the heavy d-c buses are along the left wall.

APPLICATIONS OF IGNITRON RECTIFIERS‖

Rectification by mercury-pool tubes constitutes the preferred method of obtaining d-c power at voltages of 250 to 3000, except in small amounts such as desired for control purposes. Under certain conditions they are used at 125 volts or below, but the relatively fixed arc-voltage drop results in objectionably low efficiency at output voltages below 250. Also, for the higher power requirements, ignitrons have proved attractive at alternating voltages up to 20 000.

The first commercial application of a 300-kw 275-volt ignitron rectifier was in 1937, in a coal mine. Several mining installations followed, and the ignitron has continued to be popular for mines because of its compact size, the ease with which it is made fully automatic and in small portable units so that it can be installed underground and moved as the load center changes. Its reliability and low maintenance record are also important. A 4800-ampere 280-volt electrochemical installation was made in 1939. The first 600-volt ignitron was a 3000-kw installation in railway service in 1938.

In number of units and total installed capacity ignitrons in the 600-volt electrochemical service outrank many times all other voltage and classes of service; a typical installation is shown in Fig. 10.20. The first 600-volt electrochemical installation was made at Massena, N. Y. in January 1939. By the end of 1944 about 1000 of the 12-tube 3000-kw 600-volt ignitron rectifiers had been installed for the electrolytic reduction of aluminum and magnesium. This class of ignitron rectifier is being applied to an increasing extent as power supply for light- and heavy-traction systems, and more recently they have been installed to supply 600-volt circuits in steel mills. Although those of the 600-volt class predominate, ignitrons are also used to provide direct current at all standard voltages from 250 to 3000.

The extraordinary record of continuity of performance turned in by the ignitron in most exacting of service no longer leaves any doubt as to its dependability and suitability as an industrial power device.

SUMMARY

Mercury-pool gas tubes include ignitrons, excitrons and mercury-arc rectifiers

Mercury-pool cathodes serve the dual function of supplying electrons necessary to conduction and of being the source of mercury vapor, the gas used for ionization.

Mercury cathodes are self-restoring in that mercury removed from the pool as a result of arc conduction is condensed on the tube walls and returns to the pool by gravity.

‖See Cox, "The Ignitron Mercury-Arc Rectifier," *Westinghouse Engineer*, March 1944, p 51.

The cathode spot formed by termination of the arc at cathode-pool surface is a source of abundant electron emission. A current concentration as great as 25 000 amperes per square inch has been observed. The number and size of cathode spots is a function of current magnitude.

Emission of electrons from the cathode pool is believed caused by the high-potential gradient at the pool surface, resulting from the voltage across the immeasurably thin cathode sheath. The potential gradient at the pool surface may be as great as 2×10^6 volts per inch.

Initial electron release from the cathode pool is not possible by the pool itself. An arc must be formed at the pool before emission is observed. This requires that the tube include some means to start arc conduction. Once started by whatever device provided, the initial arc can be picked up by the tube anode. Conduction is then from the pool cathode to anode.

Multianode rectifiers usually consist of either 6 or 12 anodes within a single tank with one common cathode pool. A magnetic device is provided to start the initial arc, after which the arc is maintained continuously by passing from one anode to the next.

The ignitron consists of a mercury-pool cathode, anode, and ignitor for starting the arc. The arc is extinguished whenever current falls to zero and is re-established when needed by current through the ignitor.

The principle of ignition by forming a spot at the cathode surface depends upon the junction of two materials of greatly differing resistivity. Current concentrates at the junction to enter the low-resistance material at its surface. A potential gradient of 2.5×10^6 volts per inch is manifest by this means. Electrons released from the mercury cathode by this high field initiate a cathode spot which, when enlarged, is picked up by the main anode.

Sealed-off ignitrons consist of the principal tube elements enclosed in a metal envelope, evacuated and permanently sealed.

Pumped ignitrons consist of the principal tube elements enclosed in a metal tank designed so as to be taken apart allowing replacement of any element. Accessory equipment is necessary to maintain continuously the required gas pressure within the tank.

A rotary vacuum pump (motor-driven) reduces gas pressure from atmospheric to approximately 1/10 millimeter.

A mercury-diffusion pump reduces gas pressure from a maximum of 20 millimeters to less than 1 micron (0.001 millimeter).

A McLeod gauge is used periodically to measure gas pressure with extreme accuracy.

A hot-wire gauge is used to indicate gas pressure continuously with reasonably good accuracy.

Excitation methods for firing ignitrons include:

(a) Anode firing, wherein positive voltage at the ignitron anode is momentarily connected to its ignitor by a phanotron or thyratron.

(b) Capacitor-discharge firing using a thyratron, wherein a capacitor, previously charged by a rectifying circuit, is rapidly discharged by the thyratron, the discharge current flowing through the ignitor.

(*c*) Capacitor-discharge firing using a saturating reactor, wherein the capacitor is charged through a linear reactor then discharged rapidly through the saturating reactor and ignitor.

The excitron consists of a mercury-pool cathode, a main anode, excitation anode, grid, and mechanical device, for starting the arc. Once started by the mechanical device the arc is never extinguished. As conduction to the main anode becomes nearly zero, the arc transfers to the excitation anode, and is shielded from the main anode by negative potential of the grid. Conduction to the main anode is resumed by a positive potential applied to both the main anode and grid, causing the arc to transfer immediately from the excitation to main anode.

REFERENCES

MIT Electrical Engineering Staff, *Applied Electronics*, John Wiley & Sons, New York, 1943, pp 219–30.

O. K. Marti and H. Winograd, *Mercury-Arc Power Rectifiers, Theory and Practice*, McGraw-Hill Book Co., New York, 1930, pp 210–328.

J. Slepian and L. R. Ludwig, "A New Method of Initiating the Cathode of an Arc," *AIEE Transactions*, Vol 52, June 1933, p 693.

D. D. Knowles, "The Ignitron — A New Controlled Rectifier," *Electronics*, Vol 6, June 1933, p 164.

J. H. Cox and D. E. Marshall, "Mercury-Arc Rectifiers and Ignitrons," *Electrochemical Society Transactions*, Vol 79, October 1937, p 183.

H. C. Meyers and J. H. Cox, "Excitation Circuits for Ignitron Rectifiers," *Electrical Engineering*, Vol 60, October 1941, p 943.

J. H. Cox and G. F. Jones, "Ignitron Rectifiers in Industry," *Electrical Engineering*, Vol 61, October 1942, p 713.

J. H. Cox, "The Ignitron Mercury-Arc Rectifier," *Westinghouse Engineer*, March 1944, p 51.

H. Winograd, "Development of Excitron-Type Rectifier," *AIEE Transactions*, Vol 63, 1944, pp 969-78.

Chapter 11

AMPLIFICATION

PRINCIPLES OF AMPLIFICATION

Electronic devices are frequently characterized by the exceeding small quantity to which they faithfully respond. A beam of light falling on a phototube delivers energy less than a millionth of a watt to the light-sensitive surface. A person speaking normally delivers to the air a total of but fifteen millionths of a watt, and only a small portion of this falls on a sound-responsive device. The antenna of a radio receiver picks out of the air but a few millionths of a watt. In many industrial electronic-control circuits normal currents or potentials are of the order of thousandths or millionths of amperes or volts.

Before these feeble signals can be translated into appropriate action by relays, motors, or contactors, they must be amplified, sometimes many millions of times, and often must faithfully preserve the shape of the original wave throughout this build-up. Amplification is one very large and very important component of electronics.

Pliotrons, either triodes, tetrodes, or pentodes, are used to obtain amplification. Although the details of application differ, depending upon the type of tube chosen, the fundamentals of amplification are adequately portrayed by the simple triode. As explained in Chapter 6, the voltage fed into the amplifier is the *signal voltage*. The output is often referred to as the *load voltage*. The ratio between the output or load voltage and input or signal voltage is the *gain* of the amplifier.

The principles of amplification are set forth in Fig. 11.1. From the previous discussion of tube performance contained in Chapters 6 and 7, a varying voltage applied to the grid of tube 1 obviously causes a variation in anode current i_A through the anode load resistor R_L. The instantaneous voltage applied to the grid of tube 1 is the summation of a fixed grid-bias potential E_{cc} and the instantaneous signal voltage e_g. The variable grid potential resulting from the variation of e_g causes a variable anode current i_A through resistor R_L, thus setting up a variable potential e_L across the load resistor. The variable voltage e_L appearing across the load resistor R_L represents the useful output voltage of tube 1. The voltage e_L can approach a value of μe_g as its maximum.

Frequently, the output voltage e_L of tube 1 is still too weak to actuate the desired control. Further amplification is necessary. Voltage e_L then becomes the signal voltage for tube 2 and is connected to the grid of tube 2 by a suitable coupling device. The resulting circuit is a two-stage amplifier. All devices to the left of the grid resistor of tube 2 are components of the first stage, and the components of the second stage may or may not be a duplicate of the first.

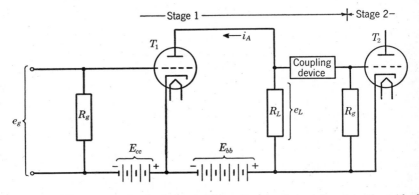

FIG. 11.1.   The output of tube 1 denoted by voltage e_L is transferred to the grid of tube 2 by a coupling device thereby multiplying the amplification of tube 1.

The pliotron tube passes only unidirectional current through its anode. However, an alternating component of current and voltage appears in the anode circuit whenever an alternating voltage is applied to the grid. Referring to Fig. 11.1, and the operating characteristics of Fig. 11.2, assume that an alternating voltage e_g is applied at the input terminals. As shown in Fig. 11.2a, the instantaneous grid voltage e_c is the addition of the bias component E_{cc} and the a-c signal e_g. The anode current then varies in a similar manner, as shown in Fig. 11.2b. The d-c component of anode current is I_{A0} corresponding to zero signal. The alternating component of anode current has an rms value I_A'. The maximum a-c component I_A' is never so large as the d-c component I_{A0}. For one half-cycle it is added to the d-c component and is subtracted from it during the next half-cycle. Thus, the anode current is a pulsating unidirectional current i_A composed of a d-c component I_{A0} and an a-c component I_A'.

The variable anode current through the load resistor R_L results in a variable anode potential as Fig. 11.2c. The d-c component E_{A0} is applied to the anode corresponding to zero signal. The a-c component E_A' results from the variable anode current through the load resistor R_L. This a-c component of anode voltage is the useful output of the amplifier circuit. It

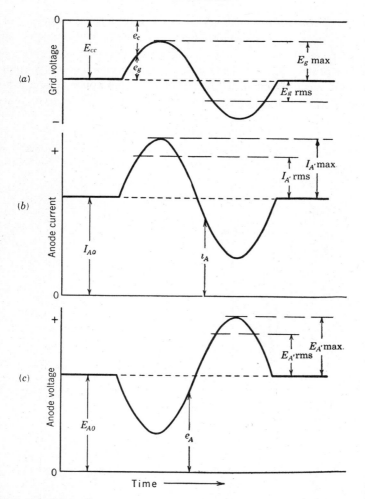

FIG. 11.2. The grid voltage, anode current, and anode voltage are all pulsating uni- · directional voltages or currents. An a-c signal, E_g rms, to the grid causes an a-c component of anode current $I_{A'}$ rms to flow. An a-c component of anode voltage $E_{A'}$, rms is the result.

may or may not be the same pattern as the input voltage wave. If the output wave shape faithfully reproduces the input wave form, the amplifier is said to operate without distortion.

Amplifier Operation

All amplifiers are broadly divided into three classifications, depending on the proportion of the cycle that anode current is allowed to flow:

Class-A Amplifier — The grid bias and alternating component of grid (signal) voltages of a class-*A* amplifier are adjusted such that anode current flows for the complete cycle of alternating grid-signal voltage.

Class-B Amplifier — The grid-bias voltage of a class-*B* amplifier is made approximately equal to the cutoff value; no appreciable anode current flows with zero grid-signal voltage, and the anode current flows for approximately one half of the alternating grid-signal voltage cycle.

Class-C Amplifiers — The grid bias of a class-*C* amplifier is appreciably greater than the cutoff voltage; no anode current flows at zero signal voltage, and anode current flows for less than one half of the grid-signal voltage cycle.

CLASS *A* AMPLIFIER

The operating features of a class-*A* amplifier are illustrated in Fig. 11.3. The grid-bias voltage is adjusted to approximately one half of the cutoff

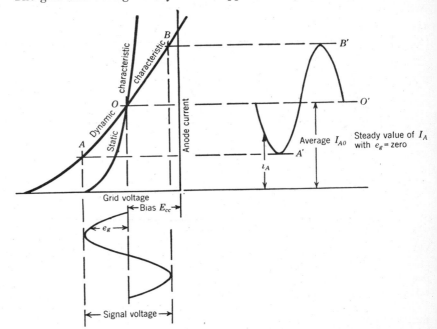

FIG. 11.3. Class-*A* amplification is typified by adjustment of the bias voltage to approximately half of the static cutoff voltage; a maximum signal e_g equal to the bias voltage, and an undistorted amplification of the signal.

voltage so that the signal voltage varies over the nearly straight portion of the dynamic transfer characteristics.

Because grid voltage is varied over only the essentially straight portion

of the dynamic characteristics, the output wave form is a reasonably faithful reproduction of the input wave. That is, a class-A amplifier does not
introduce any appreciable distortion of the input wave. If the signal has an
amplitude considerably greater than that shown in Fig. 11.3, the instantaneous grid potential may exceed cutoff voltage. Then anode current
would not flow during a complete cycle of grid signal. The qualifications for
class-A operation no longer are fulfilled, which emphasizes that both the
grid bias and the amplitude of the signal determine the class of an amplifier.

The average anode current remains unchanged at I_{A0}, because the a-c
component of anode current is symmetrical about the average value. The
load resistor must carry both the d-c average current I_{A0} and the a-c component of anode current. However, only the a-c component of anode current is effective in producing useful output of the amplifier. Hence the
the efficiency of a class-A amplifier is relatively low as is discussed later.

Class-A amplifiers are further subdivided into two classifications that
define the relative magnitude of the signal voltage. For class-A_1 amplifiers
the grid current is assumed zero throughout the entire cycle. To all practical purposes this means that the instantaneous grid voltage is maintained
negative at all times, and the peak signal voltage, as illustrated in Fig. 11.3,
does not exceed the grid-bias voltage.

For class-A_2 amplifiers grid current flows during some portion of the
cycle. This means that the grid voltage may become slightly positive as a
result of the peak signal voltage being somewhat greater than the grid-bias
voltage. With reference to Fig. 11.3, if e_g is greater than E_{cc}, the actual grid
voltage becomes positive at the maximum positive signal voltage. Grid
current flows during the portion of the cycle corresponding to any net
positive grid voltage; that is, $e_g > E_{cc}$.

If the same tubes are used, the power output of a class-A_2 amplifier is
greater than the equivalent class A_1, although some distortion is intro·
duced by class-A_2 operation.

CHOICE OF MAGNITUDE OF LOAD RESISTANCE

The choice of anode-circuit load resistance is necessarily a compromise
among the following three factors:

1. *The maximum voltage gain* is equal to the amplification or *mu* of the
tube, although this can be attained only if the load-circuit resistance is
infinite. Obviously, this is impossible, although, as noted in Fig. 11.4, a
voltage gain of 0.8μ is obtained with a load resistor four times the anode
resistance. But little additional amplification results from using more load
resistance.

2. *Minimum distortion* is theoretically obtained using a load resistance

twice the tube anode resistance. Class-A_1 and A_2 amplifiers usually are employed for voice-frequency amplification, and the load resistance is usually selected 2.0 to 2.5 times the anode resistance to assure low distortion.

3. *Maximum power output* is theoretically attained using a load resistance equal to the tube anode resistance. Power amplifiers are designed so that this condition is attained as nearly as possible.

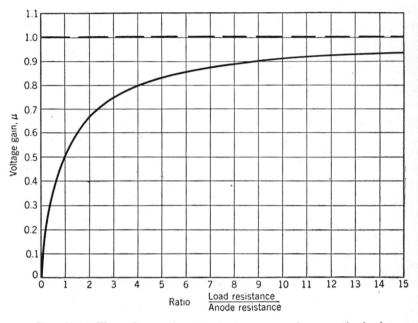

FIG. 11.4. The voltage gain at each stage approaches μ as the load resistance is increased.

The choice of the anode circuit resistance is, therefore, a compromise among these three factors. In practice, values from 2.0 to 2.5 are chosen for amplifiers designed for minimum distortion, or a value approximately equal to the anode resistance for power amplifiers.

CONSTRUCTION OF LOAD LINES

The performance of amplifiers can often be predicted with sufficient accuracy by the graphical construction of operating characteristics. The starting point for such graphical illustrations is the construction of a *load line*, which determines the distribution of the anode-supply voltage between the load resistor and the tube anode.

Assume that a circuit is designed with an anode supply of 400 volts and a load resistor of 20 000 ohms. The construction of a load line wherein the ordinate is determined by dividing the anode-supply voltage by the load resistance, resulting in 20 ma is shown in Fig. 11.5. The abscissa is equal to the anode-supply voltage.

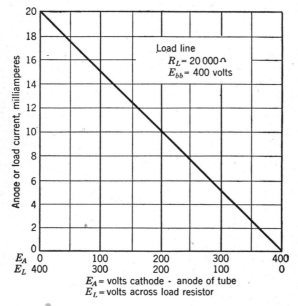

FIG. 11.5. The construction of a load line graphically illustrates the division of anode supply voltage between the load resistance and tube anode.

The figure shows that at zero anode current there is no drop in the load resistor and the full anode-supply voltage of 400 volts is available at the tube anode. At a load current of 10 ma the anode supply is equally divided with 200 volts across the load resistor and 200 volts across the tube anode. The load current can never reach 20 ma, since, for it to do so, the load resistor would consume the entire 400 volts, leaving no voltage at the tube anode terminal.

OPERATION DETERMINED BY STATIC CHARACTERISTICS

The graphical construction of operating characteristics is illustrated in Fig. 11.6. The first step is the construction of a load line upon the static anode characteristics by the method already outlined. To illustrate typically, the characteristics for a 6J5 are used in plotting Fig. 11.6.

The second step is the construction of the dynamic-transfer characteristic, the points of which are determined by the intersection of the load line with each curve of the anode characteristic. Such a curve passes through points A, Q, and B.

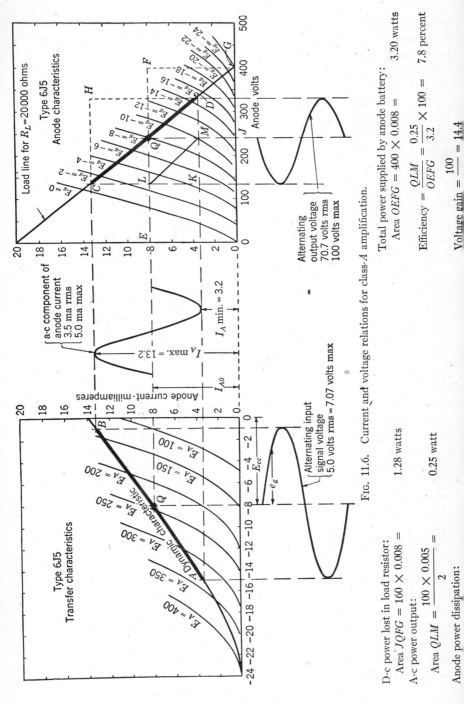

Fig. 11.6.   Current and voltage relations for class-A amplification.

Total power supplied by anode battery:

Area $OEFG = 400 \times 0.008 =$ 3.20 watts

$$\text{Efficiency} = \frac{QLM}{OEFG} = \frac{0.25}{3.2} \times 100 = \quad 7.8 \text{ percent}$$

$$\text{Voltage gain} = \frac{100}{} = 14.4$$

D-c power lost in load resistor:

Area $JQFG = 160 \times 0.008 =$ 1.28 watts

A-c power output:

Area $QLM = \dfrac{100 \times 0.005}{2} =$ 0.25 watt

Anode power dissipation:

The third step is the selection of point Q upon the anode characteristic. Point Q is known as the point of *quiescence*, or the point of operation corresponding to zero signal voltage. Point Q is chosen along the load line approximately halfway from the intersection with the anode curve for zero grid voltage to a point somewhat above the bend of the anode curves. Such a range is illustrated between points C and D. For the case illustrated, point Q is chosen at 8 ma and 240 volts. This fixes the grid-bias voltage.

Consider the operation when an a-c signal of 5 volts rms is applied to the amplifier input. The peak value of this signal is 7.07 volts, which is slightly less than the -8-volt bias and is satisfactory for class-A_1 operation.

The a-c signal voltage projected to the dynamic-transfer characteristic shows that the tube will operate between limits AB over the essentially straight portion of the dynamic characteristics.

The anode current varies from 3.2 ma minimum to 13.2 ma maximum, resulting in an a-c component of 5.0 ma maximum or 3.5 ma rms. This variation in anode current projected to the load line between limits CD shows the operating range of the tube on the anode characteristic. Point C corresponding to the maximum anode current of 13.2 ma shows that the anode voltage is 130 volts; the remaining 270 volts is consumed across the load resistor. At point D, the minimum anode current is 3.2 ma and the anode voltage 330 volts, leaving 70 volts drop across the load resistor.

The a-c component of voltage across the load resistor then varies from 130 volts minimum to 330 volts maximum. Peak-to-peak alternating voltage is then 200 volts, resulting in an rms value of 70.7 volts.

VOLTAGE GAIN

The voltage gain is the ratio of alternating-voltage output to alternating-voltage input or $70.7/5.0 = 14.4$. Compare this to Fig. 11.4 by noting that the tube anode resistance at point Q is 7500 ohms.* The load resistance is then 2.6 times the tube anode resistance for which Fig. 11.4 shows a gain of 0.73μ. The amplification factor of a 6J5 tube is 20,* and the calculated gain is therefore 14.6, which checks the graphical computation closely.

---

*These values are conveniently taken from the manufacturer's data or approximate values obtained by scaling the figure, from which:

$$\text{Anode resistance} = \frac{250 - 225 \text{ (volts)}}{0.009 - 0.0057 \text{ (amperes)}} = 7570 \text{ ohms} \quad \text{and}$$

$$\mu = \frac{240 - 200 \text{ (anode volts)}}{8.0 - 6.0 \text{ (grid volts)}} = 20$$

A more accurate graphical check can be made by referring to Chapter 6, Fig. 6.5.

DETERMINATION OF ANODE DISSIPATION, A-C POWER OUTPUT, AND EFFICIENCY

With reference to Fig. 11.6, the total power supplied by the anode battery is the average anode current times the supply voltage. It is represented by the rectangle,

$$OEFG = 0.008 \times 400 = 3.20 \text{ watts} \tag{A}$$

This total power of the anode circuit is divided into three components:
1. D-c power lost in the load resistor.
2. A-c power dissipated in the load resistor.
3. Power dissipated by the tube anode.

A *d-c power loss in load resistor* results from the average direct current I_{A0} through the load resistance. This is represented by voltage QF times the current QJ or the area of the rectangle,

$$JQFG = 160 \times 0.008 = 1.28 \text{ watts} \tag{B}$$

A-C Power Output. — If we assume the current through the load resistance to be sinusoidal,

$$I_{rms} = \frac{1}{\sqrt{2}} \times \frac{I_{max} - I_{min}}{2} = \frac{I_{max} - I_{min}}{2\sqrt{2}}$$

Voltage across the load resistance is also sinusoidal, and

$$E_{rms} = \frac{1}{\sqrt{2}} \times \frac{E_{max} - E_{min}}{2} = \frac{E_{max} - E_{min}}{2\sqrt{2}}$$

A-c power dissipated in the load resistor is then $E_{rms} \times I_{rms}$, from which;

$$\text{A-c power} = \frac{(E_{max} - E_{min})(I_{max} - I_{min})}{8}$$

Graphically, this is one eighth of the rectangle $KCHD$, conveniently illustrated by the triangle

$$MLQ = \frac{200 \times 0.010}{8} = 0.25 \text{ watt} \tag{C}$$

Anode Dissipation. — Power is dissipated as heat at the tube anode as a result of electrons flowing to it. Graphically, it is the total power supplied by the anode source with the d-c power lost in the load resistor and a-c power output subtracted. Its magnitude is what remains of the rectangle

OEFG when the two areas (B) and (C) are subtracted. This is the area *OELMJ*, calculated as follows:

Total power supplied by anode battery (A)		3.20 watts
D-c power lost in load resistor (B)	1.28 watts	
A-c power output (C)	0.25 watts	
Total of (B) and (C)	1.53 watts	
		1.53 watts
Anode dissipation		1.67 watts

Tube anode dissipation is least when the a-c power output is greatest. Conversely, the dissipation is a maximum with zero output power, at which time it is the area of rectangle *OEQJ*. When the signal voltage is zero, the entire power supplied by the anode battery is divided between power loss in the load resistor *JQFG* and the anode dissipation *JQEO*.

Efficiency. — The efficiency of the amplifier is the ratio of the a-c power output to the total power input, which is, in this case,

$$\frac{MLQ}{OEFG} = \frac{0.25}{3.2} \times 100 = 7.8 \text{ percent}$$

SUMMARY OF CLASS-*A* AMPLIFIER OPERATION

Class-*A* operation is characterized by the following features:

1. Operation is over the linear portion of the dynamic-transfer characteristic, and the output voltage is a faithful reproduction of the input signal voltage.

2. The operation efficiency is extremely low, usually less than 20 percent, because of the power loss in the load resistor by the flow of anode current with zero signal.

3. The rms value of output voltage is usually less than one third of the d-c anode battery voltage.

4. The grid-bias voltage is 50 to 60 percent of the cutoff voltage,† referring to the static-transfer characteristics.

CLASS-*B* AMPLIFIER

The anode current of a class-*B* amplifier flows for only one half of the a-c signal-voltage cycle. This is accomplished, as shown in Fig. 11.7, by adjusting the grid-bias voltage to approximately equal the cutoff voltage as determined by the dynamic-transfer characteristics.

A class-*B* amplifier amplifies positive signal voltages without appreciable distortion, but does not pass a negative signal, because this makes the grid

†With reference to Fig. 11.6, a static-transfer curve passing through *Q* reaches cutoff at approximately −14 volts.

more negative, extending it even further below cutoff. The amplified output is no longer a faithful reproduction of the incoming signal. For this reason, class-B amplification is not suited to voice-frequency amplification unless two tubes are connected in a push–pull circuit wherein one tube amplifies positive signals and the other tube negative signals. This circuit is discussed in further detail in the second section of this chapter.

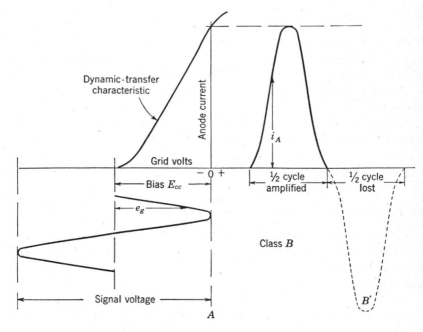

Fig. 11.7.   Class-B operation is typified by adjustment of the bias voltage to approximately the dynamic cutoff voltage, a maximum signal equal to the bias, and the flow of anode current for one-half cycle.

Class-B operation is frequently used for industrial-control applications in which all signal voltages are positive. For example, a photoelectric relay made to respond to increasing illumination may be biased to cutoff with the phototube "dark." Greater illumination of the phototube manifests a positive signal voltage and is amplified without distortion.

The grid-bias voltage is adjusted to cutoff as determined by the dynamic characteristics and not the static characteristics. With reference again to Fig. 11.6, class-B operation is obtained by adjusting the grid bias to approximately -22 volt. The approximate value can be determined by the anode supply voltage divided by μ, which in this case is $400/20 = 20$ volts.

The operating efficiency of a class-B amplifier is considerably higher than that of class-A operation. The reason for this is that the anode current is zero when the signal is zero, and loss in the load-circuit resistor at zero signal is eliminated. The theoretical maximum efficiency is 78 percent; practical values are approximately 60 percent.

Class-*B* operation is characterized by the following:

1. Anode current flows only when signal voltages are positive.

2. The grid bias is adjusted to approximately cutoff as determined by the dynamic characteristics.

3. The actual operating efficiency is relatively high — approximately 60 percent.

4. The grid voltage may become positive during strong positive values of signal voltage, during which part of the cycle grid current flows.

CLASS-*AB* AMPLIFIERS

Class-AB amplifiers are characterized by operation at a grid bias between the limits specified for class *A* and class *B*. The anode current of class-*AB* amplifiers flows for more than one-half cycle, but less than a complete cycle

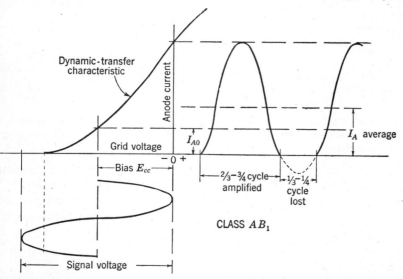

FIG. 11.8. Class-*AB*₁ operation is typified by adjustment of the bias voltage to less than the dynamic cutoff and a maximum signal such that the grid potential is always slightly negative.

as indicated in Figs. 11.8 and 11.9. The efficiency and power output of class-*AB* amplifiers is greater than with class-*A* operation. However, some distortion is introduced, because anode current flows for less than a complete cycle. For this reason class-*AB* amplifiers are usually employed in push-pull circuits as discussed further on page 220.

Class-AB amplifiers are further classified as to whether or not the grid becomes positive at any time during amplifier operation by subscript numbers 1 and 2 added to indicate that such is not, or is the case, respectively. Thus class-AB_1 operation is defined by the instantaneous grid voltage always remaining negative and is illustrated by Fig. 11.8. Class-AB_2

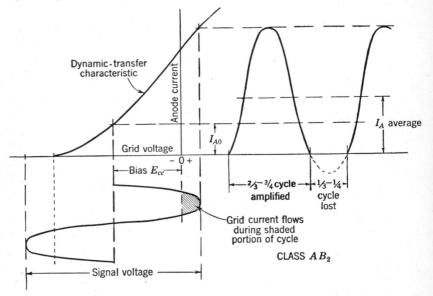

FIG. 11.9. Class-AB_2 operation is typified by the adjustment of bias to less than the dynamic cutoff and a maximum signal such that the grid becomes positive during a portion of the cycle.

operation is similar except that the instantaneous grid voltage becomes positive corresponding to a strong positive signal. This is shown in Fig. 11.9. Class-AB_2 operation delivers a larger power output than the equivalent class AB_1 but may introduce more distortion. Also grid current flows while its potential is positive.

CLASS-C AMPLIFIER

Class-C amplifiers are characterized by a grid bias so strongly negative that anode current flows for only a portion of positive signal.‡ Typical class-C operation is demonstrated in Fig. 11.10, in which even less than a complete half-cycle of anode current flows. The high distortion common to class-C amplifiers renders them useless for the amplification of voice frequencies. However, the class-C amplifier operates at the highest efficiency,

‡The principles of class-C operation are better understood by referring to Chapter 12, pp 238–44.

approximately 75 percent, and finds its field of usefulness when applied to radio-frequency power amplifiers. In such circuits, the output circuit is designed resonant to the frequency being amplified, and the harmonics introduced by class-C operation are smoothed out by the resonant action of the tuned output circuit.

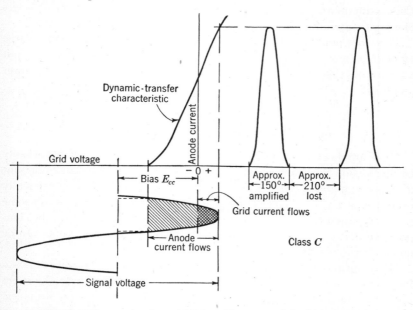

FIG. 11.10. Class-C operation is typified by adjustment of the bias to a voltage considerably greater than the dynamic cutoff, a maximum signal greater than the bias, and the flow of anode current for less than one-half cycle.

UNTUNED MULTISTAGE AMPLIFIERS

Often a single tube cannot provide sufficient amplification to operate the output device. Two or more tubes then can be connected together in cascade to obtain the desired degree of amplification. Each amplifier tube and its associated components is referred to as one stage of the amplifier. Thus, two tubes connected in cascade constitute a two-stage amplifier, and the component parts by which the first tube is connected to the second tube are referred to as the coupling.

In general, amplifiers are considered either as voltage amplifiers or power amplifiers, although the choice of words indicates a relative comparison, rather than absolute distinction. For example, voltage amplifiers are considered as those in which the load circuit drives the grid of a succeeding stage, wherein the grid is assumed to draw a negligible amount of power.

Therefore, the primary purpose of the amplifier is to produce the maximum possible voltage gain, a small power output being sufficient. On the other hand, a power amplifier is one whose load circuit is a power-consuming device such as a loud-speaker or the coil of a control relay. The voltage gain of power amplifiers is usually small, and their primary purpose is to feed the maximum amount of power into the load device. In general, all stages of a multistage amplifier, except the last, are voltage amplifiers.

This does not mean that a power amplifier necessarily handles a large amount of power. The output stage of a small portable radio does not exceed a fraction of one watt, and yet the output stage is defined as a power amplifier.

Representation of Amplifier Characteristics

Most amplifiers are designed to pass an alternating current, usually having a wide frequency range. Because of the several impedances present in every amplifier circuit, it is impossible that a circuit amplify equally every frequency over the wide range. It is then necessary to establish some practical yardstick by which the performance of one amplifier can be compared to that of another, or by which the response of one amplifier can be noted over a wide frequency range.

Many untuned amplifiers are designed primarily to handle voice or audio frequencies for the purpose of driving a loud-speaker. For these, the effect upon the human ear is the most useful comparison of their performance. The ear discriminates between sound intensities or acoustic powers, by a ratio rather than by numerical difference. For example, an ear that can barely discriminate between "silence" and a faint whisper in a quiet country room can probably just distinguish a clap of thunder from a roaring aircraft engine in loudness. The numerical difference expressed in units of sound intensity is many times greater in the latter case; yet because the *ratios* indicated for either condition are approximately equal, the ear detects these differences with approximately equal effect. If we select the logarithm of these power ratios as the comparison of one condition with another, the relative effect upon a human ear remains essentially equal, regardless of the actual level of intensity. This is done conveniently by using the *decibel*, abbreviated *db*, which is

$$\text{Power expressed in decibels} = 10 \log_{10} \frac{\text{power available}}{\text{reference power level}}$$

Various reference power levels are used, depending upon the purpose of a measurement. A reference level of 10^{-16} watt per square centimeter (at

1000 cycles) is frequently used for sound intensity, and 6 milliwatts is the reference for amplifiers applied to broadcast and public-address systems.

With reference to the preceding example, the approximate values of sound intensity are as follows:

$$P_1 - \text{Quiet room} \quad = 10^{-14} \text{ watt per square centimeter}$$
$$P_2 - \text{Whisper} \quad = 10^{-13} \text{ watt per square centimeter}$$
$$P_3 - \text{Aircraft engine} = 10^{-3} \text{ watt per square centimeter}$$
$$P_4 - \text{Thunder} \quad = 10^{-2} \text{ watt per square centimeter}$$

If we use the reference level of 10^{-16} watt per square centimeter these values expressed in decibels then become:

$$P_1 \text{ db} - \text{Quiet room} \quad = 10 \log_{10} \frac{10^{-14}}{10^{-16}} = 20$$

$$P_2 \text{ db} - \text{Whisper} \quad = 10 \log_{10} \frac{10^{-13}}{10^{-16}} = 30$$

$$P_3 \text{ db} - \text{Aircraft engine} = 10 \log_{10} \frac{10^{-3}}{10^{-16}} = 130$$

$$P_4 \text{ db} - \text{Thunder} \quad = 10 \log_{10} \frac{10^{-2}}{10^{-16}} = 140$$

The decibel reference for power measurements manifests its best use in the comparison of one condition with another, and as such is expressed by

$$\text{Number of decibels by which } P_2 \text{ exceeds } P_1 = 10 \log_{10} \frac{P_2}{P_1}$$

When P_2 exceeds P_1, the result is referred to as *decibels gain*, or, when P_2 is less than P_1, the expression becomes one of *decibels loss*.

Again, if we cite the previous example, the first condition shows that

$$\text{Decibels by which a whisper exceeds a quiet room} = 10 \log_{10} \frac{10^{-13}}{10^{-14}} = 10 \text{ db}$$

and the second condition likewise shows that

$$\left. \begin{array}{l} \text{Decibels by which a thunder clap} \\ \text{exceeds noise of an aircraft engine} \end{array} \right\} = 10 \log_{10} \frac{10^{-2}}{10^{-3}} = 10 \text{ db}$$

Thus, in either case, *the difference* between comparisons is 10 db, and the effect upon a human ear is approximately equal, regardless of the power level.§

§In the preceding idealized example, the effects of a difference in frequency of one sound from another is not considered.

If we apply these principles to audio-frequency amplifiers the gain of an amplifier is conveniently represented by

$$(\text{Output} - \text{input})\ \text{decibels} = 10 \log_{10} \frac{\text{watts output}}{\text{watts input}}$$

Fundamentally, the decibel is the logarithm of a power ratio. However if the power in either case is expended in *equal resistance values* the expression is conveniently modified to indicate a comparison of voltages, thus:

$$(\text{Voltage output} - \text{voltage input})\ \text{decibels} = 10 \log_{10} \frac{E_2{}^2}{E_1{}^2}$$

$$= 20 \log_{10} \frac{E_2}{E_1}$$

where E_1 is the input voltage $\Big\}$ across same values of

E_2 is the output voltage $\Big\}$ resistance

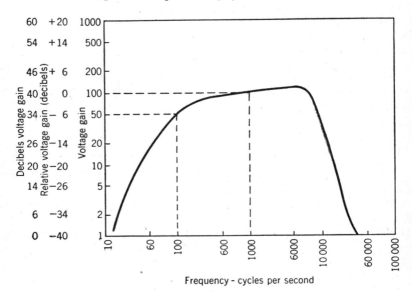

Frequency - cycles per second

FIG. 11.11. Amplifier response is commonly portrayed by logarithmic scales. *Decibels voltage gain* expresses an absolute value of stage amplification as does the numerical *voltage gain*. The *relative voltage gain* is referred to one point, in this case 1000 cycles.

The preceding equation is frequently used to express the *decibels voltage gain* of an amplifier as distinguished from the numerical *voltage gain* derived from the components of the circuits, as discussed in Chapter 6, page 95. A further modification sometimes is employed to indicate the relative decibels voltage gain. Use of the latter expression is to indicate performance relative to some point selected as a reference. For example, Fig. 11.11, if 1000 cycles is chosen as the reference point, the amplifier output at 100 cycles has decreased by the amount of 6 db. These three methods of representing amplifier characteristics are illustrated in Fig. 11.11, with a comparison of the values shown.

Manner of Coupling Amplifiers

DIRECT RESISTANCE-COUPLED AMPLIFIERS

The simplest type of two-stage amplifier is the *direct resistance-coupled* circuit, shown in Fig. 11.12. This circuit connects the output of tube 1 directly into the grid of tube 2. The input voltage e_{g1} is amplified by tube 1,

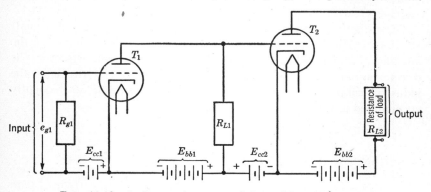

FIG. 11.12 A direct resistance-coupled amplifier connects the output of tube 1 directly to the input grid of tube 2.

and a varying voltage appears across resistor R_{L1} equal in magnitude to $K\mu e_{g1}$, where K is a fraction as discussed with reference to Fig. 11.4. The varying voltage across R_{L1} is fed directly to the grid of tube 2 constituting its input. This signal is likewise amplified to result in a larger variation of voltage across the output load resistance R_{L2}.

Operation of the direct resistance-coupled amplifier is simple. The circuit amplifies a wide range of frequencies from direct current to several thousand cycles with approximately equal gain for all frequencies. However, there are several disadvantages to the circuit, arising chiefly from the relative high cost of the power supply required. For example, two independent anode batteries‖ E_{bb1} and E_{bb2} are required because the anodes are at

‖The use of "batteries" does not indicate that dry cells or the equivalent must be used. Any type of power supply can be substituted for the "battery" although the comparison discussed is not altered by this substitution.

different potentials. These batteries represent the principal cost of the amplifier equipment. Independent batteries likewise are required for each grid and each cathode heater. Although the circuit can be modified to eliminate one of the anode sources, such modification requires that bias voltage E_{cc2} be considerably increased so that it offers no over-all advantages to the circuit of Fig. 11.12.

Another disadvantage of the direct resistance-coupled amplifier is its tendency to drift seriously as a result of changes in anode supply potentials and slight changes in tube characteristics. Anode- and grid-voltage sources cannot be maintained constant over long periods, nor does the cathode-heating potential remain exactly constant. These relatively small changes occurring in the circuit of tube 1 are amplified by the circuit of tube 2, and the effect may alter the output voltage to an objectionable degree.¶ Many different methods are used to construct high-gain direct resistance-coupled amplifiers to avoid the drift characteristic of the simple circuit of Fig. 11.12.

These disadvantages make the direct resistance-coupled amplifier unattractive to radio design engineers, because other circuits satisfactory for the amplification of a-c signals employ less costly equipment. However, the direct resistance-coupled amplifier is an extremely useful circuit to the industrial-control engineer because it amplifies a d-c signal, so frequently encountered in control-circuits.

RESISTANCE–CAPACITANCE-COUPLED AMPLIFIERS

Resistance–capacitance-coupled amplifiers are more frequently used than any other kind, primarily because they afford satisfactory operation at reasonable efficiency over a comparatively wide frequency range while their cost and weight are relatively low.

A circuit illustrating the principle is shown in Fig. 11.13. Two independent anode batteries E_{bb1} and E_{bb2} are shown to facilitate understanding of the operation, although the negative terminal of these batteries is common, and a single supply would suffice in practice. This circuit passes only alternating current to be amplified because direct current is blocked by the coupling capacitor C_{C1}.

The size of coupling capacitor C_{C1} is chosen so that its impedance to alternating current is low in comparison to the resistance of grid resistor

¶See Maurice Artzt, "Survey of D-C Amplifiers," *Electronics*, August 1945, pp 112–18.

R. G. Mezger, "A Stable Direct-Coupled Amplifier," *Electronics*, July 1944, pp 106–10, and 352–3.

Goldberg, "A High Gain D-C Amplifier for Bioelectric Recording," *Electrical Engineering*, Vol 59, January 1940, pp 60–4.

R_{g2}. An alternating voltage amplified by tube 1 and appearing across resistor R_{L1} is coupled to the circuit of tube 2 by capacitor C_{C1} and appears as an alternating voltage across resistor R_{g2}. This voltage then becomes e_{g2}, and the input to tube 2 is further amplified and results in an alternating voltage e_{L2} across resistor R_{L2}. This voltage, having been amplified in both stages, then is coupled to the output circuit by passing through coupling capacitor C_{C2}, the impedance of which is also chosen to be low for the a-c amplified voltage.

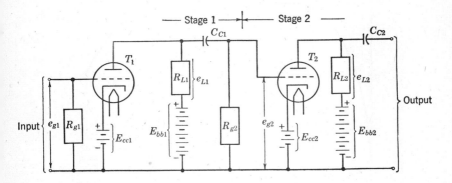

FIG. 11.13. A resistance–capacitance-coupled amplifier couples the output voltage e_{L1} of tube 1 to the input grid e_{g2} of tube 2 through capacitor C_{C1}. This circuit allows a single-anode supply source to replace the individual batteries E_{bb1} and E_{bb2}.

Coupling capacitors C_{C1} and C_{C2} perform the dual purpose of passing the alternating voltage to be amplified without appreciable loss while blocking direct current. With direct current blocked, the relatively high potential of battery E_{bb1} can be impressed on the anode of tube 1 without affecting the d-c potential applied to the grid of tube 2. The insulation between direct voltages allows a circuit arrangement whereby the two tubes can be served by a single source of anode voltage; that is, E_{bb1} and E_{bb2} can be combined.

Another important advantage of resistance–capacitance coupling results from the insulation of direct voltages by coupling capacitor C_{C1}. The drift predominant in direct resistance-coupled amplifiers is largely eliminated because a small change in the d-c potential of E_{bb1} does not affect the grid of tube 2. This means that the drift is not amplified in the second stage. The resistance–capacitance circuit is therefore more stable in operation than an equivalent direct resistance-coupled amplifier.

The circuit does not amplify all frequencies equally, although the design can be co-ordinated to result in characteristics that satisfy the human ear. Throughout the intermediate range of frequencies, the gain is reasonably constant, as illustrated in Fig. 11.14. Two factors contribute to a reduction in the gain at both ends of the frequency range.

The loss at the lower frequencies is explained by the relatively high impedance of coupling capacitor C_{C1} to a low-frequency current so that the a-c component voltage e_{L1} is divided between a drop across C_{C1} and grid resistor R_{g2}. As the frequency increases to approximately 100 cycles, the

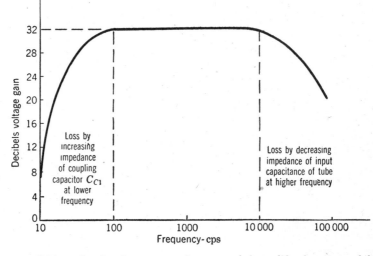

Fig. 11.14. The gain of resistance–capacitance-coupled amplifier is not equal for all frequencies because of the changing capacitive reactances at various frequencies.

voltage drop across C_{C1} becomes negligible if practical values of C_{C1} and R_{g2} are used. Above 100 cycles, then, the entire output voltage e_{L1} of stage 1 can be assumed as utilized for the input voltage e_{g2} driving tube 2.

As frequency is increased into the high range, the input capacitance of the tubes (see page 103) offers a sufficiently low impedance to the flow of high-frequency alternating current so that some of the voltage e_{g2} is shunted by the tube input capacitance. This causes a reduction in gain at the higher frequency.

A practical operating circuit is given in Fig. 11.15. It is a two-stage amplifier with pentode tubes. The operation of this circuit is exactly as described for the fundamental circuit, Fig. 11.13, except for a few added details.

In practice the grid-bias voltages represented as battery E_{cc1} and E_{cc2} in Fig. 11.13 are replaced by a series resistor R_{K1} and R_{K2} through which the tube cathode current produces a voltage drop with the polarity shown and replaces batteries as previously illustrated. These resistors are shunted by

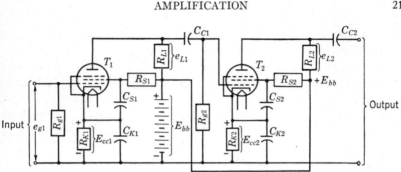

FIG. 11.15. Practical resistance–capacitance amplifiers employ pentodes. By-pass capacitors and resistors are added to the simple circuit of Fig. 11.13 to obtain a commonly used practical amplifier.

capacitors C_{K1} and C_{K2} so that alternating voltages being amplified effectively by-pass the resistors.

Screen-grid potential is obtained from the anode supply E_{bb}. The desired screen voltage is usually less than anode voltage. The difference is the amount of the voltage drop through series resistors R_{S1} and R_{S2}. Capacitors C_{S1} and C_{S2} by-pass the screen grid to the cathode, as explained on p 104.

Anode supply is indicated as a battery E_{bb}, although in practice it consists of a rectifier and filter circuit such as discussed in Chapter 9.

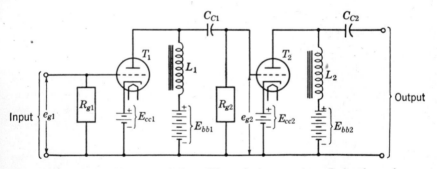

FIG. 11.16. An impedance-coupled amplifier substitutes reactor L_1 in place of a resistor. The low direct-voltage drop through the reactor decreases the voltage required for the anode supply E_{bb1} and increases the operating efficiency of the circuit as compared to resistance coupling.

IMPEDANCE-COUPLED AMPLIFIERS

The circuit of an impedance-coupled amplifier is shown in Fig. 11.16. The circuit is similar to that of a resistance-coupled amplifier, except that reactors L_1 and L_2 replace the anode circuit resistors. Strictly speaking the circuit could be called an *impedance–capacitance–resistance-coupled ampli-fier* although *impedance coupling* is the more common terminology.

The advantage of this circuit is the lower direct-voltage drop through reactors L_1 and L_2 as compared to the resistance-coupled circuit. This leads to lower anode-supply voltages E_{bb1} and E_{bb2} and consequently lower cost. Reactors L_1 and L_2 offer a high impedance to the alternating voltage being amplified and result in a large voltage input e_{g2} across the grid of tube 2.

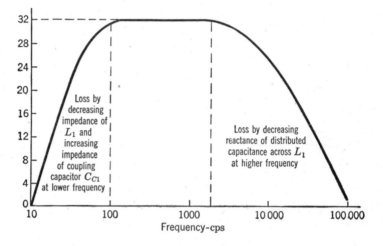

Fig. 11.17. The gain of an impedance-coupled amplifier is not equal for all frequencies because of the changing inductive reactance of L_1, the capacitive reactance of the coupling capacitor, and the distributed capacitance across L_1 at various frequencies.

The relative response characteristic of a typical impedance-coupled amplifier, Fig. 11.17, is poorer than that of an equivalent resistance-coupled amplifier, Fig. 11.14. The reason for the decrease in gain at a low frequency is the reduction in impedance value of reactors L_1 and L_2 at low frequency plus the relatively high impedance of the coupling capacitor. The gain also declines at a higher frequency because of the increasing effect of the distributed capacitance of the reactor winding and tube inter-electrode capacitance, which in effect shunts the reactance.

Impedance-coupled amplifiers were popular as audio-frequency ampli-fiers for radio before tetrodes and pentodes became available. The com-paratively large power loss in the anode-circuit resistors of the resistance-coupled amplifier so increased the size of the anode power supply that the impedance-coupling method was worthwhile. Pentodes, which greatly reduce the loss in the anode resistor, make the impedance-coupled circuit virtually obsolete.

TRANSFORMER-COUPLED AMPLIFIERS

Transformers of many types are used in amplifier coupling for several purposes. This discussion is confined to iron-core transformers used in the amplification of voice frequencies. A typical circuit, using two types of transformers, is shown in Fig. 11.18. Transformer TR_1 is an *interstage*

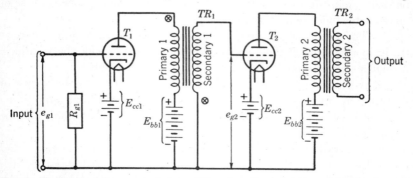

Fig. 11.18. A transformer-coupled amplifier has the advantage of a larger gain resulting from a step-up ratio of the transformer windings, and a low direct-voltage drop through the primary winding.

coupling transformer used to transfer the output voltage of tube 1 to the input of tube 2. Transformer TR_2 is an *output* transformer, connecting the output voltage of tube 2 to the load circuit. A third type, an *input* transformer, could be used to replace the grid resistor R_{g1} for the purpose of coupling the input voltage e_{g1} to the grid of tube 1, as illustrated by Fig. 11.19.

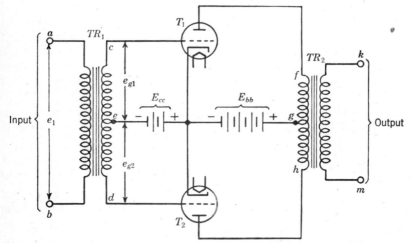

Fig. 11.19. A push–pull amplifier is used to obtain a power output approximately equal to the sum of each tube rating.

Iron-core transformers in place of resistors, capacitors, or reactors, as previously discussed, possess several important advantages:

1. The over-all voltage gain of each stage of amplification is increased approximately in proportion to the turns ratio between primary and secondary windings of the first stage transformer. However, this ratio is limited in practice to a maximum of approximately five to one because of unavoidable limitations in the physical design of the transformer.

2. The direct-voltage drop through the transformer windings is relatively low because of the comparatively low resistance of the windings. A smaller source of anode voltage E_{bb1} and E_{bb2} is the result.

3. A further advantage of transformer coupling is the simplicity of adapting the circuit to push–pull connections by merely adding a tap to the center of a secondary winding, or by design of the secondary winding a tube can be connected to a load of any desired impedance.

The disadvantages of transformer coupling are the size, weight, and especially the cost of the equipment, as compared with resistance coupling. The size of the equipment may be indirectly influenced by a further disadvantage in that transformers have a tendency to pick up magnetic coupling of stray fields causing undesirable amplifier performance. This can be eliminated by careful shielding and location of transformers.

The cost of suitable transformers is influenced by the desirability of obtaining good frequency response. If a transformer-coupled amplifier is to compare favorably in quality with a good resistance-coupled amplifier, the transformers are necessarily expensive. Attempts to reduce the size, weight, and cost of transformers invariably result in the failure of an amplifier to amplify signals at various frequencies with equal gain.

A complete analysis of the many factors influencing the performance of transformer-coupled amplifiers* is too extensive for treatment here.

Push–Pull Amplifiers

CLASS A

Many tasks for electronics require a relatively large amount of power output without appreciable distortion of voice frequencies. One common example is the output stage of radio receivers wherein the output drives the speaker coil. One method of obtaining a large power output is to connect two tubes in a push–pull circuit, illustrated in Fig. 11.19. The input voltage e_1 is divided into two signal voltages e_{g1} and e_{g2} by the secondary winding of the input transformer TR_1. The secondary winding of this transformer has a center tap, and the direction of windings is such that an instantaneous positive polarity at terminal a causes a positive polarity at secondary terminal c. Thus, when signal voltage e_1 becomes positive at terminal a, the

*See Terman, *Radio Engineers Handbook*, pp 366–75.

secondary voltage becomes positive at c and negative at d. Although the secondary voltage in windings ce–ed are in phase, the grid voltage applied to tube 1 and tube 2 is 180 degrees out of phase relative to the center tap e.

The push–pull terminology is derived from the action of anode currents through the two tubes. An increasing positive voltage applied to the grid

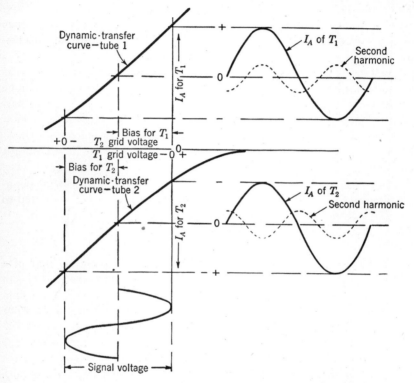

FIG. 11.20. The graphic representation of push–pull operation shows how the second-harmonic components of distortion cancel in the primary winding of the output transformer. Push–pull operation results in less distortion than an equivalent single output tube.

of tube 1 is accompanied by an increasing negative voltage applied to the grid of tube 2. The anode current of tube 1 through primary winding fg of output transformer TR_2 is then increasing at the same instant that the anode current of tube 2 through winding gh is decreasing. Thus, an increasing current in winding fg forces current through the output terminals mk in the same direction as a decreasing current in primary winding gh. The output of tubes 1 and 2 thus are combined by the center-tapped primary winding of the output transformer.

The push–pull circuit delivers more than twice as much power as one tube alone. This is explainable by the operating characteristics, Fig. 11.20.

The dynamic-transfer curve of tube 2 is inverted and aligned† so that an input signal voltage operates on the same portion of the two tube characteristics. The effect is to cancel the nonlinear characteristic of the two curves, so that the output voltage remains practically undistorted although the operation occurs over a nonlinear portion of the characteristic of each. This assumes that the tube characteristics are matched and the center-tap transformer windings are identical. With distortion reduced, the range of operation can be extended beyond that allowable for either tube operating singly.

The anode current of either tube taken alone possesses some distortion as a result of operation over a nonlinear transfer curve. The distortion can be resolved into harmonics of the fundamental frequency. The second harmonic is the most important. As illustrated in Fig. 11.20, the second-harmonic components of the two anode currents act upon the output transformers in opposite directions and therefore are canceled in the output circuit.

The reduction of distortion by a push–pull circuit accounts for its popularity as the last amplifier stage. However, the circuit is not restricted to use in the output stage, and enjoys the same advantage wherever used.

CLASS B

The circuit of a class-B push–pull amplifier is the same as that of a class-A amplifier, Fig. 11.19. As shown in Fig. 11.21, the positive loops of signal voltage are amplified through tube 1 while negative loops are amplified through tube 2. Class-B operation differs from class-A in that only one tube passes anode current at a time. During the positive half-cycles of signal voltage the anode current of tube 1 flows through primary winding fg and negative half-cycles of tube 2 through winding gh. The current in the secondary winding of the output transformer is the combined wave of both loops and is a reproduction of the original signal-voltage wave with only a small amount of distortion.

Class-B push–pull amplifiers are capable of handling a relatively large amount of power without appreciable distortion. Their principal application is in radio transmitters wherein the power level to be amplified warrants this choice.

CLASS AB

Either class-AB_1 or AB_2 operation is obtained using the push–pull circuit with all of the same principles holding. Class-AB operation has the advan-

†For an explanation of this method of representing push–pull amplifiers see MIT staff, *Applied Electronics*, pp 433–48; also Thompson, "Graphical Determination of Performance of Push-Pull Audio Amplifiers," *IRE Proc.* 21, 1933, p 595.

tage of a larger power output than the equivalent class A with only slightly more distortion. It is commonly employed in the output circuit of most radio receivers.

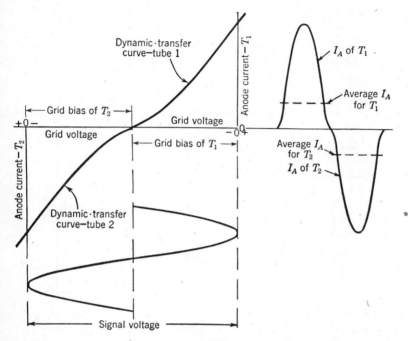

Fig. 11.21. A class-B push–pull circuit amplifies a positive signal voltage through tube 1 and a negative signal voltage through tube 2. The anode currents are added together by the output transformer producing an output wave without appreciable distortion.

TUNED AMPLIFIERS

Tuned amplifiers are of primary interest to the radio engineer and are used for the purpose of amplifying the band of so-called radio frequencies, 200 000 cycles and above. The analysis of tuned amplifiers is considerably beyond the scope of this text, and only a fundamental explanation of the purpose of a few simplified tuned circuits is presented.

Tuned Voltage Amplifiers

The principles of any tuned voltage amplifier are illustrated by the direct-coupled circuit, Fig. 11.22. The similarity to the resistance–capacitance-coupled amplifier, Fig. 11.15, is apparent except that the variable capacitor C in parallel with inductor L replaces the anode-circuit resistor. Pentodes are usually employed for this purpose, because it becomes essential to minimize the anode-grid capacitance within the tube to prevent undesirable coupling between the anode and grid circuits at these high frequencies.

The effect of the load-circuit resistance in proportion to the tube anode resistance was pointed out in connection with Fig. 11.4. In the case of tuned amplifiers, the impedance of the parallel capacitor–inductor circuit has a similar effect upon the stage gain. If the impedance of the tuned circuit is large, the stage gain is large and the gain is reduced by a smaller impedance of the tuned circuit.

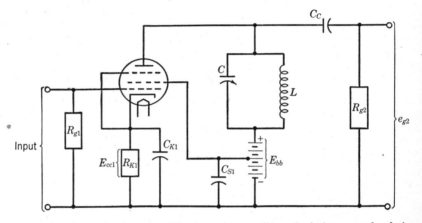

FIG. 11.22. A tuned voltage amplifier is used to amplify a single frequency by designing capacitor C and inductance L for resonance at the desired frequency.

Tuned amplifiers are used to amplify essentially a constant frequency (for each adjustment of the tuned circuit). The principle of operation is to adjust the tuned circuit to parallel resonance corresponding to the signal frequency. This condition results in a maximum impedance of the tuned circuit as further discussed in Chapter 12, page 234. The effect is to amplify the resonance frequency to which the circuit is tuned with a large voltage gain and reject amplification of all other frequencies except for a narrow band either side of the resonance frequency, as shown in Fig. 11.23. Thus the circuit possesses the characteristic of selectivity in that only a particular frequency as determined by the resonant tuning of the circuit is selected to become amplified and passed on to succeeding stages of amplification.

The selection of any other frequency to be amplified is accomplished by tuning the circuit, usually by an adjustable capacitor. This principle of selective tuning is commonly employed in radio receivers although it is equally useful in the field of communication and certain laboratory measuring devices.

Tuned amplifiers are also designed of the impedance and transformer-coupled types. Tuned transformer-coupled circuits employ transformers tuned on the primary side, on the secondary side, or with both primary and secondary sides tuned. The latter type is particularly effective for amplifying an extremely narrow band of frequencies, which allows sharp tuning of the transformer circuits.

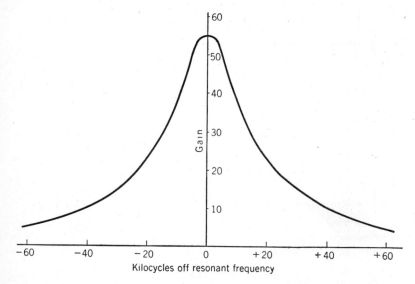

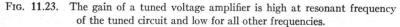

Fig. 11.23.   The gain of a tuned voltage amplifier is high at resonant frequency of the tuned circuit and low for all other frequencies.

Tuned Power Amplifiers

As discussed in connection with class-*B* and class-*C* amplifiers and illustrated by Figs. 11.7 and 11.10, anode current flows for one-half cycle or less of the alternating voltage. Such operation cannot be used directly to amplify an alternating voltage because of the obvious considerable degree of distortion resulting from class-*B* or class-*C* operation. Class-*B* and class-*C* circuits are used as radio-frequency amplifiers wherein advantage is taken of their inherently large power output and high operating efficiency. This advantage cannot be realized by the tube operating alone. It becomes necessary to co-ordinate the tube operation with a tuned output circuit. The principles of a simple tuned class-*B* or class-*C* circuit are set forth in Fig. 11.24.

A parallel circuit consisting of capacitor *C* and reactor *L* is connected in the anode circuit with their values chosen to become resonant at the frequency of the a-c signal. The capacitor and reactor together are called a *tank circuit*, derived from their action in storing energy, first in the capacitor and then in the reactor. The electrical action of the tank circuit is comparable to that of a single-cylinder gasoline engine equipped with a flywheel. A pressure impulse of relatively short duration within the cylinder of the engine sets the flywheel in motion and the stored energy of the fly-

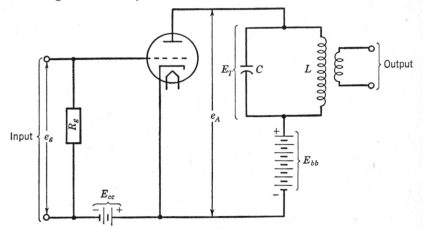

FIG. 11.24. Tuned power amplifiers utilize the flywheel effect of the *tank circuit* (parallel resonant capacitor C and reactor L) to obtain a sinusoidal load current with a tube operating on class-B or class-C characteristics.

wheel is sufficient to maintain rotation of the shaft during the interval when no pressure exerts force upon the piston. In the electrically tuned circuit anode current flowing for a half-cycle or less corresponds to the pressure exerted upon the piston in the mechanical analogy, while the electric energy stored by the tank circuit corresponds to the momentum of the mechanical flywheel.

In this way an alternating current is kept flowing within the resonant tank circuit‡ through capacitor C and reactor L. The flux through the core of reactor L is alternating and links the turns of the output coupling coil. By the co-ordinated design of component parts of the circuit, the current through the output or load is thus alternating and without appreciable distortion, although the anode current flows in approximately half-cycle peaks characteristic of class-B or class-C operation.

The simultaneous curves of anode voltage, grid voltage, and anode current typifying class-C operation are shown in Fig. 11.25. Derivation of the anode-current wave form with respect to the grid voltage has been previously discussed with class-C amplification. A positive swing of grid voltage results in anode-current flow to start the tank-circuit "flywheel" in motion, which carries the instantaneous anode voltage e_A above the d-c-

‡A more complete explanation of this principle is given in Chapter 12, p 238-9.

anode supply voltage E_{bb} to start the pattern of sinusoidal anode voltage.‡ The a-c component of anode voltage E_T is the alternating voltage across the terminals of the tank circuit. This a-c component is coupled to the load

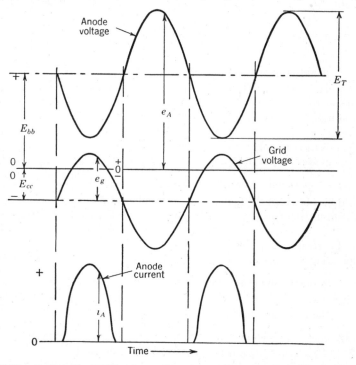

FIG. 11.25. A class-C amplifier in conjunction with a tuned-output circuit results in a sinusoidal voltage E_T across the tank. A sinusoidal current flows around the tank circuit to produce a sinusoidal voltage in the output coupling coil.

by transformer action between the tank reactor L and the output coupling coil. Thus sinusoidal alternating current in the output circuit is obtained at the high efficiency of class-B or class-C operation, although the anode-current wave form bears no apparent similarity to the input signal voltage.

SUMMARY

The *gain* of each amplifier stage refers to the amount by which the output voltage exceeds the input voltage. Gain sometimes is given as a numerical ratio, but more frequently is expressed in decibels.

The *maximum gain* theoretically possible for each stage of amplification approaches μe_g as a limit, but seldom achieves more than 80 percent of this value.

‡A more complete explanation of this principle is given in Chapter 12, p 238-9.

Class-A operation is characterized by:

Grid bias approximately one half the cutoff voltage.

Anode current flows for the complete cycle of grid-signal voltage.

Slight distortion: that is, the output wave truly reproduces the shape of signal input wave.

Operating efficiency 20 percent or less.

Least power output for a given tube rating.

Class-B operation is characterized by:

Grid bias approximately equal to the cutoff voltage.

Anode current flows for approximately one half of the grid signal voltage cycle (positive half-cycles only).

Operating efficiency approximately 60 percent.

High distortion, unless used in a push–pull circuit.

Large power output for a given tube rating.

Class-AB$_1$ operation is characterized by:

Grid bias between the limits of class *A* and class *B*.

Anode current flows for more than one half but less than a full cycle of grid signal.

Grid current does not flow (appreciably).

Operating efficiency and power output exceed comparative values for class *A*.

Class-AB$_2$ operation is characterized by:

The same as class *AB$_1$* except that grid current flows appreciably during a portion of the grid signal-voltage cycle.

Class-C operation is characterized by:

Grid bias appreciably greater than the cutoff voltage.

Anode current flows for less than one half of the grid signal-voltage cycle (positive half-cycles only).

Highest operating efficiency, approximately 75 percent.

Greatest distortion — used only with tuned output.

Largest power output for a given tube rating.

Coupling is the device or connection of several devices by which the output of one stage is transformed to the input of a succeeding stage.

Direct resistance-coupled amplifiers consist of two or more stages coupled solely by resistors. They amplify a wide range of frequencies, including a d-c signal, with nearly an equal gain for all. Two disadvantages are the comparatively high cost of a suitable power supply and a tendency toward drift over a prolonged operating interval.

Resistance–capacitance-coupled amplifiers consist of two or more stages coupled by the voltage developed across a resistor (in each anode circuit) which passes to the grid of a succeeding stage through a capacitor. The capacitor allows alternating current to pass with only a slight attenuation and yet blocks direct current. This circuit is used extensively and is popularly called a resistance-coupled amplifier. The gain for all frequencies within the audio spectrum is reasonably constant. Simplicity and low cost more than balance the single disadvantage of low operating efficiency.

Impedance-coupled amplifiers consist of two or more stages coupled by the voltage developed across an iron-core reactor (in each anode circuit), which passes to the grid of a succeeding stage through a capacitor. Operation is similar to the resistance-coupled amplifier, compared to which its operating efficiency is higher; cost, weight, and size are greater; response to the range of audio frequencies is less linear.

Transformer-coupled amplifiers consist of two or more stages coupled by a transformer whereby the primary winding couples the anode circuit to the grid of a succeeding stage by its secondary winding. Stage gain is enhanced by the transforming ratio. Operating efficiency is high. By proper design of the transformer gain for the range of audio frequencies is reasonably constant.

Input transformers are used to couple an input voltage to the grid of the first amplifier stage.

Interstage transformers are used for coupling one stage to a succeeding stage.

Output transformers are used to couple output of the final amplifier stage to the device actuated by the amplifier system.

Push–Pull amplifiers, using two tubes for each stage, usually are employed for the final stage and have the advantage of delivering the maximum power with least distortion for the materials used.

Tuned amplifiers are used for amplifying a narrow band of frequencies (for each tuning adjustment). Operation is selective in that stage gain is large for frequencies close to the tuned value while gain for those above or below the tuned value is reduced. Band width of the frequencies amplified with appreciable gain is controlled by design constants.

REFERENCES

MIT Electrical Engineering Staff, *Applied Electronics*, John Wiley & Sons, New York, 1943, pp 378–432; 459–525 and 559–84.

W. G. Dow, *Fundamentals of Engineering Electronics*, John Wiley & Sons, New York, 1937, pp 263–93 and 296–326.

F. E. Terman, *Radio Engineering*, McGraw-Hill Book Co., New York, 1937, pp 167–80; 181–314 and 314–45.

F. E. Terman, *Radio Engineers' Handbook*, McGraw-Hill Book Co., New York, 1943, pp 353–413 and 451–59.

Jacob Millman and Samuel Seely, *Electronics*, McGraw-Hill Book Co., New York, 1941, pp 573–676.

Herbert J. Reich, *Theory and Applications of Electron Tubes*, McGraw-Hill Book Co., New York, 1944, pp 124–282.

Keith Henney, *Radio Engineering Handbook*, McGraw-Hill Book Co., New York, 1941, pp 359–94 and 395–422.

W. D. Cockrell, *Industrial Electronic Control*, McGraw-Hill Book Co., New York, 1944, pp 110–19.

J. B. Hoag, *Basic Radio*, D. Van Nostrand Co., New York, 1943, pp 80–9 and 176–212.

F. H. Gulliksen and E. H. Vedder, *Industrial Electronics*, John Wiley & Sons, New York, 1935, pp 33–8.

Maurice Artzt, "Survey of D-C Amplifiers," *Electronics*, August 1945, pp 112–18.

R. G. Mezger, "A Stable Direct-Coupled Amplifier," *Electronics*, July 1944, pp 106–10 and 352–3.

H. Goldberg, "A High-Gain D-C Amplifier for Bioelectric Recording," *AIEE Transactions*, January 1940, Vol 59, pp 60–4.

B. J. Thompson, "Graphical Determination of Performance of Push–Pull Audio Amplifiers," *IRE Proc.*, Vol 21, 1933, p 595.

Chapter 12

PRINCIPLES OF OSCILLATION

De Forest had scarcely announced his three-element *audion* tube, now classified as a pliotron, in 1907, when radio engineers successfully employed the tube to obtain high-frequency oscillations. The power output obtainable from these early tubes was extremely small, although sufficient to enable detection of the extremely feeble radio signals of that era. Larger

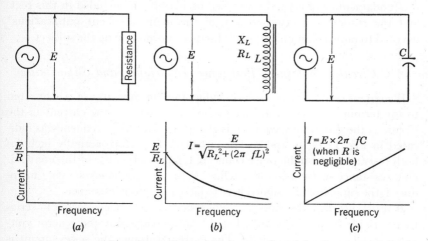

FIG. 12.1. Current through a resistance (*a*) is not affected by frequency of the impressed voltage; through a reactor (*b*) current decreases with rising frequency; and through a capacitance (*c*) current increases at higher frequency.

pliotrons were quickly developed, and soon vacuum-tube oscillators capable of 50 to 250 watts output replaced all other means of generating a radio signal. Because of the simplicity by which a vacuum-tube oscillator could be "voice-modulated," radiotelephony became a reality that has since strongly influenced our mode of living.

Until 1925 the pliotron stood alone in controlling the frequency of the oscillating circuit. Transmitters of this type are classified as *self-excited* oscillators. Early radio transmitters were subject to a frequency drift not tolerable when the transmitting stations increased in number. Professor W. G. Cady and G. W. Pierce were among the first to recognize that the piezoelectrical phenomenon offered a means of controlling frequency of

231

oscillation with a precision of approximately one cycle in one million cycles. The piezoelectrical effect results from the ability of crystalline substances, notably quartz, to vibrate mechanically at a certain specific frequency when an alternating voltage is impressed across appropriate faces of the crystal.

Thus, vacuum-tube oscillators are broadly divided into two classifications: (1) self-excited oscillators, whose frequency is subject to some variation (unless complicated refinements are used), and (2) crystal-controlled oscillators, whose frequency remains constant. The relative simplicity of the self-excited oscillator makes it extremely useful in industrial fields where constant operating frequency is not required, particularly applied to induction and dielectric radio-frequency heating (Chapter 14). Crystal-controlled oscillators are used largely in radio transmission. Hence, only the fundamentals of crystal-controlled oscillators are included in this text, and the reader is referred to any of the many excellent publications* devoted to radio communication for further information on the subject.

A-C Circuits Containing Resistance, Inductance, and Capacitance

If a circuit containing resistance, inductance, or capacitance is connected to the terminals of a variable-frequency a-c generator, the current in the circuit as the generator frequency is changed varies with frequency as indicated in Fig. 12.1a, b, and c. The circuit of Fig. 12.1b actually includes both resistance and inductance connected in series because of the unavoidable resistance of the reactor winding. Without serious error being introduced, the capacitor is assumed here to have negligible resistance.

If resistance R, inductance L, and capacitance C are connected in series to a variable-frequency source, Fig. 12.2a, the capacitor and reactor voltages must be added vectorially. The current through the series circuit is manifest by a difference between the inductive and capacitive reactances. Inductive reactance increases as the source frequency is raised while capacitive reactance behaves in the opposite manner. At some particular frequency these two reactances become equal, and, being opposite in sign, they cancel to render the impedance of the series circuit a minimum. Hence, the current becomes a maximum, limited only by the resistance, at a frequency f_r, Fig. 12.2a, known as the *resonant frequency* of the series circuit.

If the reactor (with its inherent resistance) and capacitor are connected in parallel, Fig. 12.2b, the resultant circuit is most readily conceived by referring to the susceptance of each branch.† Inductive susceptance, b_L,

*Such as Terman, *Radio Engineering*, pp 374–85.
†See R. R. Lawrence, *Principles of Alternating Currents*, pp 150–72 and 220–9, McGraw Hill Book Co., New York, 1922.

decreases as the source frequency is raised, while the capacitive susceptance, b_C, becomes greater (and of opposite sign). At the resonant frequency, f_r,

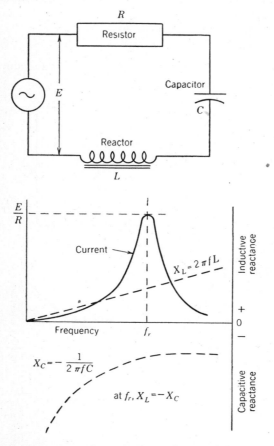

FIG. 12.2. (a) A series-resonant circuit manifests a minimum impedance at resonant frequency.

these susceptances are equal and opposite making the impedance of the parallel circuit of greatest magnitude. The line current is least at the resonant frequency f_r, as Fig. 12.2b shows.‡

‡Parallel resonance of reasonably low-loss circuits can be described in two additional ways. One defines it as occurring when the line current is exactly in phase with the applied voltage. Still another definition requires that the inductive reactance be exactly equal to the capacitive reactance. Under usual circumstances, the resonant frequency to satisfy either of these definitions is so nearly the same that no distinction between the definitions is required.

The characteristics of a series-resonant circuit are typified by the following properties:

1. The frequency at which the circuit becomes resonant is

$$f_r = \frac{1}{2\pi\sqrt{LC}}$$

2. Line current is a maximum; impedance is a minimum and equal to the resistance of the circuit.

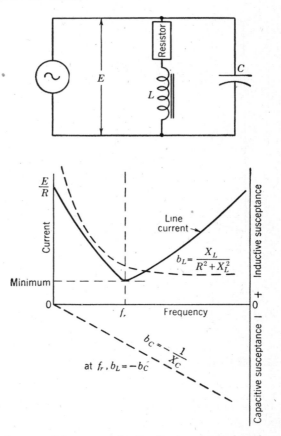

FIG. 12.2.   (*b*) A parallel-resonant circuit offers maximum impedance (minimum susceptance) at resonant frequency.

3. Line current is in phase with the impressed voltage (the power factor of the circuit is unity).

4. If the circuit resistance is small, the voltage drop across the capacitor and the reactor is greater than the impressed generator voltage.

5. Voltages across the capacitor and the reactor are numerically equal (approximately), but these voltages are nearly vectorially opposed.

Parallel resonance is characterized by the following properties:

1. If the resistance is small in comparison to the inductive and capacitive reactances, the resonant frequency is close to

$$f_r = \frac{1}{2\pi\sqrt{LC}}$$

2. Line current is a minimum; impedance is a maximum.

3. Line current is in phase with the impressed voltage.

4. The current circulating in the parallel circuit itself is much larger than the line current.

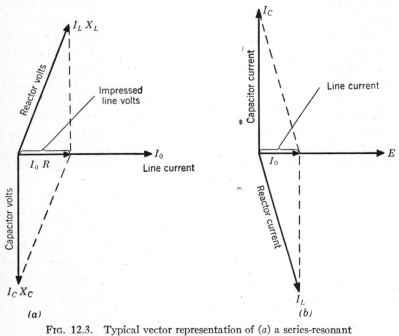

Fig. 12.3. Typical vector representation of (a) a series-resonant circuit and (b) a parallel-resonant circuit.

A comparison between series and parallel resonance is illustrated by the vectors, Fig. 12.3a and b. Series resonance, Fig. 12.3a illustrates large voltages across the reactor and capacitor in comparison to the impressed line voltage. Each of these is displaced approximately 90 degrees from the impressed voltage. Parallel resonance, Fig. 12.3b illustrates reactor and capacitor currents much larger than the line current. Each is displaced approximately 90 degrees from the line current.

A comparison between these two types of resonance can be summarized by saying that in a series-resonant circuit high voltages appear across the component parts, whereas in a parallel-resonant circuit, a high current circulates in the component parts. As the current surges back and forth in a parallel resonant circuit, the energy is alternately shifted between the magnetic field of the coil (reactor) and the electric field of the capacitor, losing a certain portion of the total energy into the resistance of the circuit during each cycle. To maintain oscillations the power source supplies an amount of energy during each cycle equal to that expended in the circuit resistance.

A mechanical analogy frequently used to explain visually the properties of a resonant circuit is the familiar single-cylinder steam engine, with its valve mechanism and flywheel. If the engine operates at no load, uniform rotation (oscillation) is maintained by the periodic application of power by the piston. The power impulses by the piston must be delivered at the proper point of the mechanical cycle and must have sufficient magnitude to make up for the losses in the engine, mostly friction.

Two factors of a resonant circuit are most important: (1) the resonant frequency of the circuit, and (2) a comparison between the total energy in the circuit and that which is dissipated in losses. The latter factor is referred to as the *quality* of the resonant circuit and is designated as the Q of the circuit.

In electronic practice, nearly all of the circuit resistance is within the reactor itself, and the circuit quality becomes

$$Q = \frac{X_L}{R}$$

This expression is commonly used by radio engineers in the design of resonant circuits of relatively low power. The industrial engineer is usually more interested in the current in a resonant circuit. Most oscillating circuits are sufficiently low loss to allow the following modification:

$$Q = \frac{X_L}{R} \times \frac{I^2}{I^2} = \frac{IX_L \times I}{I^2 R} = \frac{\text{volt} \times \text{amperes}}{\text{watts}} = \frac{\text{kva}}{\text{kw}}$$

The ratio *kva/kw* of a resonant circuit is a factor of merit. To maintain sustained oscillation the kva/kw ratio of a circuit must be above a certain minimum figure. The load§ drawn from an oscillator has the effect of reducing the ratio; hence, it can be appreciated that the maximum loading permissible is dependent upon the ratio inherent in the circuit. The

§As described, this Q is known as the loaded Q of the circuit. If the loaded Q is not much lower than the unloaded Q, the energy transfer efficiency is poor.

ratio used in practical electronic circuits varies. Sometimes it is as low as 10 and occasionally as high as 500. An average figure is perhaps 50.

If the resistance of a resonant circuit is small, it has a high kva/kw ratio and "tunes" sharply to the resonant frequency. If the circuit resistance is large, the ratio is small and no sharply defined resonant peak exists. Figure 12.4 shows this.

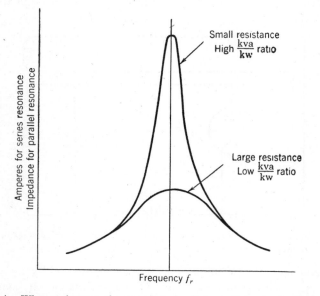

FIG. 12.4. When resistance of a resonant circuit is small tuning to the resonant frequency is sharp, whereas a large resistance makes the tuning peak broad.

The circuit comprising a capacitor and reactor is commonly referred to as the *tank* circuit because of its characteristic storing of energy and the relatively large current circulating within the boundary of a parallel-resonant circuit.

Oscillator Principles

Pliotron tubes are used to produce electric oscillation from a fraction of one cycle to several billion cycles per second. The ability to generate oscillations is dependent upon the amplifying property of pliotrons in that the power within the anode circuit is greater than the power applied to the grid circuit. If a part of the amplified power is *fed back* from the anode to the grid by any one of several types of coupling devices and is given the proper phase relation with respect to the anode, continued amplification sufficient to overbalance the circuit losses produces sustained oscillations. Circuits functioning in this manner are classified as *self-excited* oscillators and in industrial terminology are called *radio-frequency generators*.

Sustained oscillations can be produced by a self-excited oscillator only when two principal conditions are satisfied. First, the power transferred from the anode circuit to the grid circuit must be slightly greater than the circuit losses (plus power expended in the load) divided by the circuit amplification factor. Second, the feed-back power must be in the proper phase relation with the signal to become regenerative.

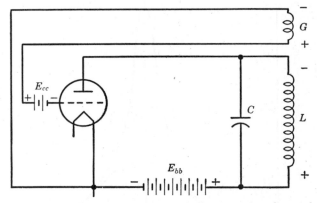

FIG. 12.5. The fundamentals of a feed-back oscillator consist of a tank circuit C and L, a feed-back coil G, anode supply voltage E_{bb} and grid bias E_{cc}.

The fundamental principle of operation is manifested by the circuit of Fig. 12.5 in which a pliotron is connected with a tank circuit, consisting of capacitor C and the air-core reactor L. Anode battery E_{bb} is the source of power for the generation of oscillations within the tank circuit. Grid bias is obtained from battery E_{cc}, and grid coil G is the coupling to feed back some of the energy from tank coil L to the grid of the tube.

Oscillations are started by connecting the anode battery E_{bb}. Electrons immediately flow from the tube cathode to anode and charge the capacitor C with negative polarity at the top. Anode current rapidly diminishes as the voltage across C subtracts from E_{bb} to leave only a small positive voltage applied to the tube anode. The capacitor is now fully charged, and the anode current is practically zero. Electrons stored by the capacitor then flow through the tank coil L. This constitutes a coil current, and the electric charge of the capacitor is transferred to a stored magnetic field of the coil. The electron flow continues in the same direction as the magnetic field diminishes, coming out of the coil and entering the bottom terminal of the capacitor. The voltage across C is then reversed with negative polarity at the bottom. While the magnetic field of the coil is thus decreasing, the voltage induced in grid coil G is in a direction to make the grid even more negative than the bias voltage and to prevent the flow of anode current. The electron flow then reverses with electrons flowing out of the bottom terminal of the capacitor and upward through the tank coil, again increasing the coil magnetic field, in the opposite direction. The coil magnetic field then

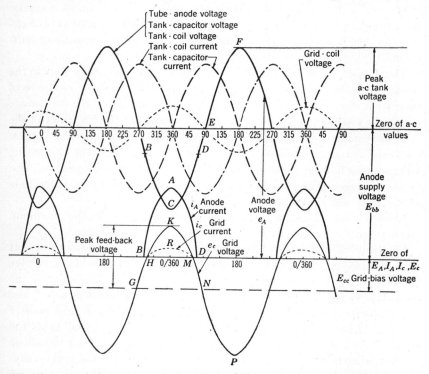

FIG. 12.6. Typical constants of a feed-back oscillator. An alternating voltage appears across the tank circuit although the tube anode voltage is a rapidly pulsating unidirectional voltage. The oscillator is a generator of radio-frequency voltage, although power is derived from the anode supply.

collapses, and electrons once more flow into the top terminal of the capacitor. This time, the decreasing magnetic field links the grid coil G in the direction to make the grid positive. Anode current from battery E_{bb} again recharges capacitor C, replenishing electron energy lost in resistance of the circuit during the previous part of the oscillating cycle. The electron flow then reverses, with electrons leaving the top terminal and flowing into the tank coil, and the cycle is repeated.‖

‖Actually, the build-up to the full magnitude of oscillation requires several cycles and is not accomplished in a fraction of one cycle as suggested by the above explanation. However, the principle by which oscillations are started is not altered by this technical inconsistency.

The several properties of oscillation are given in Table 12.1 throughout a complete cycle, beginning with the instant of connecting the anode battery and assuming that the full magnitude of oscillation is attained within the first 45 degrees.‖ In this table, the (−) sign denotes one unit of electron charge on the tank capacitor, and each arrow denotes one unit of magnetic field stored by the tank coil. The magnetic field is shown relatively clockwise for one-half cycle and counterclockwise during the remaining half-cycle.

The data of Table 12.1 is graphically reproduced in Fig. 12.6 to help the reader visualize the several variations occurring throughout one cycle of oscillation. An alternating voltage is not actually applied to the tube anode as may be supposed. The anode voltage is pulsating at the frequency of the tank oscillations, but remains positive at all times. An alternating voltage does exist across the tank coil and capacitor, the zero axis of the alternating voltage being halfway between the minimum and maximum pulsating-tube anode voltages and displaced above the zero of d-c values by the magnitude of the anode-supply voltage.

Anode current flows for less than a complete half-cycle, the maximum anode current coinciding with the minimum tube anode voltage.

Practical self-excited oscillators operate under class-C conditions in that their grid bias greatly exceeds the cutoff voltage and the feed-back voltage is sufficient to drive the grid potential positive during a portion of the oscillating cycle. For these conditions a fixed grid bias is undesirable,¶ and the simple bias battery E_{cc} of Fig. 12.5 is replaced by a grid resistor R_g, Fig. 12.7a, and capacitor C_g. The combination is referred to as the *grid-leak* method of obtaining self-bias. The operation is similar to a diode rectifier wherein the feed-back voltage excites the circuit, the grid rectifying with R_g a resistance load, and C_g partially smoothing the load voltage. As feed-back voltage drives the grid positive, grid current through R_g causes a voltage drop across the resistor, negative at the grid terminal. C_g is charged to nearly the resistor drop potential. As the cycle progresses, feed-back voltage no longer makes the grid potential positive. Grid current ceases but the charge of C_g remains to establish a negative grid bias. Thus, the circuit becomes self-biasing. Some of the capacitor charge leaks off through R_g, to be replaced as the grid again becomes positive. As stable conditions are reached, the amount of charge lost from C_g during one part of the cycle is equaled by that amount replenished while grid current flows. Thus, the a-c component or radio-frequency grid current is by-passed through the grid capacitor, leaving the d-c component to flow through the resistor. The constants are chosen such that R_g multiplied by the d-c component of grid current results in the required bias voltage, and C_g offers a

¶See MIT staff, *Applied Electronics*, pp 603–11.

low reactance (in comparison to R_g) to the flow of radio-frequency current.

An alternative grid-leak circuit, Fig. 12.7b, connects resistor R_g directly between the tube cathode and grid. The operation of this circuit is similar, possessing the advantage that d-c grid current does not pass through the grid coil circuit.

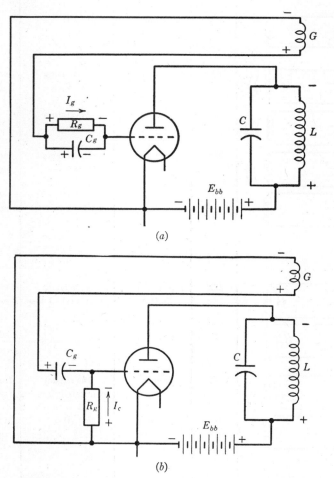

(a)

(b)

FIG. 12.7.   Self-biasing by a grid-leak uses either circuit (a) or (b). The grid rectifies while its potential is positive, passing grid current through resistor R_g, furnishing the source of bias voltage. Capacitor C_g serves as a smoothing filter.

Either of these grid-leak circuit arrangements contribute to more stable operation of self-excited oscillators. Consider that a condition reduces the amplitude of oscillation. The voltage fed back to the grid is likewise decreased, and the magnitude of grid current is reduced. Decreased grid

TABLE 12.1

Tank	Angle	Capacitor Negative Charge	Tank Coil Field	Grid Coil, Volts
(circuit diagram)	0+	Maximum — top	0	0
(circuit diagram)	45°	Decreasing — top	Increasing clockwise	Increasing positive
(circuit diagram)	90°	0	Maximum clockwise	0
(circuit diagram)	135°	Increasing — bottom	Decreasing clockwise	Increasing negative
(circuit diagram)	180°	Maximum — bottom	0	Maximum negative
(circuit diagram)	225°	Decreasing — bottom	Increasing counterclockwise	Decreasing negative
(circuit diagram)	270°	0	Maximum counterclockwise	0
(circuit diagram)	315°	Increasing — top	Decreasing counterclockwise	Increasing positive
(circuit diagram)	360°/0°	Maximum — top	0	Maximum positive
(circuit diagram)	45°	Decreasing — top	Increasing clockwise	Decreasing positive

– – – – Denote units of electron charge.

+ + + + Denote units of positive charge.

⤳   Denote units and direction of magnetic field.

TABLE 12.1 (*Continued*)

Capacitor Volts	Capacitor Current	Tank Coil Current	Grid Voltage	Grid Current	Anode Current	Anode Voltage
Maximum negative	0 After charging	0	0	0	Maximum	Minimum
Decreasing negative	Increasing positive	Increasing negative	Slightly positive	Slightly positive	Decreasing	Increasing
0	Maximum positive	Maximum negative	Slightly negative	0	0	Equal to battery
Increasing positive	Decreasing positive	Decreasing negative	Increasing negative	0	0	Increasing
Maximum positive	0	0	Maximum negative	0	0	Maximum equal to battery plus tank voltage
Decreasing positive	Increasing negative	Increasing positive	Decreasing negative	0	0	Decreasing
0	Maximum negative	Maximum positive	Equal to negative bias	0	0	Equal to battery
Increasing negative	Decreasing negative	Decreasing positive	Slightly positive	Slightly positive	Increasing	Decreasing
Maximum negative	0	0	Maximum positive	Maximum positive	Maximum	Minimum equal to battery minus tank voltage
Decreasing negative	Increasing positive	Increasing negative	Slightly positive	Slightly positive	Decreasing	Increasing

current charges C_g to a lesser degree, effectively reducing the grid-bias voltage. This in turn results in a greater anode current and partially re-establishes the original amplitude of oscillations. Should the oscillation ampl tude rise above normal, a larger feed-back voltage causes an increased grid current to make the bias even greater. Anode current is thus reduced and the amplitude of oscillation held more nearly to a constant level. In this way, the self-bias circuit serves to promote stability.

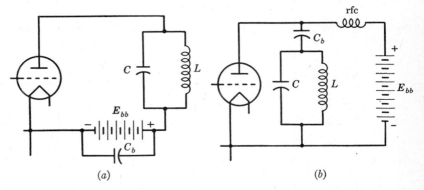

FIG. 12.8. The anode supply voltage is either (a) series fed or (b) parallel-fed. Circuit (b) can be grounded at the tube cathode, tank, and negative anode supply, whereas circuit (a) does not offer this flexibility.

The anode-supply voltage E_{bb} is connected by either a *series-fed* circuit, Fig. 12.8a or a *parallel-fed* circuit, Fig. 12.8b. In a practical oscillator using the *series-fed* circuit, the source of anode voltage E_{bb} is shunted by a capacitor C_b to provide a low-impedance path around E_{bb} for the high-frequency currents. The series-fed connection requires that the anode-supply voltage and tank coil (or a part thereof) be connected between the tube cathode and anode. This is not always possible (see Fig. 12.11) or is occasionally undesirable.

Another connection is the *parallel-fed* circuit, Fig. 12.8b, in which the anode supply E_{bb} is connected to the tube anode through an air-core radio-frequency choke. The tank circuit is connected to the tube anode through a blocking capacitor C_b. Anode direct current from the supply readily passes through the radio-frequency choke, but high-frequency current of the tank-circuit oscillations cannot pass through the choke to the anode-supply circuit. Likewise, the high-frequency current passes readily through capacitor C_b, while anode direct current cannot pass through the capacitor into the tank circuit. The parallel-fed connection offers the advantage that d-c anode potential can be applied without the necessity of passing through the tank coil.

Oscillator Circuits

Although self-excited oscillator circuits are of many types, practically all industrial units can be classified into three basic groups. Many individual variations* of each of the following circuits are possible, such as the use of either the series-fed or the parallel-fed anode-supply connection and either of the grid-leak connections. However, the basic identity of each circuit is unaltered.

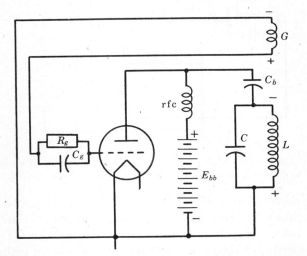

Fig. 12.9. The tuned-anode circuit employs a separate grid coil *G* to derive feed-back voltage; adjusted by varying the turns and coupling between coils *G* and *L*.

The *tuned-anode*† circuit of Fig. 12.9 employs a separate grid coil *G* magnetically coupled to the tank coil *L*. The magnetic coupling between grid coil and tank coil induces the feed-back voltage by which the grid is controlled. With reference to the characteristic operating curves, Fig. 12.6, the magnitude of feed-back voltage largely controls the anode current and thus influences the oscillator output. The feed-back voltage is varied by adjusting the turns of grid coil *G* and also by the relative alignment (that is, coupling) between coils *G* and *L*. The popularity of the tuned-anode circuit

*Design considerations are not given here. For information in regard to the design of oscillators see references such as:

Terman, *Radio Engineers' Handbook*, pp 480–510.

Terman, *Radio Engineering*, pp 349–85.

MIT staff, *Applied Electronics*, pp 596–619.

The Radio Amateurs' Handbook; see Chapter, Radio-Frequency Power Generation, of any recent edition.

†This circuit is more commonly known as the *tuned-plate* connection although "anode" is used here, in keeping with industrial terminology, for this electrode of the tube.

results from its flexibility. It allows the wide range of grid-coupling adjustment frequently required, particularly for industrial-heating applications.

The *Hartley* circuit, Fig. 12.10, employs a tapped tank coil. In effect, the tank coil is used as an autotransformer, in which the section L_1 is coupled to

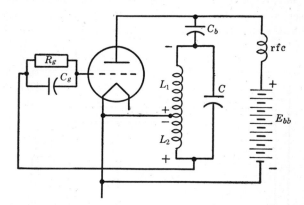

FIG. 12.10. The Hartley circuit employs a tapped tank coil as an autotransformer to derive the feed-back voltage from the L_2 portion of the coil.

the anode circuit while section L_2 is coupled to the grid and becomes the feed-back circuit. The radio-frequency tank-coil current circulates through the entire coil to set up instantaneous polarities as indicated. The magnitude of the feed-back voltage is adjusted by a change in the position of the cathode tank-coil tap, which changes the ratio between L_1 and L_2.

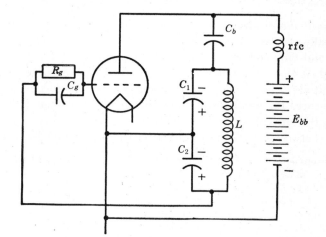

FIG. 12.11. The Colpitts circuit employs two capacitors to divide the tank voltage. The feed-back voltage appears across capacitor C_2.

The simplicity of the Hartley circuit and the fact that relatively few parts are required for its construction make it desirable. No separate grid coil is necessary, the tank coil performing a dual purpose of a tank reactor and feed-back transformer. The Hartley circuit is well adapted to the generation of frequencies up to several megacycles, but at higher frequencies the number of turns in the tank coil is decreased to such a point as to make the location of a tap difficult or impossible.

The *Colpitts* circuit, Fig. 12.11, employs two capacitors C_1 and C_2, connected in series in the tank circuit. The instantaneous polarity across the

FIG. 12.12. An industrial oscillator showing (1) tank coil, (2) tank capacitor (pressurized nitrogen type with high-voltage terminal at bottom), (3) triode oscillator tube, (4) cooling fins (called radiator) for air-cooling the oscillator tube, (5) cathode heating transformer, (6) radio-frequency choke for parallel-fed d-c anode supply, (7) grid resistor, (8) grid capacitor and (9) pressure gauge to indicate tank capacitor nitrogen pressure.

(Courtesy Westinghouse)

capacitors is such as to feed back a grid voltage in the proper phase relation to sustain oscillation. The magnitude of the feed-back voltage is adjusted by the ratio of capacitance C_1 to C_2. The total tank-circuit voltage is divided inversely proportional to the two capacitances, and if either or both are made variable, the feed-back voltage can be readily adjusted to the necessary value.

The Colpitts circuit is one example necessitating a parallel-fed anode supply. The series-fed connection cannot be used here because d-c anode current cannot flow through the anode-circuit capacitor, C_1, Fig. 12.11, required in the tank circuit. The parallel-fed connection avoids this, as the figure shows.

Oscillator Operation

Graphic analysis of oscillator operation is best shown by using the *constant-current* pliotron characteristic. The constant-current characteristic of a WL-892 power triode, commonly used in industrial-power oscillators is illustrated in Fig. 12.13. These curves clearly show that in order to maintain any chosen anode current at a constant value, if anode voltage is decreased, the grid voltage must be made more positive. They also show the characteristic of grid current flowing. For all negative values of grid potential, grid current is zero or slightly negative, regardless of the applied anode voltage. When the grid potential is positive, grid current flows, the value depending upon both the grid and anode potentials.

Typical operating characteristics are drawn on the constant-current characteristic, Fig. 12.14, with only the most important lines ($I_A = 8, 4, 2,$ and 0 amperes) shown. Point A is placed along one of the lines of constant anode current and located so as not to exceed either the maximum peak anode current or grid current allowed by the tube design. For the case illustrated, this corresponds to a peak anode current of 8.0 amperes and a peak grid current of 0.80 ampere. The anode voltage supply, E_{bb} is 8000 volts. With reference to both Figs. 12.6 and 12.14, the anode voltage varies sinusoidally with the axis corresponding to the anode-supply voltage, reaching a minimum at point C. During its decline anode voltage passes through B, at which point the anode current is zero and just beginning to flow. Anode current then increases from B as the anode voltage further decreases to C, the anode current rising along successive constant-current lines from B to a maximum at A. The tube loading follows the intersection of each constant-current line with the straight line AB, hence, this line on the characteristic is known as the *load line*. As the anode voltage rises from C to D, the anode current decreases and is again zero at D. The electrical degrees expanded by anode voltage in traversing B–C–D form the angle during which anode current flows.

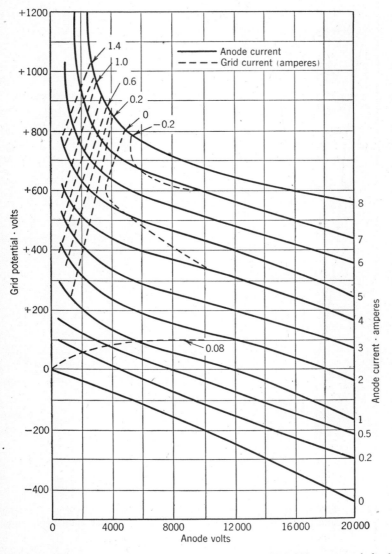

Fɪɢ. **12.13.** Constant-current characteristics of a type *WL*-892 power triode frequently used for industrial radio-frequency generators.

The extension of the load line to its intersection with the anode-supply voltage determines the grid-bias voltage, point *E*. The grid voltage is sinusoidal about the bias voltage as an axis, Fig. 12.6 and 12.14. As the grid voltage rises sinusoidally from *G* to its peak at *K*, grid current begins to flow at *H* corresponding to zero grid voltage. The angle of grid-current flow

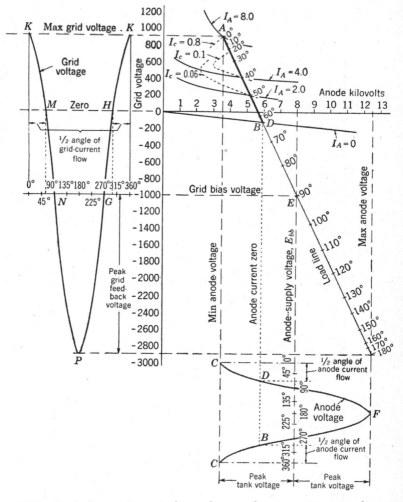

FIG. 12.14. Typical operation superimposed upon the constant-current characteristics. Anode and grid currents flow less than a half-cycle; the tube anode voltage varies above and below the anode supply by an amount equal to the peak radio-frequency tank voltage. The peak grid voltage is equal to the bias plus the maximum feed-back voltage.

is the number of degrees required for the grid voltage to traverse the portion HKM (more clearly evident in Fig. 12.6) of the grid-voltage cycle. The grid voltage is symmetrical about the bias and reaches a maximum negative value at P, equal to the bias voltage plus the peak grid voltage.

The operation must also satisfy both the average anode-current and average-grid-current ratings for the tube. The average anode current is

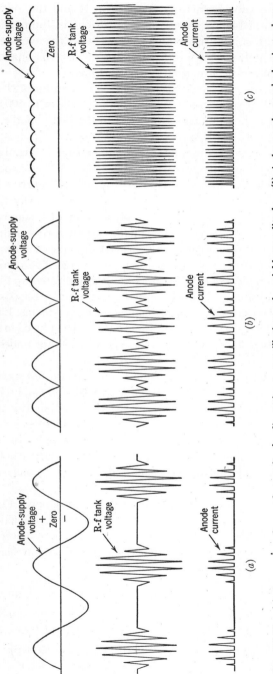

Fig. 12.15. (a) An a-c anode supply results in discontinuous oscillations of variable amplitude. (b) A d-c anode supply having a large ripple results in continuous oscillations of variable amplitude. (c) A d-c anode supply with little or no ripple results in continuous oscillations of constant amplitude. The largest power output using a given tube is obtained by a well-filtered anode supply (c).

calculated by the wave form from the peak at A and the angle of flow, BCD.‡ For Fig. 12.14, the average anode current is approximately one fourth of the peak current or 2.0 amperes. Likewise, the average grid current is approximately one fifth of the peak value or 0.16 ampere. Both of these satisfy the average current ratings of the tube.

The maximum anode voltage, point F, Fig. 12.6 and Fig. 12.14, is equal to the anode voltage supply plus the peak tank voltage or 12 500 volts. The maximum negative grid voltage, P, is equal to the bias plus the peak grid feed-back voltage or -2900 volts.

If an a-c supply is used as the anode voltage source, Fig. 12.15a, the oscillations vary in amplitude and are discontinuous. The anode-current pulses are variable. No anode current flows during the negative half-cycle of the anode-supply voltage. A particular tube cannot deliver so much power if the anode is fed from an a-c supply as from a d-c supply, because the anode current is limited to a maximum current corresponding to the positive peak of the a-c supply voltage, whereas the power output is averaged over a complete cycle of the anode-supply voltage. The average power output is considerably less than the peak value as indicated by Fig. 12.15a.

A further disadvantage of using a-c anode excitation, is the possibility of creating radio interference in near-by communication systems. Each time a group of oscillations start or stop, interference may be induced in surrounding communication lines, rendering this type of oscillator undesirable for industrial use.

If the anode supply is obtained from a single-phase full-wave rectifier without filter, Fig. 12.15b, the oscillations are variable in amplitude but are continuous. The anode-current pulses are likewise variable. If it is assumed that the same tube is used as for the previous example, the average is considerably increased by the use of a rectified anode supply. In practice, a single-phase rectified anode supply is usually filtered sufficiently to provide a more constant amplitude of oscillations and a greater ratio of average-to-peak values than indicated by Fig. 12.15b.

A three-phase full-wave rectifier for the anode supply, Fig. 12.15c, maintains a nearly constant amplitude of oscillation and equal pulses of anode current. Therefore, a particular tube delivers more power with this type of anode supply than with either the single-phase rectifier or an a-c anode supply.

Frequency Stability with Crystal-Controlled Oscillators

One effective method of maintaining a nearly constant oscillating frequency is by the use of the piezoelectrical properties or a quartz crystal,

‡For a determination of these average values see Terman, *Radio Engineering*, p 325, or Terman, *Radio Engineers' Handbook*, p 447.

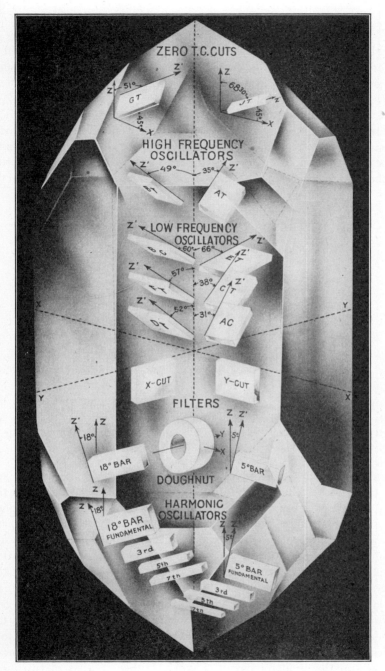

FIG. 12.16. The electrical axis of a quartz crystal runs through its hexagonal corners (*x*) and (*y*), the mechanical axis through its sides, and tne optical axis through the long dimensions of the crystal. (*Courtesy Crystal Products Company*)

253

Fig. 12.16. Slabs taken from the crystal are known as *cuts* and are named in accordance with the axis and angle of the cut. Various cuts used for stabilizing oscillator frequency as well as those used for certain specialized filters are indicated in the figure.

If voltage is applied to a crystal in the direction of one axis, a mechanical stress results in the direction of another axis. Conversely, a mechanical pressure in the direction of its mechanical axis causes electric charges to appear on the faces of the crystal through its electrical axis. The polarity of the electric charge and the direction of mechanical pressure are directly

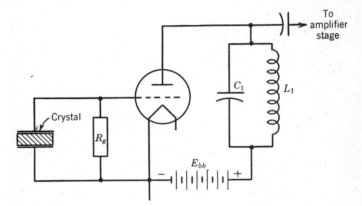

FIG. 12.17. A simple crystal-controlled oscillator employs a tank coil and capacitor in the tube anode closely matched to the crystal resonant frequency. Oscillating frequency is governed by the crystal in the tube grid circuit because of its higher Q as compared to the anode tank.

related, such that a reversal of one causes a reversal of the other. Each crystal possesses a mechanically resonant frequency depending upon the type of cut and its principal dimensions. If an alternating voltage is applied across the crystal faces and the electrical frequency adjusted to the mechanical resonant frequency of the crystal, sustained vibration of the crystal results at the expenditure of extremely small power input. The vibrating frequency of each crystal is remarkably constant, thus maintaining the alternating voltage across the crystal faces at a constant frequency.

One type of crystal oscillator,§ Fig. 12.17, connects the crystal to the grid circuit of an oscillator tube using a conventional tank circuit C_1–L_1 in the anode circuit. A properly resonating crystal is electrically equivalent to a series-resonant tank circuit of extremely low loss. With this conception of the crystal the oscillator circuit, Fig. 12.17, then consists of two inde-

§Crystal oscillators are more completely covered by a text devoted to radio, such as Terman, *Radio Engineers' Handbook*, pp 484–98, Terman, *Radio Engineering*, pp 374–85.

pendent tank circuits; one the anode L_1–C_1, the other in the grid circuit, or the crystal itself. The anode tank L_1–C_1 is designed to resonate at the crystal frequency as near as possible while failure of the anode-tank circuit to maintain this exact frequency gives way to the constant oscillating frequency of the crystal because of the much lower losses of the crystal or grid-circuit oscillation.

Because a crystal is limited to relatively small amounts of power and for other reasons affecting frequency stability crystal-controlled oscillators are practically restricted to low power output of not more than 100 watts. Crystal control is usually applied to a small *master oscillator*, the output of which is multiplied by one or more stages as may be required to control the frequency of the final output tube.

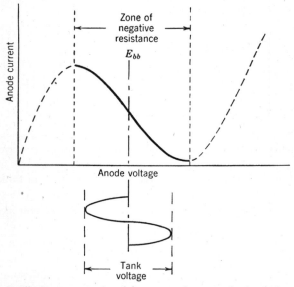

FIG. 12.18. Oscillations are produced by connecting a tank circuit in series with a negative-resistance device, or one across which a decreasing voltage results in an increasing current. Secondary emission from a tetrode anode produces this characteristic if the anode voltage is less than the screen voltage.

Dynatron Oscillator

The *dynatron oscillator* depends upon a negative characteristic of resistance|| of the circuit feeding the oscillating-tank circuit. That is, the current through the negative-resistance circuit must *increase* as the voltage *decreases*, Fig. 12.18.

||See Herold, "Negative Resistance and Devices for Obtaining It," *IRE Proc.*, Vol 23, October 1935, p 1201.

Such a negative characteristic of resistance is readily obtained by applying the proper voltages to the elements of a pliotron tetrode. As explained in Chapter 7, page 101, if the anode voltage is operated at a potential less than the screen voltage, electrons are released from the anode surface by secondary emission, and the characteristics of Fig. 7.2 and Fig. 12.18 are obtained.

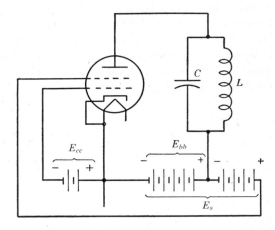

FIG. 12.19. The dynatron oscillator depends upon the negative-resistance characteristic of a tetrode operated with its anode potential less than the screen voltage.

A dynatron oscillator is constructed by connecting the tank circuit in series with the anode, Fig. 12.19, and supply voltage E_{bb}. The screen voltage E_s is greater than the anode voltage E_{bb}. The grid voltage E_{cc} is adjusted to obtain the desired operating characteristic.

Because of the negative characteristic of the tube anode, a decrease in anode voltage results in an increase in anode current. This operation follows the principles previously illustrated in Fig. 12.6 and summarized by Table 12.1.

Beat-Frequency Oscillators

The commercial testing of the response characteristic of radio receivers and other laboratory procedures often requires a signal source varying continuously over the audible frequency range, say 10 to 20 000 cycles. The construction of an oscillator to meet these requirements designed according to the previous principles would be difficult because of the components necessary to build a tank circuit of this frequency and the difficulty of making the oscillations continuously variable over this frequency range.

One method of accomplishing the desired result by a convenient single-dial control is the *beat-frequency* oscillator, represented by the block diagram, Fig. 12.20. The circuit consists of two similar oscillators, one of which is adjusted to a fixed frequency and the frequency of the other made adjustable by a variable capacitor in the tank circuit. The output of these two oscillators is connected to a detector circuit¶ consisting of tube T,

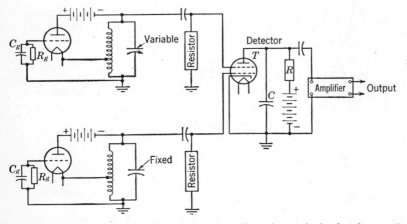

FIG. 12.20. Block diagram of a beat-frequency oscillator for producing low frequencies over a wide range. Voltage of a fixed-and variable-frequency oscillator are mixed by a detector, and the *difference-frequency* voltage is amplified to the desired output level.

capacitor C, and resistor R. Output of the detector circuit, with the aid of a filtering circuit not shown in the figure, is made responsive only to the difference in frequency between the two oscillators. The difference-frequency output is then amplified to the desired level.

The operation is explained with the aid of Fig. 12.21. Assume that the fixed oscillator frequency be represented by the relatively high-frequency wave (*a*), 100 000 cycles. Assume the variable-frequency oscillator to be adjusted to a somewhat lower frequency, (*b*), as 80 000 cycles. The mixed input to the detector circuit is then a summation of waves (*a*) and (*b*) producing the wave (*c*). Both the frequency and amplitude of the resultant wave (*c*) are variable and depend upon the relation between the original waves (*a*) and (*b*). If the amplitudes of waves (*a*) and (*b*) are equal, the amplitude of (*c*) is sinusoidally variable from zero to a maximum of twice (*a*) or (*b*), as illustrated in the figure. Envelope of the mixed wave (*c*),*

¶The block diagram of Fig. 12.20 represents the principle of electronic mixing within the detector tube. For practical problems concerning their design, see Terman, *Measurements in Radio Engineering*, pp 298–303.

*For a discussion of the envelope characteristic when waves (*a*) and (*b*) are not of equal amplitude, see Terman, *Radio Engineers' Handbook*, pp 567–71.

which represents its changing amplitude is sinusoidal at a frequency one-half the difference between (a) and (b), or 10 000 cycles for the example illustrated. The beats resulting from the mixture of (a) and (b) occur at a frequency equal to the difference between them. This is twice the envelope frequency, as Fig. 12.21c shows.

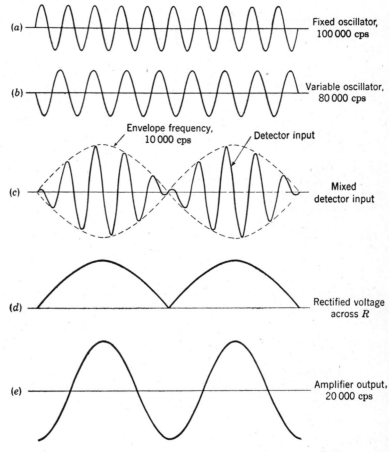

(a) ————————— Fixed oscillator, 100 000 cps

(b) ————————— Variable oscillator, 80 000 cps

Envelope frequency, 10 000 cps   Detector input

(c) ————————— Mixed detector input

(d) ————————— Rectified voltage across R

(e) ————————— Amplifier output, 20 000 cps

FIG. 12.21.   Typical voltages across the components of a beat-frequency oscillator, Fig. 12.20.

The detector tube rectifies† the mixed wave (c) in such a way that only the upper half of the wave envelope is effective in the resultant voltage across resistor R, as shown by Fig. 12.21d. The variable component of this resistor voltage is then amplified and the output adjusted to the desired

†The function of resistor R, capacitor C, and the tube elements to manifest detection are explained in Chapter 13, p 269.

magnitude. As Fig. 12.21e illustrates, the frequency of the output is thus equal to the difference-frequency of (a) and (b).

Be it observed that a relatively low frequency (20 000 cycles) results from the addition of two high frequencies (100 000 and 80 000 cycles). Also, by the principles illustrated, if the frequency of the variable source is changed to 99 000 cycles, the output frequency becomes 1000 cycles. In this way the variation of one source frequency over a relatively small range (80 000 to 99 990 cycles) results in variation of output frequency from 20 000 to 10 cycles. Oscillators for generating the two relatively high source frequencies are readily constructed by the foregoing principles, and the adjustment of frequency necessary of one source is within the limits easily obtained without undue design complications.

The principle of obtaining a third frequency by beating two other frequencies together is employed in every superheterodyne radio receiver. Here, the frequency of a local oscillator is beat against the frequency of the received signal to obtain a third frequency, referred to as an *intermediate* frequency. The object of this system is to convert the received signal whose frequency varies over a wide range to a constant intermediate frequency. This is accomplished by adjusting the local oscillator to a frequency equal to the incoming frequency plus the desired intermediate frequency. When these are mixed, the resulting intermediate frequency, maintained constant regardless of the input-signal frequency, is most effectively amplified by an amplifier tuned for the intermediate frequency. Thus, the intermediate stages of amplification are tuned and operate with high gain, as discussed in Chapter 11. The more detailed principle of a superheterodyne receiver are excellently described by any handbook devoted to radio engineering.

SUMMARY

Current through a reactor decreases as the frequency of the exciting source is raised.

Current through a capacitor increases as the frequency of the exciting source is raised.

Resonance of a series circuit containing resistance, inductance, and capacitance is observed when the inductive and capacitive reactances are equal and opposite. Resonance of a similar parallel circuit is observed when the inductive and capacitive susceptances are equal and opposite.

Series resonance is characterized by:

(a) Maximum line current. Impedance is a minimum at the resonant frequency, and is equal to the resistance of the circuit.

(b) Line current is in phase with the impressed voltage.

(c) Voltages across the reactor and capacitor exceed the impressed voltage, if circuit resistance is small.

Parallel resonance is characterized by:

(*a*) Minimum line current. Impedance is a maximum at the resonant frequency.

(*b*) Line current is in phase with the impressed voltage.

(*c*) Current circulating within the parallel circuit exceeds the line current, if circuit resistance is small.

Quality or Q of a resonant circuit is a measure of the ratio of energy within a resonant circuit, as compared to the losses in it. Two expressions commonly used to denote this are

$$Q = \frac{X_L}{R} \quad \text{or} \quad Q = \frac{\text{kva}}{\text{kw}}$$

Self-excited oscillators are those wherein the oscillating frequency is governed by the circuit constants according to

$$\text{Frequency} = \frac{1}{2\pi\sqrt{LC}}$$

A change in the value of either inductance or capacitance changes the oscillating frequency.

A *tank circuit* consists of a reactor coil (usually air-core) and a capacitor connected in parallel, the values of which are chosen to result in parallel resonance at the desired frequency.

Sustained oscillation of self-excited oscillators requires that

(*a*) Power transferred (fed back) from the anode to the grid circuit must be greater than the circuit losses (plus power expended in the load) divided by the circuit amplification factor.

(*b*) Feedback must be in the proper phase relation to become regenerative.

Self-bias is usually employed wherein rectification of a positive grid potential manifests a voltage across a grid resistor, partially sustained by a paralleling grid capacitor as the grid feed-back voltage reverses polarity.

The *grid-leak* method of self-biasing promotes a more constant amplitude of oscillations, because bias voltage is a function of the oscillation amplitude. Any amplitude change reflects in a bias change of the sign required to restore oscillations to their normal amplitude.

The *tuned-anode* circuit employs a separate grid coil as the means of deriving feed-back voltage. Adjustment of feedback is by the number of coil turns and its coupling with the anode-tank coil.

The *Hartley* circuit employs a tapped tank coil functioning as an autotransformer to derive feed-back voltage. Adjustment of feedback is by location of the tap.

The *Colpitts* circuit employs two series-connected capacitors across the tank coil to divide the radio-frequency voltage. Feedback is derived across one capacitor, and adjustment is by the relative capacitor values.

The *piezoelectrical* properties of a quartz crystal show mechanical stress along one crystal axis to be related to electrical stress along another axis. Sustained vibration of the crystal is obtained when a small power, of the crystal resonant frequency, is applied across faces of a properly prepared crystal.

Resonant frequency of a properly prepared quartz crystal is extremely constant — approximately one part in one million.

A crystal is electrically equivalent to a tank circuit with inductance, capacitance, and very low resistance. Hence, its Q is very large.

Crystal oscillators make use of (*a*) the constant vibrating frequency and (*b*) extremely high Q of a crystal to control the oscillating frequency. Inductance and capacitance of the tank-circuit components are adjusted to match the crystal frequency as near as possible. The lower losses within the crystal circuit force oscillations at crystal frequency rather than at resonant frequency of the tank components.

Beats resulting from the addition of two waves of different frequency occur at a rate equal to the difference-frequency.

Beat-frequency oscillators, making use of the foregoing principle, employ two oscillators of relatively high frequency, one whose frequency is fixed and the other variable. The output of these is added; the mixed wave detected then amplified to obtain a low-frequency output, continuously variable over a wide frequency range.

REFERENCES

MIT ELECTRICAL ENGINEERING STAFF, *Applied Electronics*, John Wiley & Sons, New York, 1943, pp 596–619 and 697–701.

W. G. Dow, *Fundamentals of Engineering Electronics*, John Wiley & Sons, New York, 1937, pp 326–34.

F. E. TERMAN, *Radio Engineers' Handbook*, McGraw-Hill Book Co., New York, 1943, pp 480–530.

F. E. TERMAN, *Radio Engineering*, McGraw-Hill Book Co., New York, 1937, pp 349–91.

KEITH HENNEY, *Radio Engineering Handbook*, McGraw-Hill Book Co., New York, 1941, pp 283–320.

J. H. MORECROFT, *Principles of Radio Communication*, John Wiley & Sons, New York, 1933, pp 77–354.

J. B. HOAG, *Basic Radio*, D. Van Nostrand Co., New York, 1943, pp 90–97 and 218–28.

E. W. HEROLD, "Negative Resistance and Devices for Obtaining It," *IRE Proc.*, Vol 23, October 1935 p 1201.

F. E. TERMAN, *Measurements in Radio Engineering*, McGraw-Hill Book Co., New York, 1935, pp 298–303.

The Radio Amateurs' Handbook, American Radio Relay League, Inc., West Hartford, Conn.; see Chapter, "Radio-Frequency Power Generation," of any recent edition.

Chapter 13

MODULATION AND DETECTION OF CARRIER WAVES

Many examples of modulation and detection fall within common experience, although they may not be so recognized. The larynx causes variations in atmospheric pressure that are carried to the ear. The ear detects these pressure waves and conveys to the brain a stimulus reproducing the speaker's voice. Among Indians, intelligence was transmitted visually by puffs of smoke allowed to ascend skyward in some coded regularity. The smoke served as a carrier of information and the eye of an observer as a detector.

A more restricted meaning of *modulation* applying to the field of electrical engineering is* "the process of producing a wave, some characteristic of which varies as a function of the instantaneous value of another wave, called the *modulating* wave."

One common example of modulation is the telephone transmitter and receiver. Here the wave to be modulated is direct current, illustrating a liberal interpretation of the definition just given. Modulation is afforded by the voice pressure waves affecting the transmitter diaphragm in such way as to change the electrical resistance of the transmitter. Current through the series circuit, which includes the telephone receiver, is thus changed in such form as to manifest transmission of a modulated wave and is detected by the receiver.

In these examples modulation of the medium of transmission is direct. Such principles are not applicable to transmission by radio, because radiation is not possible by direct current in the antenna nor is it practical at frequencies common to speech or music. Employing circuits and antennas of economic proportions, space radio is not used as a medium of transmission below several hundred kilocycles. Clearly then, some means is necessary to interrelate the audible frequencies associated with speech and the higher frequencies required for radio transmission. Modulation affords this interrelation whereby audible (low) frequencies are effectively raised to a higher frequency for practical transmission through space by radio. It is this feature of modulation that makes possible the entire development of radio broadcasting. Rivaling this in importance is the means by which

*"Standards on Transmitters and Antennas," *IRE*, New York, 1938, p 3.

many bands of frequencies are simultaneously transmitted over a single-wire circuit to make possible many simultaneous telephone conversations. Without this efficient use of trunk lines, the cost of long-distance telephone communication would exceed present rates by many times.

In radio, the sound or intelligence is not transmitted directly, but is superimposed upon a wave acting as a *carrier*. This signal, neither seen nor heard, is propagated through space at approximately the speed of light.

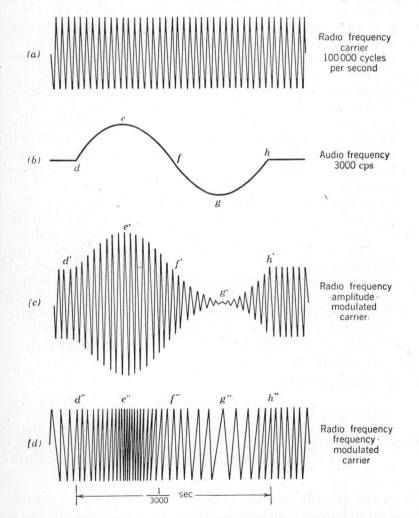

FIG. 13.1. An unmodulated carrier wave (*a*) of high frequency is combined with a low-frequency audio wave (*b*) to produce an amplitude-modulated (*c*) radio-frequency wave, or (*d*) a frequency-modulated carrier.

Equipment for the transmission of intelligence by a high-frequency carrier wave performs two functions: (1) The high-frequency carrier wave is generated, and (2) the carrier wave is modulated to carry a component of intelligence with it to the distant receiver. The receiving equipment performs the dual task of separating the component of intelligence from the carrier wave, and translating this component back into its original form, usually speech.

The process of modulation is graphically illustrated by Fig. 13.1. Let a radio-frequency carrier wave of 100 000 cycles be represented at (a), by which it is desired to transmit an audio-frequency signal of 3000 cycles shown at (b). The function of the modulating equipment is to mix these waves in such a way that (b) is transmitted along with (a).

One method of accomplishing this result is to control the amplitude of the carrier frequency in proportion to the instantaneous values of the audio-frequency signal.† This method is known as *amplitude* modulaton. The result is Fig. 13.1c showing several cycles of the unmodulated carrier with modulation beginning at d'. As the audio-frequency signal rises to its positive maximum at e, a positive modulation peak results at e'. The audio-frequency signal extends through f at zero, continuing to a negative maximum at g, where the carrier amplitude reaches its minimum at g'. Figure 13.1b and c illustrates a particular condition whereby the modulating signal is sinusoidal and its peak amplitude $e-g$, equal to the carrier amplitude. The *positive modulation peak* e' of the modulated wave (c) becomes twice the unmodulated amplitudes d', and the *negative modulation peak* g' becomes zero. Under these conditions the carrier wave is said to be 100-percent-modulated, representing the maximum amplitude of a symmetrical modulating signal that can be transmitted by the carrier without distortion. In practical examples the modulating signal is seldom symmetrical, requiring that the modulation factor be expressed separately for positive and negative peaks, as

Percent positive modulation

$$= 100 \times \frac{\text{maximum amplitude} - \text{unmodulated amplitude}}{\text{unmodulated amplitude}}$$

Percent negative modulation

$$= 100 \times \frac{\text{unmodulated amplitude} - \text{minimum amplitude}}{\text{unmodulated amplitude}}$$

The percent negative modulation cannot exceed 100 or else no signal is transmitted. Positive modulation exceeding 100 percent is possible and is

†For a mathematical analysis of amplitude modulation see MIT staff, *Applied Electronics*, pp 632–8.

called *overmodulation*. Either of these conditions is rare, the usual value of modulation being considerably less than 100 percent.

Another method by which a carrier can be modulated is by altering its frequency in relation to the audio-frequency signal without changing its amplitude. This process is known as *frequency modulation*, Fig. 13.1d. The frequency of a frequency-modulated carrier wave deviates from the unmodulated frequency by an amount proportional to the amplitude of the audio signal, while the rate at which the frequency is altered depends upon the frequency of the audio signal.‡ In the case illustrated, maximum carrier frequency occurs at e'', which is coincident with the positive modulation peak. The minimum is at g'', the negative modulation peak. The rate at which the carrier frequency makes this change corresponds to the audio frequency, assumed at 3000 cycles.

These are the two principal methods by which voice communication is carried either through space by radio or over wire by power-line or telephone carrier systems. Amplitude modulation is popularly abbreviated AM, and frequency modulation, FM.

Producing Amplitude-Modulated Carrier Waves

The function of modulation is to combine the relatively low-frequency audio wave with a relatively high-frequency carrier wave, the result being a

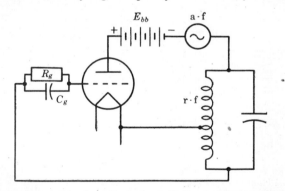

FIG. 13.2. Illustrating one basic method of amplitude modulation, the low- or audio-frequency signal is combined with the high or radio-frequency voltage in the anode circuit of the oscillator.

high-frequency wave containing the components necessary to transmit the audio intelligence with the carrier. Figure 13.2 illustrates one principle by which the high-frequency carrier can be modulated within the anode circuit

‡For a discussion of frequency-modulated waves see MIT staff, *Applied Electronics*, pp 627–32 and 703–15.

of the oscillator generating the carrier signal. In this circuit the alternating audio-frequency voltage is connected in series with the d-c anode supply E_{bb}. Anode voltage then varies in proportion to the modulating audio-frequency voltage. As explained in Chapter 12 by the aid of Fig. 12.15a, b, and c, page 251, when anode potential is variable, the anode-current pulses and a-c tank-circuit voltage are similarly variable. Thus, the amplitude of tank-circuit voltage, that is, carrier amplitude, is modulated by the audio-frequency voltage of the anode circuit.

A comparison of this system of modulation and the usual "60-cycle" generator is worthy of note. Consider the field excitation of a conventional synchronous generator to be sinusoidally altered at a rate of once each second. The amplitude of voltage across the generator terminals varies in proportion to the variance of excitation. Hence, the output at 60 cycles can be thought of as modulated at one cycle, and, when it is stepped up in frequency, the analogy is comparable to the vacuum-tube system.

ANODE MODULATION§

The principles of the simple circuit of Fig. 13.2, whereby an audio-frequency voltage is introduced into the anode circuit of an oscillator are illus-

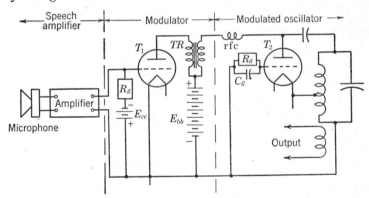

FIG. 13.3. Radio-frequency voltage of the oscillator tank-circuit is amplitude-modulated by the microphone audio-frequency coupled to the oscillator anode circuit through modulator tube T_1 and transformer TR.

trated by the circuit of Fig. 13.3. An audio-frequency voice signal originates at the microphone, is amplified by a class-A, or class-B speech amplifier, and is fed to the grid of modulator tube T_1. The modulator tube further

§The methods of modulation given here describe only the fundamentals of two basic arrangements. Details of many circuits commonly used are given more completely in handbooks devoted to radio engineering such as MIT staff, *Applied Electronics*, pp 638–54, and Terman, *Radio Engineers' Handbook*, pp 531–51.

amplifies the voice signal and terminates in the primary winding of coupling transformer TR. A suitable anode supply E_{bb} is common to the anode circuit of modulator tube T_1 and oscillator tube T_2. The audio-frequency voice signal is reproduced in the secondary winding of TR and modulates the d-c anode supply of the oscillator circuit. The high-frequency voltage across the oscillator tank circuit is thereby modulated in response to the voice signal.

Direct modulation of a self-excited oscillator, as Fig. 13.3, is seldom used for the high frequencies common to space radio transmission, because the degree of modulation affects the operating frequency of the oscillator. A system more frequently employed is indicated by the block diagram of Fig. 13.4, wherein tube T_2 is operated as a class-C amplifier driven by a

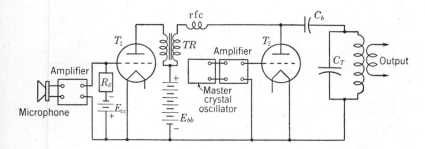

FIG. 13.4. A high frequency controlled by the master crystal oscillator and finally amplified by T_2 is amplitude-modulated by the audio frequency from microphone to modulator tube T_1 coupled to the anode circuit through transformer TR.

master crystal-controlled oscillator and amplifier, as discussed in Chapters 11 and 12. Modulator tube T_1 is then coupled to the anode circuit through coupling transformer TR and modulates the high-frequency voltage across the tank circuit. The principles of the class-C amplifier are closely related to oscillator operation except that the frequency is controlled by the excitation applied to its grid circuit. If this system is used, the frequency of the carrier-wave remains unchanged by the degree of amplitude modulation.

When the modulating signal is introduced into the anode circuit, Fig. 13.4, the power required to produce the modulation component is supplied by the modulator tube T_1, and the power required to produce the carrier component from tube T_2. If the carrier wave is completely modulated, the peak voltage across transformer secondary winding TR must equal the anode supply E_{bb}. It follows that one half of the instantaneous input to T_2 is supplied by the modulator tube and the remaining half by the anode supply E_{bb}. For this reason, tube T_1 often assumes proportions comparable with the final power-output tube T_2, to manifest a high level of amplitude modulation.

GRID-BIAS MODULATION

Another method of modulation introduces the audio-frequency modulating voltage with the high-frequency excitation into the grid circuit, Fig. 13.5, of the output tube and is commonly called *grid-bias* modulation. Voice frequency from the microphone is amplified and modulator tube T_1 feeds into coupling transformer TR, the secondary winding of which is in

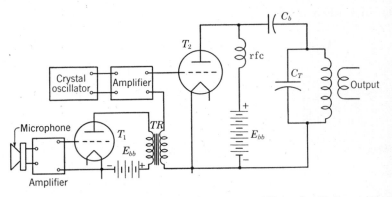

FIG. 13.5. The radio-frequency output of power amplifier tube T_2 is amplitude-modulated by the audio-frequency of the microphone, modulator tube T_1, and transformer TR coupled in the grid circuit of the power amplifier.

series with the high-frequency excitation voltage from a suitable crystal oscillator and amplifier in the grid circuit of output tube T_2. Thus, the instantaneous grid voltage of tube T_2 is the sum of the high-frequency excitation voltage and audio-frequency secondary voltage of TR. Several refinements required in an actual working circuit‖ are omitted, and Fig. 13.5 is simplified to typify the principle of grid-bias modulation.

The scheme of grid-bias modulation has the advantage that the audio-frequency amplifier and modulator tube T_2 can be smaller than the equivalent components required for anode modulation, because both the high-frequency excitation and audio-modulating voltages are amplified through the output tube T_2. However, it is also true that the output tube operates at lower efficiency when modulated through its grid with the result that the output components must be increased in size to obtain a given power output. Hence, the over-all costs of comparative systems using either grid-

‖See Terman, *Radio Engineers' Handbook*, pp 535-40.

bias or anode modulation are about equal. Both systems are in general use. The grid-bias circuit is likely to introduce the more distortion of the two, although special refinements of the circuit minimize this disadvantage.

Demodulation or Detection of Amplitude-Modulated Waves

A modulated carrier wave transmitted by space radio or along a wire system contains components of both the high-frequency carrier and audio-frequency voice signal. Only the audio-frequency voice signal comprises the medium of intelligence transmitted. The receiving equipment must discriminate between the two components rejecting the high-frequency carrier and amplifying only the audio-frequency component. Separation of these two components of the modulated carrier waves is known as *detection* or *demodulation*.

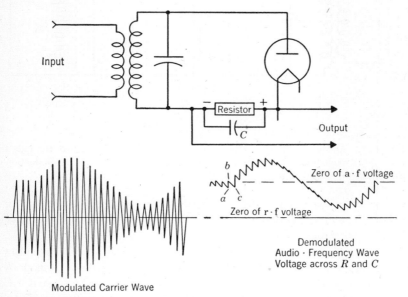

Fig. 13.6. Amplitude-modulated carrier waves are detected by a small kenotron. Half-wave rectification charges C by the voltage drop across the resistor. Average value of the capacitor voltage reproduces the original audio frequency.

One of the many systems of detection employs a small kenotron rectifier tube with a resistance load and filter capacitor, Fig. 13.6, commonly known as diode detection. Rectified half-cycles of the carrier cause a voltage drop across the resistor, positive at the cathode terminal. The function is illustrated at the right of Fig. 13.6, wherein one rectified positive half-cycle of the carrier raises the voltage across the resistor and capacitor from a to b.

During the negative half-cycle of the carrier the voltage across C decreases from b to c. The result is a series of saw-tooth waves having an envelope corresponding to the original audio-frequency wave by which the carrier signal was modulated. The graphic representation of Fig. 13.6 greatly exaggerates the magnitude of the saw-tooth waves. The actual distortion by this method of demodulation is relatively small.

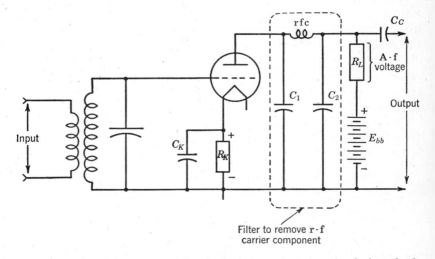

FIG. 13.7. Anode detection amplifies the modulated incoming signal through the triode, then demodulates the wave by rectification in the anode circuit. Reproduction of the modulating signal appears as an audio-frequency voltage across R_L.

The audio-frequency voltage across the resistor–capacitor circuit is connected to an amplifier and increased to the desired output level to complete the desired transmission of intelligence.¶

Anode detection, Fig. 13.7, employs a pliotron operating as a rectifier. Bias voltage is obtained by anode current through cathode resistor R_k, resulting in a voltage drop across this resistor, smoothed by capacitor C_k. Component values are chosen to develop a bias voltage sufficient for tube cutoff. Rectification in the anode circuit results, as reference to Fig. 13.8 shows. The modulated carrier is applied to the grid. Positive half-cycles of the carrier result in anode current peaks, A', B', E', F' through the anode load resistor R_L, while carrier negative half-cycles, C, D, are blocked because they simply add to the tube negative grid potential, normally biased to cutoff. High-frequency components of the carrier through the tube anode are by-passed through C_1 and blocked from load resistor R_L by

¶For the design of diode detectors and circuit modifications, see Terman, *Radio Engineers' Handbook*, pp 553–62.

a filter such as C_1, high-frequency reactor (rfc) and C_2. Thus, the average voltage across R_L, noted in Fig. 13.8, reproduces the original audio-frequency voltage by which the carrier was modulated. The d-c component of voltage across R_L is blocked by coupling capacitor C_C, Fig. 13.7, and only its a-c component amplified by succeeding stages.

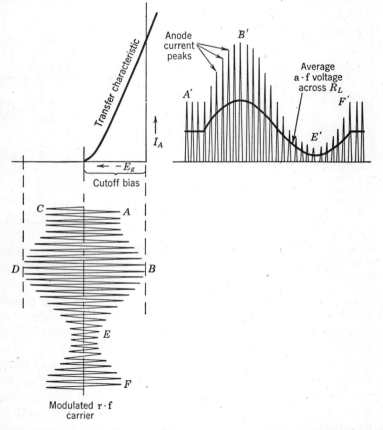

Fɪɢ. 13.8.   Bias of the anode circuit detector is adjusted to cutoff. An alternating voltage applied to the grid is then rectified. Average value of the rectified wave reproduces the original audio-frequency modulating signal.

Because a relatively small voltage variation on the grid results in a much larger change in voltage across R_L, this circuit serves the dual purpose of detection and amplification. It has a further advantage in that the grid current is minute, so that little power is taken from the input circuit.

A grid-leak detector circuit, Fig. 13.9, is the equivalent to a combination of the diode detector of Fig. 13.6, plus one stage of amplification by the pliotron. In this case, the grid functions as a virtual anode, the grid and cathode rectifying to effect the voltage across the grid resistor R_g, exactly as described for Fig. 13.6. The audio-frequency component of voltage across R_g varies the applied grid voltage above and below an average bias determined by the constants of R_g and C_g. This voltage is amplified to result in an audio-frequency voltage across load resistor R_L, the anode circuits, Figs. 13.7 and 13.9, having the same function.

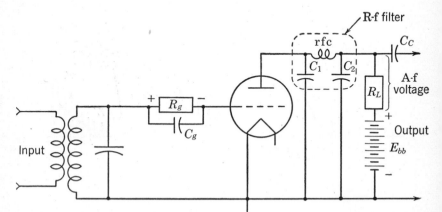

FIG. 13.9. The grid-leak detector circuit combines diode detection with one stage of amplification. In this case, the tube cathode and grid elements serve to rectify and demodulate the signal, as shown by Fig. 13.6.

Of these three detection methods, the diode circuit is the most popular, because it functions with a lower distortion (when properly designed) and because it can rectify a higher voltage than other methods. Its disadvantage is that it is relatively insensitive, although multipurpose tubes combining a diode and pentode in a single envelope make possible diode detection followed by one stage of amplification using a single tube. The anode detector has an advantage in that little power is absorbed from the input circuit, but operation of the tube at cutoff results in low over-all sensitivity, and distortion is relatively large. The grid-leak circuit was once popular, because it offered the advantage of high over-all sensitivity, although distortion is large. These latter methods now are considered inferior to the diode circuit using a multielement tube to detect and amplify by a single tube.

Producing Frequency-Modulated Carrier Wave

The growing popularity of frequency modulation results from the desire to separate "noise" from the transmitted signal of intelligence. Electrical disturbances, atmospheric and man-made, are primarily amplitude-modulated. For this reason, AM is inherently subject to unavoidable background noise when these disturbances are mixed with the intelligence signal. FM avoids this by making possible the separation of the disturbance and intelligence signals. This is done by transmitting the intelligence signal as frequency-modulated. Atmospheric disturbance interfering with the modulated carrier en route to the receiver are largely amplitude-modulated and can be separated by the receiving equipment, leaving the frequency-modulated intelligence signal to be detected without interference. Thus, FM possesses an advantage over AM.

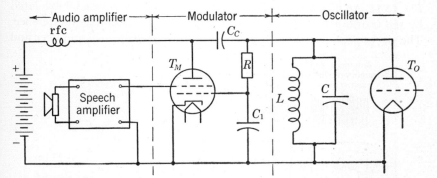

FIG. 13.10.   Radio-frequency waves of the oscillator are frequency-modulated by audio-frequency of the microphone and modulator tube T_M. Modulator T_M, known as a *reactance tube*, affects reactance of the oscillator tank-circuit, thereby changing the frequency in proportion to the amplitude and frequency of T_M grid voltage.

The basic principle of frequency modulation* of a high-frequency carrier is illustrated by Fig. 13.10. In this case, the audio-frequency response of the microphone is enlarged by the speech amplifier and fed to a modulator tube T_M. One grid of the multigrid modulating tube is connected to the audio amplifier. The anode of tube T_M is connected directly across the tank circuit LC of the oscillator tube T_0 through a coupling capacitor C_C. The high-frequency voltage across the oscillator tank circuit is the source of power to circulate current through the anode of tube T_M. The control grid of T_M is connected into the oscillator-tank circuit through resistor R and capacitor C_1. The constants of R and C_1 are chosen to shift the grid voltage 90 degrees out of phase with the tank-circuit voltage. In this way, the anode current through tube T_M becomes 90 degrees out of phase with the tank-circuit current.

*The discussion of frequency modulation given here is confined to a brief description without analysis. For further details see MIT staff, *Applied Electronics*, pp 627–32 and 703–15; also, Terman, *Radio Engineers' Handbook*, pp 578–88, and Reich, *Theory and Applications of Electron Tubes*, pp 338–45.

The modulator tube T_M affects the tank circuit LC as though the reactance of the tank circuit were changed and the oscillator frequency varied in proportion to the response of tube T_M to the audio-frequency input. Tube T_M is known as a *reactance tube*, and its function is to modulate the oscillator frequency in response to the amplitude of the audio frequency as dictated by the microphone.

DEMODULATION OF FREQUENCY-MODULATED CARRIER WAVES

The elements of an FM receiver are illustrated by the block diagram, Fig. 13.11. An incoming carrier wave is assumed to be frequency-modulated by the transmitter and amplitude-modulated by undesirable interference. The signal is passed through a conventional high-frequency amplifier and

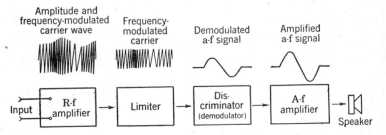

FIG. 13.11. Frequency-modulated waves are received by first passing through a *limiter* to remove the undesired affects of amplitude modulation. They are demodulated by a *discriminator*, and then amplified sufficiently to operate the speaker.

increased to the desired level without change in shape or frequency. The undesirable effect of amplitude modulation by interference is first eliminated by passing the signal through a *limiter* circuit, leaving only the frequency-modulated carrier. The next element is known as a *discriminator*, employed to demodulate the carrier wave, leaving only the original audio-frequency component by which the carrier wave was originally modulated. The audio-frequency component is then amplified to the required level to reproduce the intelligence of transmission, represented as the loud-speaker.

The *limiter* is basically a class-A amplifier using a sharp cutoff type of tube having a characteristic such as $B-A-C$, Fig. 13.12. A signal of variable amplitude is previously amplified such that a signal E_{S1} represents the minimum amplitude desired. The signal negative half-cycle reaches the tube cutoff B, and the positive half-cycle approaches the saturated point C. An incoming signal of amplitude E_{S1} passes through the limiter without change. An incoming signal E_{S2} of larger amplitude $E-D$ is such that area f of the negative half-cycle is beyond the cutoff point B and is clipped by the limiter action of the tube. Likewise, area g of positive half-cycle is clipped at C, the saturation end of the characteristic. Because limits B and C are adjusted to conform with the minimum amplitude E_{S1} of the incoming signal, the carrier amplitude is confined within the limits B'–D' of the limiter circuit output.

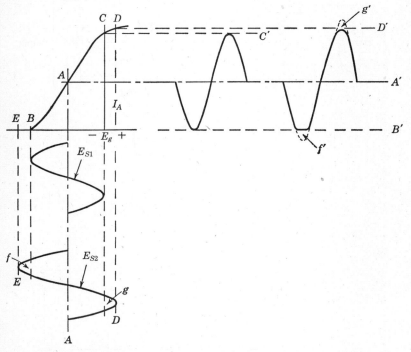

FIG. 13.12.   Incoming signals of magnitude E_{S1} pass through the *limiter* without change of magnitude or form. Larger input signals, E_{S2} are clipped at f by the cutoff and at g by the saturation characteristics of the limiter tube.

One type of *discriminator* or demodulation circuit, Fig. 13.13a, receives the frequency-modulated carrier output from the limiter circuit and terminates in a tank circuit L_0C_0, tuned to the resonant frequency of the *unmodulated* carrier wave. Another tank circuit, L_1C_1, coupled with L_0C_0 is tuned to a resonant frequency f_1 somewhat below the unmodulated carrier frequency f_0. Another tank circuit L_2C_2 is tuned to a frequency f_2 above the unmodulated carrier frequency. These two tank circuits are connected to diode rectifiers terminating, respectively, in load resistors R_1 and R_2.

An alternating voltage across L_1C_1 causes a voltage drop E_1 across resistor R_1 reaching a maximum value corresponding to the resonant frequency of L_1C_1, Fig. 13.13b. Voltage E_2 from the L_2C_2 tank reaches a maximum corresponding to the resonant frequency of this circuit. The output voltage E_3

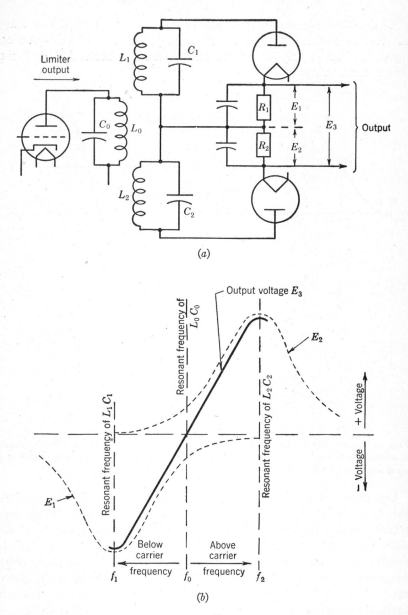

FIG. 13.13. One type of discriminator circuit (a) connects the modulated wave to tank L_0C_0 tuned to the *unmodulated* carrier frequency. Coupled to the first tank is L_1C_1 resonant *below* the carrier frequency and L_2C_2 resonant *above* the carrier frequency. (b) The voltage across R_1, R_2, varies in both magnitude and polarity in proportion to *deviation* of signal frequency from the unmodulated carrier frequency.

is a summation of E_1 and E_2. If the incoming signal corresponds to resonance of L_0C_0 voltages, E_1 and E_2 are equal and opposite, such that output E_3 is zero. A carrier frequency less than f_0 makes the upper output terminal positive, and the magnitude of positive potential is proportional to the frequency *deviation* from f_0. A carrier frequency greater than f_0 makes the lower output terminal positive.

The discriminator circuit transposes any deviation of the carrier frequency into an audio-frequency output voltage, its magnitude proportional to the deviation frequency and its rate of change corresponding to the rate of frequency change, demodulating the carrier according to the original principle of applying the frequency modulation.

Suppressing the Carrier Wave — Single-Sideband Transmission

An amplitude-modulated carrier wave, such as Fig. 13.1c, can be resolved into three component parts: (1) having a frequency of the carrier, (2) having a frequency less than the carrier by the amount of the modulating frequency, and (3) having a frequency greater than the carrier by the

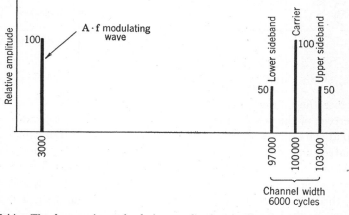

Fig. 13.14.   The frequencies and relative amplitudes manifest by 100 percent amplitude modulation of a 100 000-cycle carrier by a 3000-cycle sinusoidal frequency.

amount of the modulating frequency. To illustrate a specific case, Fig. 13.14, assume a carrier wave of 100 000 cycles to be 100 percent amplitude-modulated by a 3000-cycle sinusoidal audio-frequency signal. The modulated carrier wave can be resolved into three component frequencies: a *lower sideband*, the *carrier*, and the *upper sideband*. The *lower sideband* has a frequency of 97 000 cycles, 3000 cycles less than the carrier, while the *upper sideband* frequency is 103 000 cycles, or 3000 cycles greater than the carrier frequency. Transmission of this signal requires a *channel* or *band width* of

6000 cycles, double the audio-wave frequency. For 100-percent modulation, the relative amplitudes show that each sideband is one half the amplitude of the carrier component. The relative amount of power transmitted by each component is proportional to the square of its amplitude, so that each sideband transmits 25 percent as much power as the carrier itself. Thus, of the *total* power transmitted, each sideband transmits $16\frac{2}{3}$ percent and the carrier $66\frac{2}{3}$ percent,† if it is assumed that the carrier is 100-percent modulated. To state these quantities in another way, if it is assumed that an unmodulated carrier transmits 10 kw, when modulated 100 percent the total power in the signal rises to 15 kw with $2\frac{1}{2}$ kw transmitted by each sideband.

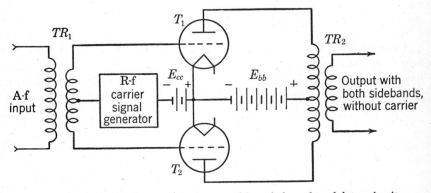

FIG. 13.15.   Carrier frequency is suppressed by a balanced-modulator circuit.

Because the carrier wave does not transmit intelligence, but requires $66\frac{2}{3}$ percent of the power of the signal, the same intelligence can be transmitted at the expense of considerably less power if the carrier component is eliminated. One method by which this is accomplished is the balanced-modulator circuit, Fig. 13.15, wherein the modulating audio frequency is applied to the grids of two modulator tubes T_1 and T_2, 180 degrees out of phase, through the center-tapped secondary winding of TR_1. The radio-frequency carrier is applied to the grids of T_1 and T_2 in the same phase relation. The output of tubes T_1 and T_2 is combined in the primary of output transformer TR_2 such that the carrier signal, applied to the grids in phase is canceled to zero‡ while the out-of-phase audio frequency becomes additive.

†A more complete discussion of sidebands and amplitude modulation will be found in MIT staff, *Applied Electronics*, pp 632–8, and Terman, *Radio Engineering*, pp 11–13 and 415–17.

‡For analysis of the circuit operation see MIT staff, *Applied Electronics*, pp 688–90. Modulation with the carrier suppressed is also accomplished by using copper-oxide rectifiers. Modulators of this type are commonly used in telephone communication. See Terman, *Radio Engineers' Handbook*, pp 552–3.

This function is known as *carrier suppression*. With reference to the previous example, Fig. 13.14, addition of the balanced modulator to the system transmits the lower sideband at 97 000 cycles and the upper sideband at 103 000 cycles and suppresses the carrier frequency of 100 000 cycles. The power required to transmit the same intelligence is reduced to one-third that of the former system.

It is neither necessary nor desirable to transmit *both* the upper and lower sidebands to transmit intelligence. Communication equipments in which one of the sidebands is eliminated are called single-sideband systems. Thus, it is possible to suppress the carrier component, eliminate one sideband, and transmit only one of the sidebands. This is accomplished by passing the modulated wave through a selective band-pass filter, which allows undisturbed passage of all frequencies between the carrier and one sideband and effectively attenuates the frequency between the carrier and the opposite sideband.§ With reference again to Fig. 13.14, assume it is desired to transmit only the upper sideband. The modulated wave, with carrier suppressed by a balanced modulator, is passed through a selective filter designed to transmit all frequencies between 100 000 and 103 000 cycles, while stopping the passage of frequencies between 97 000 and 100 000 cycles. In this particular instance, only a single frequency of 103 000 cycles is transmitted because the carrier is assumed to be modulated by a single 3000-cycle frequency.

The single-sideband system, together with suppression of the carrier wave, offers the merit of the greatest transmission efficiency because with only one sideband transmitted, representing 25 to $33\frac{1}{3}$ percent of the power required to transmit the usual amplitude-modulated signal. A further advantage is the narrower channel required for transmission of the same intelligence; for example, Fig. 13.14, the 3000-cycle audio-wave is transmitted using a single frequency of 103 000 cycles. If the carrier is modulated by frequencies from 0 to 3000 cycles, transmission occupies a band width of 3000 cycles or from 100 000 to 103 000 cycles. This compared to the conventional system of transmitting carrier and both sidebands illustrates that the single-sideband system affords transmission of the same intelligence using only one-half the band width.

Reception of suppressed-carrier signals‖ is accomplished by combining the received signal with a signal generated by an oscillator at the receiving location. With the carrier and one sideband suppressed, the signal generated

§For a more recent system of single-sideband generation see R. C. Cheek, *Westinghouse Engineer*, November 1945, pp 179–83; also M. A. Honnell, "Single Sideband Generator," *Electronics*, November 1945, pp 166–8.

‖R. V. L. Hartley, "Relations of Carrier and Side Bands in Radio Transmission," *Proc. IRE*, Vol 11, February 1923, p 34.

locally at the receiving station can differ slightly from the carrier frequency without seriously impairing the results.

Single-sideband transmission is used in carrier-line communication over telephone-wire lines and has also been recently adapted for power-line carrier communication over power-transmission lines.

Industrial Applications of Carrier

In addition to the use of carrier current for telephony, electric power companies employ it for the transmission of voice and other signals over high-voltage power lines. This use is extensive and is at present undergoing rapid growth.

Transmission of voice currents superimposed on a high-frequency carrier wave over power lines from one station to another many miles away — even a hundred or more — had its beginning in the early '20's, but the applications have had their real growth since about 1935. It is estimated that by the beginning of 1947 carrier signals were being transmitted over 20 000 circuit-miles of high-voltage lines in the United States. One of the longest most extensive power-line-carrier systems is that applied to the sectionalized 270-mile 287-kv lines between Boulder Dam and Los Angeles. Power-line carrier has also been applied to the extensive high-voltage TVA and Bonneville systems. Representative power-line carrier equipment is shown in Fig. 13.16.

Carrier has been developed for the transmission of different types of intelligence:

1. Voice communication permits operators located at different parts of the system to talk together.

2. Carrier relaying makes possible extremely rapid, automatic protection of power lines during fault conditions. The location of a fault is determined by appropriately located relays, which, if the fault is outside the zone protected by them, transmit a blocking signal over carrier that prevents the circuit breakers from operating. In other words on the occasion of a fault all breakers operate except those prevented from doing so by carrier-transmitted signals. The speed of operation is exceedingly rapid, the total time including relay operation being only 1 to 3 cycles (on a 60-cycle system).

3. With carrier telemetering, indications of the power flowing at different points in the system, or other electrical quantities, can be transmitted to a common dispatching point. Associated with this system is the transmission of power indication across a power-interchange point or power generated by different units about the system for automatic load control. Telemetering signals are simply impulses of current sent at a duration or

FIG. 13.16. A high-power single-frequency automatic simplex communication carrier set, which includes dial-telephone features. As many as ten line extensions can be selectively called. Automatic compensation holds the voice levels constant at all points.

(*Courtesy Westinghouse*)

(a)

(b)

(c)

Fig. 13.17. These three panels are the (a) transmitter, (b) receiver, and (c) modulator, respectively, of a power-line-carrier system that provides ten tones or channels for a variety of carrier functions.   (Courtesy Westinghouse)

frequency proportional to the quantity metered, which can be almost anything — current, voltage, power, power factor, or reactive power.

    4. By carrier supervisory control an operator of a power system is able
to operate circuit breakers or other types of equipment at one or more distant substations. Also he can ascertain (that is, supervise) continuously the
physical position (that is, determine whether open or closed) of any circuit
breaker. Further, should any breaker change its position, it can be made to
register that fact, over carrier, to the control point. Signals for the control
and supervision of circuit breakers over carrier consist of coded impulses.
Each breaker is provided with a code, or "number." Thus, when an operator desires to "communicate" with a particular circuit breaker, he presses a

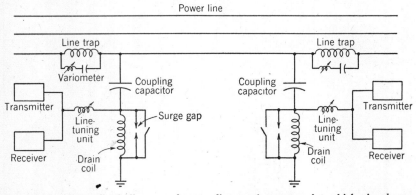

Fig. 13.18. Generalized diagram of power-line carrier system by which signals are
transmitted and received by each of two distant points on the line.

button on his carrier panel corresponding to that breaker. Automatically
the carrier wave is modulated by the code of impulses corresponding to that
breaker, or point as it is called. The modulated wave thus transmitted is
received at the distant station and demodulated, and connection is made
to the control of the breaker assigned that code. An acknowledging code of
signals is usually returned to the operator to assure him that the proper
breaker has been selected and that its control — and that of no other
breaker — awaits his direction. Once connected to that distant breaker, he
can send another code of signals either to open or to close it as desired,
which action if successfully completed is automatically acknowledged by
the carrier apparatus associated with the breaker. Likewise, the operator,
by other codes, can inquire as to the actual position of a breaker or can re-
ceive other information that the supervisory system is established to
provide.

    The systems for accomplishing any of these major functions are essen-
tially the same, shown in single-line diagram, Fig. 13.18. The carrier wave

is generated and modulated by the desired signals by some of the methods described earlier in this chapter with typical equipment pictured in Fig. 13.17. The modulated carrier is fed through a line-tuning unit and a coupling capacitor in series to the transmission line. The line-tuning unit is an inductive reactance for neutralizing the capacitive reactance of the coupling capacitor. Line traps, which are tuned choke coils, prevent the dissipation of the carrier signal over undesired lines. These devices are illustrated in Figs. 13.19 and 13.20.

FIG. 13.19. Power-line-carrier transmitter and receiver stations are sometimes located outdoors, as in a substation yard. Above the voice receiver–transmitter panel is the combination coupling capacitor and line-tuning unit, while the horizontal reactor immediately behind the capacitor is the line trap.

(Courtesy Westinghouse)

FIG. 13.20. A remote power-line-carrier station. The transmitter and receiver, with the telephone headset, is in the cabinet, near the ground, while directly above it is the coupling capacitor and line-tuning unit.

(Courtesy Westinghouse)

It is common practice to perform several of these functions with a single carrier equipment. For example, in addition to controlling circuit breakers, several metering or position indications can be carried over a supervisory-control channel, and the quantities measured can be controlled simultaneously. Demand and integrating metering can also be sent over the carrier supervisory-control channel. During the demand interval the meter at the sending end stores up impulses proportional to the integrated kilowatt-hours. At the end of the demand interval, the metering assumes control of the carrier channel for a short time and sends through a number of pulses in rapid succession, corresponding to the accumulated kilowatt-hours during the demand interval, such as 15 minutes. The receiving meter responds to this total number of impulses in each particular group. This is a demand indication. It also runs the integrating meter ahead by an amount corresponding to the number of impulses in that group and thus corrects the integrating meter each 15 minutes to the proper value. In so doing, it utilizes the carrier channel only a brief part of the total time so that it is available the remainder of the time for supervisory-control functions.

If voice communication is to be operated over the same carrier channel as is used for supervisory control, it is desirable to use one supervisory-control point for ringing and to lock out the supervisory-control equipment while the telephone conversation is taking place.

To economize on the carrier-frequency spectrum and to increase the selectivity from noise interference, a carrier channel can be modulated by a number of audio tones. Each tone can be used for one carrier function, except for transmission of voice signals. Speech transmission requires a greater band width than one tone makes available; hence, usually six tones are reserved for audio transmission, giving reasonably undistorted speech. As many as ten separate audio-tone channels can be operated over a single-carrier channel.

SUMMARY

Modulation, as applied to the field of electrical engineering, is "the process of producing a wave, some characteristic of which varies as the function of the instantaneous value of another wave, called the *modulating* wave."

A *carrier wave* is the unmodulated high-frequency signal generated by the transmitting apparatus. It does not transmit any medium of intelligence.

Amplitude modulation varies the carrier-signal amplitude in proportion to the instantaneous amplitude of the modulating wave.

Frequency modulation varies the carrier-signal frequency in proportion to the instantaneous amplitude of the modulating wave.

Amplitude-modulated waves are produced in several ways, of which two basic methods are:

(a) Anode modulation, wherein the modulating signal affects the carrier amplitude within the oscillator- (or amplifier-) tube anode circuit.

(b) Grid-bias modulation, wherein the modulating signal affects the carrier amplitude within the oscillator- (or amplifier-) tube grid circuit.

Demodulation or *detection* is the process of separating the modulating component from a modulated carrier wave, the component then duplicating the original modulating wave.

Detection of amplitude-modulated waves is principally accomplished by three basic methods:

(a) Diode detection wherein the modulated wave is rectified by a small half-wave kenotron.

(b) Anode detection wherein the modulated wave is rectified by a pliotron biased to cutoff.

(c) Grid-leak detection, wherein the modulated wave is rectified by the grid and cathode elements of a pliotron and then amplified by the cathode, grid, and anode.

Frequency-modulated waves are produced (one method) by varying the oscillator (or amplifier) tank-circuit capacitive reactance in proportion to the instantaneous amplitude of the modulating wave. A modulating tube so employed is known as a reactance tube. The change in tank-circuit reactance thus controlled affects the instantaneous carrier frequency.

Detection of frequency-modulated waves comprises:

(a) A limiter circuit, for eliminating the principal effects of amplitude modulation caused by atmospheric disturbances.

(b) A discriminator circuit, wherein a deviation in the frequency of the modulated wave either above or below the unmodulated carrier frequency results in a proportional amplitude of circuit output voltage. The voltage manifest by this action duplicates the original modulating signal.

Components of a modulated carrier are:

(a) The carrier wave itself, having a frequency f_c.

(b) The upper sideband, having a frequency f_c plus the modulating frequency (or frequencies).

(c) The lower sideband, having a frequency f_c minus the modulating frequency (or frequencies).

Relative power of these components of an amplitude-modulated wave, modulated 100 percent by a sinusoidal modulating wave are:

(a) Carrier wave..........$66\frac{2}{3}$ percent of the total power
(b) Upper sideband.......$16\frac{2}{3}$ percent of the total power
(c) Lower sideband.......$16\frac{2}{3}$ percent of the total power

The *channel* required for transmission of a modulated signal is represented by the spread of frequency from the maximum upper-sideband frequency to the minimum lower-sideband frequency.

Suppression of the carrier wave makes possible a reduction in the power required to transmit a given signal, because the carrier is not required for the transmission of intelligence and is the largest component of the modulated wave.

Single sideband is the name given to transmission by suppressing both the carrier and one of the sidebands. Only the signal essential to the transmission of intelligence is transmitted. Efficiency is highest and channel width narrowest for this method.

Power-line carrier is the name given to the transmission of communication signals over electric-power lines by a high-frequency (50 to 150 kc) carrier wave. Amplitude-modulated, frequency-modulated, and single-sideband systems are used for this purpose.

Carrier voice communication permits operators located at different parts of a power system to talk together.

Carrier relaying makes possible rapid and automatic protection of power lines against fault conditions.

Carrier telemetering makes possible the indication of load conditions at several remote points to be transmitted to a common dispatching point.

Carrier supervisory control permits operation of remote circuit breakers (and other devices) by a central system operator.

REFERENCES

MIT ELECTRICAL ENGINEERING STAFF, *Applied Electronics*, John Wiley & Sons, New York, 1943, pp 624–715.

F. E. TERMAN, *Radio Engineers' Handbook*, McGraw-Hill Book Co., New York, 1943, pp 531–88.

F. E. TERMAN, *Radio Engineering*, McGraw-Hill Book Co., New York, 1937, pp 11–13 and 393–461.

HERBERT J. REICH, *Theory and Applications of Electron Tubes*, McGraw-Hill Book Co., New York, 1944, pp 283–346.

KEITH HENNEY, *Radio Engineering Handbook*, McGraw-Hill Book Co., New York, 1941, pp 322–58.

R. C. CHEEK, *Westinghouse Engineer*, November 1945, pp 179–83.

M. A. HANNELL, "Single Sideband Generator," *Electronics*, November 1945, pp 166–8.

Chapter 14

HEATING BY HIGH FREQUENCY

Throughout the entire history of the electrical industry designers have been confronted with the problem of heat generation associated with a rapidly fluctuating current. In most electric apparatus, such as motors, generators, transformers and power-transmission lines, the heat caused by the flow of alternating current must be classified as one of the losses contributing to inefficiency. This has been a loss engineers have sought diligently to avoid, not only because it represented a decrease in operating efficiency, but also because the disposal of the heat is often a troublesome problem. In a-c heating this heat loss which is avoided elsewhere, is sought and cultivated.

It was long ago recognized that the losses manifest by an a-c flow could be put to practical use. Heaviside, Ferranti, Thomson, Colby, Steinmetz, and Kjellin are all familiar investigators who reported the practicability of heating by induction as early as 1890. During these years, at least three patents were granted on the design of induction furnaces for the melting of metals. The contribution of E. F. Northrup and the furnaces bearing his name are well known since about 1915.

With such a background, the process of induction heating would seem to be so thoroughly established as to leave little cause for modern mystery. Some believe that the art of induction heating is something new, born of World War II. Such is not the case, although established principles have recently been extended so as to reach into a range of applications heretofore untouched.

There are two classifications of a-c heating, based on the character of the material to be heated. *Induction heating* is applicable to electrically conducting substances, mostly metals, in which currents are induced to flow by transformer action. *Dielectric heating* is accomplished with relatively nonconducting substances or electrical insulators. The power-generating equipment required for the two types of heating differs only in that dielectric heating is performed at much higher frequencies than is induction heating, although the division is by no means sharp.

In heating by induction, eddy-current and sometimes hysteresis losses of the material are involved. Current induced into the material because it is located in a strong alternating magnetic field circulates against the re-

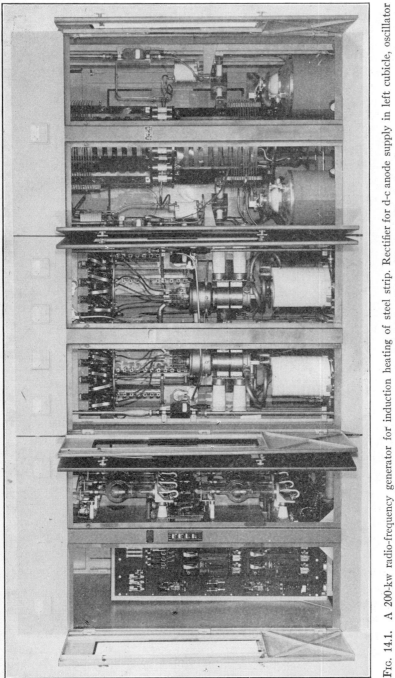

FIG. 14.1. A 200-kw radio-frequency generator for induction heating of steel strip. Rectifier for d-c anode supply in left cubicle, oscillator tubes in center cubicle, and tank circuit in right cubicle. (*Courtesy Westinghouse*)

sistance of the material itself. Heat is generated proportional to the square of the current circulating and the resistivity of the material, that is, in accordance with the familiar Ohm's law.

FIG. 14.2.   As tin plate passes through these coils, excited by the radio-frequency generator of Fig. 14.1, the tin is heated to the flow point rapidly.

(*Courtesy Westinghouse*)

Until about 1925, induction heating based on this action was used almost exclusively for the melting of metals, now classified as *through heating*. About that time, the automotive industry began to seek a means to surface-harden bearing parts in a relatively thin layer. Engineers solved the problem by applying the skin-effect theory of alternating currents. The old established principles of induction heating were used, but with the frequency raised so as to make the current induced in the parts being heated flow in a thin layer, close to the surface. In this way, only the surface of the part was affected, and the desired hardening pattern was obtained. This method was found successful, and immediately the field of induction heating expanded to include a demand for new sources of a-c power at a frequency considerably higher than can be obtained using rotating machinery, now accepted as being of the order of 10 000 cycles. It is this class of applications to which this chapter is devoted.

Heating by dielectric losses results from the periodic stressing and displacement of the atoms of the material itself acting as the dielectric of a capacitor, when subjected to a strong alternating electric field. Materials ordinarily classed as insulators are heated dielectrically by the dielectric losses produced in them by alternating electric fields.

INDUCTION HEATING

Radio-Frequency Generators and Applications

Vacuum-tube self-excited oscillators for industrial applications of both induction and dielectric heating are classified as radio-frequency generators, because they serve as a source of radio-frequency power. They extend

FIG. 14.3. A 20-kw 450-kc radio-frequency generator for induction-heating applications.
(*Courtesy Westinghouse*)

the generation of alternating current into frequencies far beyond those possible with practical rotating generators, that is, above 10 000 cycles. The principles of self-excited oscillators are treated in Chapter 12, and the operation of units used for industrial application conform to the principles there set forth.

When more radio-frequency energy is required than can be obtained from a single oscillator tube, two or more tubes are connected in parallel, or sometimes in a push–pull circuit. To review the characteristics of oscillator operation as they pertain to induction-heating applications, refer to Fig. 12.14, of Chapter 12. Also note: (1) The maximum anode voltage that can be used depends upon the rating of vacuum oscillator tube chosen, (2) the peak alternating voltage across the tank circuit is approximately equal to the d-c anode supply voltage, and (3) the rms value of a-c tank-coil voltage is approximately 70 percent of the d-c anode voltage.

As the several examples shown on pages 322-38 make evident, induction-heating problems are usually resolved into two considerations: (1) the power required to raise the temperature of the material being heated, and (2) the magnetic force necessary in the heating coil to induce the required current into the material. The latter requirement is invariably linked with the current flow obtainable from the radio-frequency generator. The current rating of a generator depends upon the capacitance used in the tank circuit. As just stated, the voltage is fixed in proportion to the tube rating. Together these constants establish the kilovolt-ampere rating of a generator, which is usually equal in importance to its kilowatt rating. The larger the tank-circuit capacitance, the higher is the kva /kw ratio of the generator and the higher is the radio-frequency current rating. The amount of capacitance to use becomes a design problem of balancing the factors of losses in the tank circuit, the desired radio-frequency output current, and cost of the equipment. Although no exact agreement among the several manufacturers of generating units exists, typical values of the radio-frequency current, radio-frequency voltage, and kva /kw ratio of several sizes are exhibited in Table 14.1.

Induction heat using vacuum-tube oscillators is relatively expensive as compared to any other form of heating. This is a result of a higher initial equipment cost, the cost of tube replacement, and the higher cost of electric energy because the over-all efficiency is lower. A-c heating is yet relatively young, so that costs can be expected to decline, although cost comparable to other forms of heat cannot be expected for a long time, if ever.

Cost alone, however, does not tell the story. To its credit, induction heating has three virtues:

1. Most metal pieces can be heated more quickly inductively than by any other method.

2. Heating can be confined to the desired area, which may be a small fraction of the total.

3. Heating starts instantly when radio-frequency power is applied and stops instantly when radio-frequency power is removed.

FIG. 14.4. The 20-kw radio-frequency generator of Fig. 14.3 showing the three-phase rectifier section (right) and air-cooled oscillator tubes with air filter compartment (left).
(*Courtesy Westinghouse*)

These virtues frequently outweigh the relatively high cost of the method. By induction heating:

(*a*) Results are attainable not possible by other methods of heating.

(*b*) By taking advantage of its speed, other component costs may be reduced.

(*c*) The quality of a product is improved.

(*d*) The heat is confined to the area required, leaving the remainder of the part unheated.

Fig. 14.5. A 20-kw radio-frequency generator showing rectifier transformer and contactor section (left) and tank circuit, and protective relays in right compartment.

(*Courtesy Westinghouse*)

The method by which a radio-frequency generator is made to heat a metal piece is by some form of coil either surrounding or in close proximity to the part to be heated. The coil is usually called a *work coil* and the metal being heated called the *work*. Radio-frequency current from the generator is passed through the work coil, and current is induced into the work.

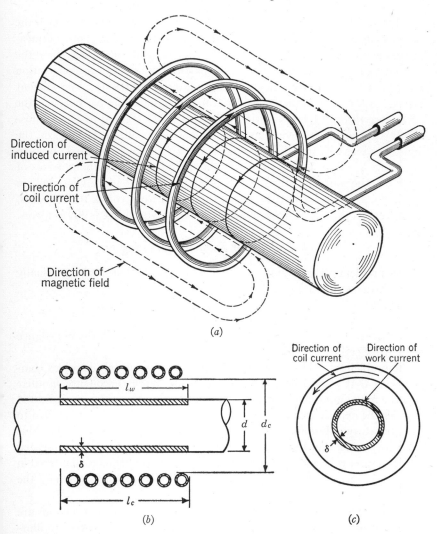

Direction of
induced current

Direction of
coil current

Direction of
magnetic field

(a)

l_w

d d_c

δ

l_c

(b)

Direction of   Direction of
coil current   work current

δ

(c)

FIG. 14.6.   As high-frequency current flows through the coil (a) a countercurrent
flows around the periphery of the work piece. The heating is concentrated (b) and (c)
near the surface of the piece and approximately within the coil.

One of the most common forms of work coils is the multiturn coil,
Fig. 14.6a. Current flowing through the work coil in one direction is
opposed by a countercurrent flowing in the opposite direction along the
surface of the work piece. The intensity of magnetic field is greater in the
center of the coil than on the outside; hence, material placed inside the coil
is heated at better efficiency than that placed on the outside of the same

coil. If the work material is magnetic, the depth δ, Fig. 14.6b, to which the induced current penetrates the work is influenced by the magnetic permea-- bility, the intensity of magnetic field, the resistivity of the material, and the frequency. If the work material is nonmagnetic, the depth of penetration depends only upon frequency and the material resistivity. The current induced in the work is then considered to flow around the periphery of the work piece through a cross section whose thickness is equal to δ and whose length is approximately equal to the length of work coil. In this respect, the circuit behaves as a transformer, Fig. 14.6c, with a short-circuited one-turn secondary winding. If it is considered as a transformer without losses of any kind, the ampere-turns in both primary and secondary windings are equal. Thus, if the current through a three-turn work coil is 100 amperes, the current in the one-turn secondary winding or work piece is 300 amperes.

Calculations for Induction Heating

The problem of applying equipment for induction heating usually reduces to a consideration of the following factors:

1. The rating of the radio-frequency generator required.
2. The design of the work coil.
3. Accessory equipment that may be required to match the impedance of the work coil to the radio-frequency generator.

The problem of calculating all of these factors accurately involves complications that should be undertaken only by those thoroughly familiar with the many unusual circumstances. Many problems are too complicated even for the experienced man to calculate accurately. The resort is then to the laboratory. Manufacturers of induction-heating equipment offer this laboratory service for the solution of unusual problems. The data presented in this chapter is intended to point out a few of the problems encountered in applying induction-heating equipment and to show methods whereby the more common problems can be solved.

Before the more detailed computations of practical heating problems are presented, the following general treatment of fundamentals serves to illustrate the origin of the theory whereby greater detail is later derived. Proof of formulas is not given, although any reader interested in the derivation of methods presented will find the source of fundamentals given in the list of references with the chapter.

Where Induced Currents Flow

If a multiturn coil surrounds a solid cylindrical metal work piece, Fig. 14.6a, an alternating current in the coil induces current to flow around the work piece in the opposite direction. If the frequency is sufficiently high, current concentrates along the inside surface of the coil and near the outside of the work piece. The crowding of current toward the outside surface, known as *skin effect*, causes the greatest heating at the surface of the work piece.

Reduction in the current density below the surface decreases exponentially, making exact calculations tedious. However, the problem is simplified if it be assumed that the total current is integrated and confined within a fictitious layer near the surface. The thickness of this fictitious layer is defined as δ the *depth of current penetration*. Within it the current density is assumed to be uniform and below it the current suddenly falls to zero. The total current within the layer is the same by this assumption as though integrated from the true exponential distribution.

Within reasonable approximation, the depth of current penetration serves the dual purpose of (1) telling how far below the surface the work piece is heated and (2) defining the boundary of a fictitious conductor through which the work current is assumed to be confined. With reference to Fig. 14.6b and c, the work current can be thought of as flowing through a one-turn coil whose cross section depth is δ, width l_w, and the length of path equal to the average periphery of the "turn." This is the shaded boundary of the figure.

To see how this induced current results in heating the work piece, first determine the depth of current penetration* which is given by

$$\delta = 3170 \sqrt{\frac{\rho}{\mu f}}, \text{ in.} \qquad (1)$$

The induced current then flows through a path whose resistance is

$$\begin{array}{l} \text{Resistance of path} \\ \text{through which work} \\ \text{current flows} \end{array} = \frac{\text{resistivity} \times \text{average periphery}}{\text{cross section}} = \frac{\rho P}{\delta l_c} \qquad (2)$$

where

P = average length of current path (inches)

If this is treated as though it were a transformer with a one-turn secondary winding the ampere-turns of the primary (work coil) is equal to the ampere-turns of the secondary. Because the secondary winding is a single-turn, the work current is then equal to the coil ampere-turns,* all losses neglected.

$$I_w = \text{coil amperes} \times \text{coil turns} = I_c T_c \qquad (3)$$

When these two factors are combined, the total power input to the work

*See Table 14.2 for explanation of units used in formulas.

piece becomes

$$\text{Total power input} = I_w{}^2 R_w$$

$$= (I_c T_c)^2 R_w = (I_c T_c)^2 \frac{\rho P}{\delta l_c} \tag{4}$$

Because induction-heating problems normally deal with the rate of heating, one is usually concerned more with the density of heat induced in the work, than with the total power input. Equation 4 is readily modified to obtain the power density by dividing by the surface area inductively heated (assuming the periphery of the work piece to be the same as the average periphery of work-current path), and changing the formula to employ turns per inch of the work coil. The density of heating then becomes

$$\text{Watts per square inch} = (I_c N)^2 \frac{\rho}{\delta} \tag{5}$$

If the value of δ, given by eq 1 is substituted, the most useful form of heating density becomes

$$\text{Watts per square inch} = 3.16 \times 10^{-4} (I_c N)^2 \sqrt{\mu \rho f} \tag{6}$$

For all nonferrous metals, such as aluminum, brass, and copper, commonly called nonmagnetic, $\mu = 1$ which can be substituted in any of the preceding equations. The permeability to use in these formulas when magnetic material such as iron are used becomes a matter of considerable experiment. Empirical data reveals that a reasonable value of permeability for iron at normal saturation is given by

$$\mu = 1.8 \frac{B}{H}$$

For normal saturation of iron and steel commonly heated $B = 18\,000$, and the empirical expression for permeability reduces to*

$$\mu = \frac{1.8 \times 18\,000}{H} = \frac{32\,400}{H} \tag{7}$$

If the peak magnetizing force, $H = 0.70 \dfrac{I_c N}{K_1}$ is substituted in eq 7 an alternate expression for the permeability is obtained by

$$\mu = \frac{46\,300}{I_c N} K_1 \tag{7a}$$

*See Table 14.2 for explanation of the units used in formula.

Either (7) or (7a) is used with reasonable approximation for iron and some steels when the temperature is below the Curié point (approximately 1300 F). When the iron becomes hotter than this, its permeability is reduced to unity. Hence, $\mu = 1$ is used for iron and steel heated above approximately 1300 F.

Formulas previously given are accurate only when the current penetration is small compared to the minimum dimension of the piece heated, say for less than one-third the thickness or diameter. Furthermore, the power input is correct only when the length of coil is large compared to the spacing between the coil and the work piece, although the correction factor K_1, given by Fig. 14.15, can be reasonably well applied for coils having more than one turn.

Calculation of Equipment Necessary for Induction Heating

With the foregoing general conception of how the work piece is heated by induced current, it is possible to develop formulas more specifically devoted to the application of heating various materials and shapes. Most problems can be solved, within the limits of practical accuracy, by following a procedure as suggested below and by use of the formulas on pages 300 to 316. It must be realized that most of the formulas given were derived by making certain assumptions, or apply within given limits, or both. When used within the limits stated with each equation, commercially accurate results can be expected.

The physical properties of many common metals will be found in Table 14.5, page 348. These constants are given in units suitable for use in the equations of this chapter.

To determine the equipment required for a specific application:

1. Determine the thermal power required. This involves the rate of heating of the material required to satisfy specified conditions of production. For this, knowledge of the material properties is necessary. See Table 14.5.

2. Estimated radiation, convection, and conduction losses. If appreciable, they must be added to the thermal power, for the work coil must induce the total of (1) and (2) into the work piece.

3. Determine the density of power put into the material being heated, that is, watts per unit volume, or, in some cases, watts per unit surface area.

4. Calculate the magnetizing force required to establish the power density set forth by (3).

5. Assume a preliminary coil design. Further calculations may prove the first design impractical. A modified design is then assumed and the calculations repeated.

6. Calculate the coil current from the known magnetizing force and coil dimensions.

7. Calculate the coil voltage from the known magnetizing force and dimensions of coil and work piece.

8. Calculate the coil copper loss from the known coil current and effective coil resistance at the frequency used.

9. Add the total of (1) thermal power (2) radiation, convection, and conduction losses and (3) coil copper loss to obtain the total watts output required of the radio-frequency generator.

10. Determine the volt-amperes required of the radio-frequency generator by the product of coil current and voltage.

11. The radio-frequency generator watts output, radio-frequency current, and volt-amperes must satisfy the requirements of the application.

12. If the requirements of (10) cannot be met by the radio-frequency generator, it may be possible to arrive at an economical choice of equipment by:

(a) Modifying the coil design.

(b) Using capacitors to improve the coil power factor.

(c) Using a current transformer.

(d) A combination of (a) and (b) or (c).

13. The water flow and pressure necessary to cool the coil sometimes require careful attention.

Each factor of this procedure is described more completely on the pages following.

1. CALCULATION OF THERMAL POWER

The power required to raise the temperature of the material from a starting temperature to the desired final temperature within a specified heating time is known as the *thermal power*. It is an expression of the rate of heating and does not include losses of any kind. Thermal power is calculated by the formula:

$$P = 17.6 M c \Delta T \text{ watts} \tag{8}$$

where
M = rate of material heated in pounds per minute
c = specific heat of the material
ΔT = temperature rise in degrees Fahrenheit
P = thermal power in watts

Table 14.5 gives the specific heat c of many of the materials commonly used. Other data for calculating thermal power are determined by the application.

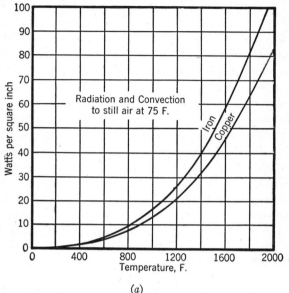

(a)

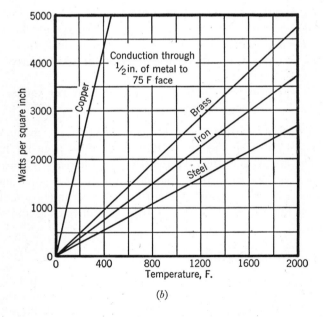

(b)

Fig. 14.7.   Typical radiation and convection loss (a) and conduction (b) through ½ inch of metal.

2. RADIATION, CONVECTION, AND CONDUCTION LOSSES

The loss by radiation and convection is usually small by comparison with other factors and can be neglected. However, some circumstances do warrant consideration of the loss, for which the data of Fig. 14.7a are given.

The loss by conduction may be of considerable importance. When the material to be heated passes continuously through the coil, conduction losses need not be considered, because eventually the entire volume is heated, and flow from the heated portion to a cooler portion is equalized by the continuous processing. But, if a small portion of the total volume is heated by a coil, heat flows from the heated portion to the unheated volume of the metal. The amount thus transferred by conduction must be supplied by the coil or else the desired volume is not elevated to the expected temperature. This condition is manifest to the greatest extent in thin-case surface-hardening applications where practically all the power put into the material is expended in conduction, the amount of thermal power being negligible.

The loss by conduction is

$$P_k = 2.03 \times 10^{-3} \frac{KA\Delta T}{l} \text{ watts} \tag{9}$$

where P_k = power by conduction (watts)

A = surface area normal to the flow of heat (square inches)

l = length of path in direction of heat flow (inches)

ΔT = temperature difference between surfaces (degrees Fahrenheit)

K = thermal conductivity† (Btu per hour per square foot per degrees Fahrenheit per inch)

Assistance in estimating the loss by conduction for many common applications is given by Fig. 14.7b. Results obtained from the figure are based on the assumption that the temperature difference is between surfaces spaced one-half inch apart; that is, the material one-half inch away from the heated portion is cold. When the average temperature difference is used with Fig. 14.7b, the results satisfy typical brazing and soldering applications.

3. CALCULATION OF POWER DENSITY

Power density is the total power input to the material heated divided by the volume of metal within the coil. The total power input is the sum of thermal power by (1) and radiation and conduction losses (if any) by (2).

---

†If (9) is used with data expressing thermal conductivity in calories per second per square centimeter per degree centigrade per centimeter, multiply the constant by 2903.

The volume of metal within the coil is taken as that within the coil cylinder. The volume that may be heated by fringing flux beyond the coil ends is not considered, thus:

$$PD = \frac{\text{total power input (watts)}}{\text{volume of metal in coil (cubic inches)}} \text{ watts per cubic inch} \qquad (10)$$

Power density is computed for a hollow cylinder on the basis of the volume of a solid cylinder having the same outside diameter (as the hollow cylinder), because, insofar as the induced current is concerned, the hollow and solid work pieces behave identically.

4. CALCULATION OF PEAK MAGNETIZING FORCE

Calculation of the peak magnetizing force required at the surface of the work piece to obtain a given power density (eq 10) is the most hazardous factor of induction-heating problems. Many theoretical formulas have been derived and have already been supported by laboratory verifications. These simplify the task of making reliable calculations. However, it must be observed that all formulas given for this procedure have definite limitations, because they are based on several assumptions. The practical limitations of each of the formulas presented herewith are given.‡ They yield commercially accurate results only when used within the limitations stated. They must not be extended to include a broader application.

Formulas for determining the peak magnetizing force of a few of the more common applications are given in the following:

*Solid Magnetic Cylinder**

$$H = \left(\frac{PD \times d}{0.438\sqrt{f\rho}} \right)^{\frac{2}{3}} \qquad (11)$$

Equation 11 is valid only when

$$d\sqrt{\frac{\mu f}{\rho}} \geqq 13\,400 \qquad (11a)$$

The value of resistivity ρ used in (11) or (11a) should correspond to the *average* temperature of the material being heated. This can be obtained by

$$\rho_{\text{hot}} = \rho_{70\,\text{F}} \left[1 + \alpha(T_{\text{hot}} - 70) \right]$$

For the values of α and $\rho_{70\,\text{F}}$, see Table 14.5.

The value of μ used in (11a) must be obtained by first solving (11) for the

‡For calculations beyond the range of limitations given in this text, see references 6 and 14.

*See Table 14.2 for explanation of units used in formula.

peak magnetizing force H. Then

$$\mu = \frac{32\,400}{H} \qquad (7)$$

Hollow Magnetic Cylinder*

Equation 11 is applied to hollow magnetic cylinders by figuring the power density on the basis of a solid cylinder having the same outside diameter. However, the wall thickness of the hollow cylinder must be greater than the depth of current penetration, thus:

$$t_w \geqq 3170 \sqrt{\frac{\rho}{\mu f}}$$

The value of resistivity ρ used in this equation must correspond to the resistivity of the material at *maximum* temperature.

Magnetic Strip or Slab*

$$H = \left(\frac{PD \times t}{0.218\sqrt{f\rho}}\right)^{\frac{2}{3}} \qquad (12)$$

The equation is valid only when

$$t\sqrt{\frac{\mu f}{\rho}} \geqq 9500 \qquad (12a)$$

where ρ corresponds to the resistivity of the material at the average temperature. μ is determined by (7), given previously.

Nonmagnetic Strip or Slab*

$$H = \sqrt{\frac{PD \times t}{1.30 \times 10^{-3}\sqrt{f\rho}}} \qquad (13)$$

The equation is valid only when

$$t\sqrt{\frac{f}{\rho}} \geqq 9500 \qquad (13a)$$

where the value of ρ corresponds to the resistivity of the material at the average temperature.

Solid Nonmagnetic Cylinder*

$$H = \sqrt{\frac{PD \times d}{2.59 \times 10^{-3}\sqrt{f\rho}}} \qquad (14)$$

*See Table 14.2 for explanation of units used in formula.

The equation is valid only when

$$d\sqrt{\frac{f}{\rho}} \geq 13\,400 \tag{14a}$$

where the value of ρ corresponds to the resistivity of the material at the average temperature.

Thick-wall Hollow Nonmagnetic Cylinder*§

$$H = \sqrt{\frac{PD \times d}{2.59 \times 10^{-3}\sqrt{f\rho}}} \tag{15}$$

the equation is valid only when

$$d\sqrt{\frac{f}{\rho}} \geq 13\,400 \tag{15a}$$

and

$$t_w \geq 3170\sqrt{\frac{\rho}{f}} \tag{15b}$$

The value of ρ used in (15) and (15a) should correspond to the resistivity of the material at the average temperature. However, the value of ρ in (15b) must correspond to the resistivity of the material at the maximum temperature.

Thin-Walled Hollow Nonmagnetic Cylinder*§

$$H = 0.442 \frac{W[\rho^2 + 2.5(t_w{}^2 f^2 d^2 \times 10^{-15})]}{\rho t_w f^2 d^2 \times 10^{-15}} \tag{16}$$

The equation is valid only when

$$t_w < 3170\sqrt{\frac{\rho}{f}} \tag{16a}$$

that is, depth of current penetration greater than wall thickness and

$$\frac{d}{t_w} \geq 10 \tag{16b}$$

The value of ρ used in (16) shou'd correspond to the resistivity of the material at the average temperature. However, the value of ρ in (16a) must correspond to the maximum temperature.

*See Table 14.2 for explanation of units used in formula.

§Reference to "thick"- or "thin"-wall hollow cylinders is purely relative to frequency used and ratio of wall thickness to diameter; note limits of formulas.

*Power Input to Nonmagnetic Cylinder**

An alternate form of eq 13 is sometimes useful when the peak magnetizing force is known and the power put into a nonmagnetic cylinder is to be calculated.

$$W = 6.48 \times 10^{-4} H^2 \sqrt{\rho f} \qquad (17)$$

This equation is convenient for the calculation of the loss in work coils or metallic supports that may of necessity be located within the field of the coil. It is valid only when the wall thickness of the piece, if hollow, is greater than the depth of current penetration. The value of ρ should correspond to the resistivity of the material at the average temperature.

Heating by Proximity Effect‖ — Flat Nonmagnetic Plate

If a conductor carrying alternating current lies parallel to a flat plate, Fig. 14.8, the magnetic field from the conductor creates currents in the surface of the plate near the conductor. If the depth of current penetration

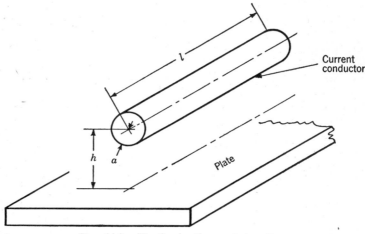

Fig. 14.8.   Heating by the proximity effect.

into the plate (eq 1, page 297) is small compared to the thickness of the plate and to the separation between the conductor and plate, the power input to a nonmagnetic plate is

$$P = 5.05 \times 10^{-5} \frac{I_c^2 l \sqrt{\rho f}}{\sqrt{h^2 - a^2}} \text{ watts} \qquad (18)$$

*See Table 14.2 for explanation of units used in formula.
‖For further details of heating by proximity effect see reference 6.

where P = total power input to plate (watts)
I_c = conductor current (amperes)
ρ = resistivity of plate at average temperature (ohm-inches)
f = frequency (cycles)
l = length of conductor (inches)⎤
h = height above plate (inches) ⎬ See Fig. 14.8
a = conductor radius (inches) ⎦

Equation 18 is valid only when

$$\sqrt{h^2 - a^2} \geqq 3.17 \times 10^4 \sqrt{\frac{\rho}{f}} \tag{18a}$$

The value of ρ used in (18a) must be the resistivity of the material at maximum temperature.

Heating by the proximity effect as given by eq 18 can be applied to a single-turn circular coil around a nonmagnetic cylinder, provided the coil conforms closely to the surface of the cylinder. In this case, the length l used in (18) should be the circumference of the cylinder.

5. FIRST APPROXIMATION OF COIL DESIGN

Design of the work coil is most often dictated by mechanical limitations of the application. The coil length is usually fixed by the length of piece to be heated, although, if a continuous process is involved, considerable flexibility in the choice of coil length is possible. In general, it is desirable to design a work coil with two objectives: (1) Use as many turns as practical, and (2) fit the coil as closely to the piece to be heated as possible. These objectives tend to result in the lowest possible radio-frequency current load on the generator.

A practical design is often a compromise based on experience. For example, it would be impractical to construct a large diameter coil of 1/8-inch tubing just for the sake of including the maximum possible turns. Such a coil would be difficult to support mechanically, if not impossible to cool, because of the limited water flow that could be forced through such a small tube. Close spacing between the coil and piece to be heated is desirable to assure high heating efficiency, although the practical minimum is dictated by the electric-arcing clearance necessary to prevent flashover between the coil and work piece. More often, the heating pattern desired requires some sacrifice of best heating efficiency.

Although the objectives previously recommended for the first approximation are satisfactory as a guide, experience is necessary before the final design may be acceptable. The several examples on pages 322 to 338 illustrate some of the factors involved in coil design.

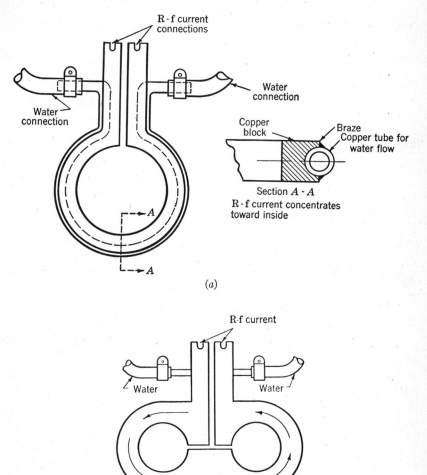

(a)

(b)

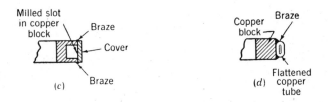

(c)   (d)

FIG. 14.9. Single unit (a) or multiple unit (b) inductor blocks are machined from copper blocks with cooling-water passage around the periphery of the block. Several suggestions for providing a passage for cooling water are evident.

A concentration of induced current is often required to obtain localized heating. Such cases are best solved by the use of single-turn *inductor blocks*. These are, in effect, single-turn coils offering the advantage of mechanical rigidity, the possibility of machining to accurate dimensions and to fit the contour of an odd-shaped work piece. Several suggestions for the construction of inductor blocks are offered in Fig. 14.9. A common construction is that of Fig. 14.9a, formed by milling a groove in the outer periphery of a copper block, its internal bore being machined to fit over the work piece with the required clearance. A copper tube is then brazed into the outside groove. The radio-frequency current concentrates toward the inside periphery. Heat as a result of copper loss flows by conduction to the water-cooled outer tubing whence it is carried away by the cooling water. An inductor block for heating two pieces simultaneously, Fig. 14.9b and Fig. 14.10, is constructed similarly, but must be slotted between paths to conduct the current around the entire periphery.

FIG. 14.10.   A two-unit inductor block brazes the parts of smoke shells. One station is loaded while the other is heating, transfer to a common radio-frequency generator being accomplished by a manual double-throw switch. (*Courtesy Induction Heating Corporation*)

In making coils for heating the inner surface of a part, such as the interior of a cylinder or hole, it is well to remember that the radio-frequency current concentrates toward the inside surface of the coil turns. Because of this, the surface to be heated is spaced from the effective coil current not only by the amount of mechanical clearance but also by the thickness of the coil tubing as well, Fig. 14.11a and b. If round tubing is used, Fig. 14.11a, the effective spacing to the work surface is greater than if flattened tubing, Fig. 14.11b is used. Hence, greatest efficiency of heating is manifest by the coil design of Fig. 14.11b.

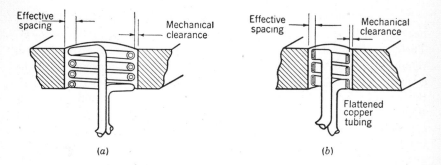

FIG. 14.11.   Coils for heating the surface of an internal bore must have as little mechanical clearance as possible. The effective spacing of a coil wound of round tubing (*a*) is greater than flattened tubing (*b*).

FIG. 14.12.   Pancake coils are used to heat surfaces when it is impractical to place the work piece within a helical coil.
(*Courtesy Westinghouse*)

FIG. 14.13.   The teeth of this internal gear are heated by an inductor block and are hardened by quenching with water sprayed through an annular nozzle or quench ring integral with the inductor block.   (*Courtesy Westinghouse*)

Pancake coils, either round or oblong, Fig. 14.12, are used to heat a flat surface that cannot be surrounded by a coil. These operate at a lower efficiency than close-fitting cylindrical coils, although this efficiency is not too poor when the spacing between the coil and the work piece is small.

Internal gears are hardened by a special form of inductor block, Fig. 14.13, serving also as a quench ring to apply the quenching medium

FIG. 14.14. This battery of four two-position work tables and radio-frequency generators affords semiautomatic operation for quantity production of brazed parts. The
hood above each work table is connected to an exhaust air system to remove fumes.
(*Courtesy Induction Heating Corporation*)

rapidly as soon as the gear teeth are brought to the proper temperature.
The gear is rotated slowly in the magnetic field to assure uniform heating.

Multiple-station work tables, Fig. 14.14, are used for semi-automatic
heating of pieces for quantity production. They usually consist of two sets
of fixtures to hold one or more pieces simultaneously, a manually operated
double-throw switch for transferring the radio-frequency generator to
either set of coils, and a timer for automatic control of the process. An
operator loads one set of fixtures while the other is heating. The radio-
frequency generator is thus used a larger proportion of the time.

6. CALCULATION OF COIL CURRENT* (MULTITURN COILS)

When the peak magnetizing force required to accomplish a given heating
rate has been determined by one of the preceding methods, the coil current

*See Table 14.2 for explanation of the units used in formula.

necessary to establish the field intensity is computed by the following relation, providing the coil consists of *more than a single turn:*

$$I_c = \frac{1.43 \times H}{N} K_1 \qquad (19)$$

or

$$I_c = \frac{1.43 \times H \times l_c}{T_c} K_1 \qquad (19a)$$

where K_1 is an empirical factor given by Fig. 14.15, which depends upon the ratio of coil length to the spacing between the coil internal diameter and piece to be heated.

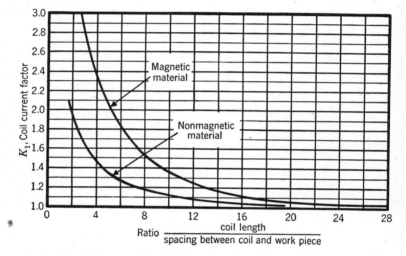

FIG. 14.15.　The coil-current factor K_1 is a function of the ratio of spacing between the coil *internal* diameter and work piece and coil length.

7. CALCULATION OF COIL VOLTAGE* (MULTITURN COILS)

The voltage induced in the turns of the coil because of the flux within the coil is

$$E_i = \sqrt{2}\pi f T_c \phi_0 \times 10^{-8} \text{ volt (rms)} \qquad (20)$$

The total flux, ϕ_0, is vectorially composed of a portion of flux in the air space between the coil and the work piece and a portion of flux within the work piece itself. In addition to the "internal" coil voltage resulting from this total flux, some voltage drop must be added because of current flowing through the resistance of the coil and flux passing through the copper turns of the coil. The total voltage across the coil is then composed of three

*See Table 14.2 for explanation of the units used in formula.

factors: (1) voltage caused by flux in the air space between the coil and work piece, (2) voltage caused by flux within the work piece, and (3) voltage caused by resistance drop in the coil and flux within the turns of the coil. The last factor can usually be neglected unless the application is one of heating materials of low resistivity and particularly accurate computations are desired.

Voltage Caused by Flux in Air Space

The voltage induced in the coil because of flux in the air space between the inside cross-sectional area of the coil and the work piece is

$$E_a = 28.6fT_cH(A_c - A_w) \times 10^{-8} \text{ volt (rms)} \tag{21}$$

where
A_c = the inside area of the coil (square inches)
A_w = the area of the work piece (square inches)

The voltage calculated in this manner is reasonably correct for either round or rectangular coils if the coil length is greater than four times the minimum inside coil dimension (diameter of round coil or inside thickness of rectangular coil) when heating a nonmagnetic material. If magnetic material is heated (below the Curié point), the voltage should be multiplied by a factor of approximately 0.7 when the minimum inside coil dimension is one-fourth the length. The factor approaches 1.0 when the minimum inside coil dimension is one-tenth the length.

Voltage Caused by Flux in the Work Piece* Nonmagnetic Material

The voltage induced in the coil because of flux that penetrates a nonmagnetic work piece is calculated within reasonable accuracy¶ by

$$E_w = 28.6fT_cH[A_w(P - jQ)]10^{-8} \text{ volt} \tag{22}$$

where P and Q have the following values:
Nonmagnetic cylinder

$$P = Q = \frac{6310}{d\sqrt{\dfrac{f}{\rho}}} \tag{22a}$$

ρ = resistivity of material at maximum temperature

Equation 22a is valid only when $d\sqrt{f/\rho} \geq 13\,400$.

*See Table 14.2 for explanation of units used in formula.
¶For a more accurate calculation see reference 6.

Nonmagnetic strip

$$P = Q = \frac{8000}{t\sqrt{\dfrac{f}{\rho}}} \tag{22b}$$

ρ = resistivity of material at maximum temperature

Equation 22b is valid only when $t\sqrt{f/\rho} \geqq 9\,500$.

Voltage Caused by Flux in the Work Piece* Magnetic Material

The voltage induced in the coil because of flux that penetrates a magnetic work piece is calculated with reasonable accuracy on the assumption that flux penetrates the material at a constant value B to a depth δ_f below the surface. It is further assumed that the magnetic material is saturated and the density $B = 18\,000$. On this basis, the total flux included with a cylindrical work piece is approximately $18\,000\pi d\delta_f$ where

$$\delta_f = 17.6\sqrt{\frac{H\rho}{f}} \text{ in.} \tag{23}$$

ρ = resistivity of the material at maximum temperature.

The voltage induced in a cylindrical coil by a cylindrical work piece then becomes

$$E_w = 0.0162df T_c\delta_f \text{ volts} \tag{24}$$

If the work piece is a thin slab, the total flux within the piece is approximately $18\,000\ 2w\delta_f$, and

$$E_w = 0.0103wf T_c\delta_f \text{ volts} \tag{25}$$

where δ_f cannot have a value greater than $t/2$.

Voltage Caused by Resistance of the* Coil and Flux Penetrating the Coil Turns

The voltage across the coil resulting from radio-frequency current through the coil resistance is the product of the coil current and effective a-c coil resistance at the frequency used. A method for determining the effective coil resistance is given on page 315. Some voltage also results from the penetration of flux within the coil turns (copper tubing). For the usual form of closely spaced coil it is sufficiently accurate to assume this numerically equal to the coil resistance drop but 90 degrees displaced in phase. The

*See Table 14.2 for explanation of the units used in formula.

two voltages are then represented by

$$E_{ir} = I_c R_c + j I_c R_c \tag{26}$$

Summation of Coil Voltage

The total coil voltage is then computed by vectorial addition of the three factors previously given above and summarized as follows:

1. Voltage due to flux in the air space, by (21).
2. Voltage due to flux in the work piece, by (24) or (25).
3. Voltage due to coil resistance and flux in turns, by (26).

The numerical value of the total coil voltage is obtained by taking the square root of the sum of the squares of real and imaginary terms of voltage. Frequently, the voltage due to coil resistance and flux in the coil turns is too small to affect the total significantly, and the "internal" coil voltage is used by the vectorial addition of the first two factors already given.

8. COIL COPPER LOSS

The copper loss within the work coil is computed by the square of the current through it multiplied by its effective resistance, that is, by Ohm's law. However, the effective coil resistance at the frequency usually employed is many times greater than its "d-c resistance" and is dependent upon the coil shape as well as on the total length of conductor. Empirical data gathered by many tests indicate that the a-c resistance of the usual single-layer closely spaced coil of copper tubing from 1/8 to 1/2-inch outside diameter of circular cross section, with diameter greater than five times the conductor diameter and length equal to or greater than the (coil) diameter, is calculated with reasonable accuracy by

$$R_c = K_2 R_{dc}(0.0967 \times D_t \sqrt{f} + 0.25) \text{ ohms} \tag{27}$$

where R_c = effective coil resistance at frequency used (ohms)
   D_t = outside diameter of conductor
   R_{dc} = d-c resistance of a coil with same dimensions, but made with a *solid* conductor of same material and conductor diameter D_t (ohms)
   f = frequency (cycles)
   K_2 = an empirical factor (see Fig. 14.16).

Equation 27 is valid only when the depth of current penetration is less than the wall thickness of the conductor. For the usual 0.035-inch-wall annealed-copper tubing the minimum frequency is 10 000 cycles.

For convenience, the a-c resistance of several popular sizes of annealed-copper tubing, at a frequency of 450 kc, is given in Table 14.3. These values apply only to coils of circular cross section having several turns and are computed for a temperature of 100 F.

If the coil cross section is oblong instead of circular, the K_2 factor of Fig. 14.16 cannot be applied. Tests made with oblong coils having a width equal to or greater than five times the thickness indicate that $K_2 = 2.5$ yields reasonably correct results over the range of frequency commonly employed.

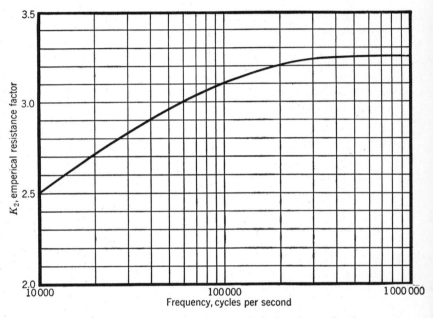

FIG. 14.16. Empirical factor K_2 for the calculation of a-c coil resistance.

The effective coil resistance R_c at the frequency used is obtained either by eq 27 or from Table 14.3, by multiplying the resistance per inch by the length of tubing in the coil. Some allowance for the length of coil leads should be included.

$$\text{The coil copper loss} = I_c{}^2 R_c \text{ watts} \tag{28}$$

9. TOTAL POWER LOAD ON RADIO-FREQUENCY GENERATOR

The total power load on the radio-frequency generator is the summation of

1. The thermal power input to the work piece (eq 8).
2. Radiation/convection/conduction losses (Fig. 14.7 or eq 9).
3. Coil copper loss (eq 28).

The total of these three factors represents the smallest rating of the radio-frequency generator that satisfies the application.

10. VOLT-AMPERE LOAD ON RADIO-FREQUENCY GENERATOR

The volt-ampere load on the radio-frequency generator is the product of coil current I_c, eq 19 or 19a and coil voltage E_c, obtained by the method of paragraph 7.

11. RATING OF THE RADIO-FREQUENCY GENERATOR

For the radio-frequency generator to be suitable for the application, its rating must satisfy all of the following:

(*a*) The watt rating must be equal to or greater than the total power load, paragraph 9.

(*b*) The generator radio-frequency current rating must be equal to or greater than the coil current, I_c, eq 19.

(*c*) The generator kilovolt-ampere rating must be equal to or greater than the load kilovolt-amperes, paragraph 10.

12. MODIFICATION OF THE LOAD TO MATCH RADIO-FREQUENCY GENERATOR

The first requirement of paragraph 11 must be met without modification. That is, the watt rating of the radio-frequency generator must be equal to or greater than the power load. If this is the case and yet the radio-frequency generator rating is deficient in its other factors, some modification of the load circuit is necessary. This is often accomplished by one or more of the following methods, listed in their order of preference.

(*a*) Modification of coil design. The most frequent form of overload is the coil current. Provided the volt-ampere rating is not also exceeded, it is usually possible to modify the coil design to reduce the coil current without altering the power input to the work piece. The first attempt should be to increase the number of coil turns, other dimensions remaining unchanged. The application can be recalculated without much difficulty and results in a higher coil voltage. The compromise possible by this change is often limited by the physical requirements of the coil, the maximum permissible coil voltage, or both, although the possibilities of this method should be fully explored before one proceeds to a more complicated modification.

The *rate* of heating can sometimes be reduced by heating several pieces simultaneously. For example, the production of one piece heated at the *rate* of three fpm can be equaled by three pieces heated simultaneously at the *rate* of one fpm, Fig. 14.17a. The coil current required for the latter example is less than that for the former; yet the power load is the same for both cases. Two or more coils are connected in series to one generator, the total generator voltage being the sum of the individual coils. As before, the volt-ampere load is the product of coil current times the total circuit voltage.

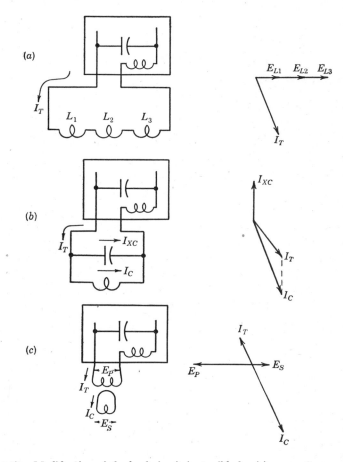

FIG. 14.17. Modification of the load circuit is possible by (a) connecting several coils in series to heat a number of pieces simultaneously, (b) an external capacitor connected across the coil for power-factor correction, (c) a current transformer between the coil and the radio-frequency generator.

(b) When the coil has been designed to result in the least possible radio-frequency current and yet this exceeds the generator rating, it may be possible to connect an external capacitor across the coil, Fig. 14.17b.

Whether or not this method can be applied is readily checked by

$$\frac{\text{Coil voltage} \times \text{coil current}}{\text{load watts}} \leqq 80\% \times \frac{\text{generator rated volt-amperes}}{\text{load watts}} \tag{29}$$

Equation 29 merely states that the load Q must not be greater than 80 percent of the Q of the radio-frequency generator. If this condition is observed, it is probable that an external capacitor can be connected across the coil. For an approximation of the value of the capacitor required, the desired current through it is found by subtracting the generator rated current from the required coil current. The difference is the approximate current that must be carried by the capacitor, from which

$$C = \frac{I_{xc}}{2\pi f E_c} \times 10^6 \ (\text{microfarads}) \tag{30}$$

where $\quad I_{xc} =$ current through the capacitor (amperes)

$E_c =$ coil voltage (volts)

$f =$ frequency (cycles)

(c) Applications restricted to coils having a single or few turns often require a coil current many times greater than the generator current rating. The resort is to a current transformer, Fig. 14.17c. The losses of the transformer primary winding, its secondary winding, and leads from secondary winding to coil must then be added to those already calculated as previously. A precaution in the use of a current transformer is that leads from the transformer secondary winding to the coil must be short and designed for the lowest possible inductance, or else the high current desired in the coil circuit is not obtained.

13. CONSIDERATION OF WATER FLOW THROUGH COILS

The copper loss of the coils themselves must be carried away by water flowing through the hollow coil conductor. Frequently, coils are machined from a solid copper block, such as single-turn inductors, in which case copper tubing is brazed to the solid block and the heat of losses removed by water flow through the surrounding tube. Whatever the construction may be, some friction drop of water flow through the tubing is encountered, and a pressure is necessary to result in the required flow.

The volume of water necessary to remove the loss within the coil is

$$Q = 1.57 \frac{\text{watts loss}}{T_2 - T_1} \ \text{cubic inches per minute} \tag{31}$$

where $\quad Q =$ water flow (cubic inches per minute)

$T_1 =$ temperature of inlet water (degrees Fahrenheit)

$T_2 =$ temperature of outlet water (degrees Fahrenheit)

The friction drop through tubing may require consideration of special means to obtain the necessary water pressure, especially when small tubing is employed. As Fig. 14.18 shows, coils of small tubing wound on a small

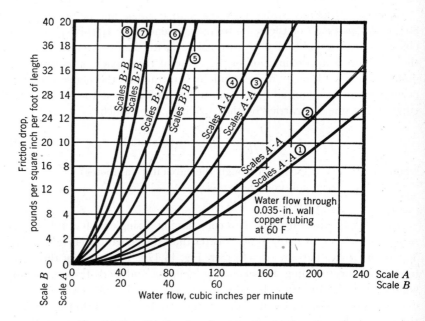

FIG. 14.18. Friction drop because of water flow through ⅛-in. and 3⁄16-in. copper tubing of various forms.

1 3⁄16-in. OD straight tubing
2 3⁄16-in. OD tubing coiled to 15⁄16-in. ID
3 3⁄16-in. OD tubing flattened to ⅛-in. straight piece
4 3⁄16-in. OD tubing flattened to ⅛-in. coiled 15⁄16-in. ID
5 ⅛-in. OD straight tubing
6 ⅛-in. OD tubing coiled to ⅝-in. ID
7 ⅛-in. OD tubing flattened to 3⁄32-in. straight piece
8 ⅛-in. OD tubing flattened to 3⁄32-in. coiled ⅝-in. ID

diameter or partly flattened may require an appreciable pressure for their cooling. The friction drop through larger tubes, Fig. 14.19, is usually so small as to make consideration of their cooling unnecessary. However, the friction drop through reducing fittings should not be overlooked. A common offender is the reduction from 1/4-in. pipe size to a smaller copper tubing. As shown by Fig. 14.20, the friction drop through fittings of this type may become an appreciable part of the total system for some installations.

When high pressures are anticipated as manifest by the use of Figs. 14.18,

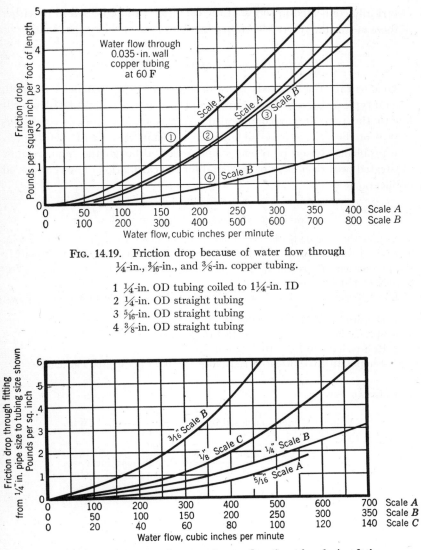

FIG. 14.19.   Friction drop because of water flow through
¼-in., ³⁄₁₆-in., and ⅜-in. copper tubing.

1 ¼-in. OD tubing coiled to 1¼-in. ID
2 ¼-in. OD straight tubing
3 ⁵⁄₁₆-in. OD straight tubing
4 ⅜-in. OD straight tubing

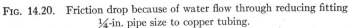

FIG. 14.20.   Friction drop because of water flow through reducing fitting
¼-in. pipe size to copper tubing.

14.19, and 14.20, special precautions can be taken. Sometimes, the water-
flow circuit for the coil is isolated from the electric circuit of the radio-
frequency generator by the use of rubber or Saran tubing. In this way, the
water-flow circuit of several coils electrically connected in series is isolated
such that the water flow is effectively paralleled, even though the coils are

electrically connected in series. If the condition cannot be solved by either of these means the resort is then to a booster pump of the required rating.

Typical Examples of Induction Heating

To illustrate the methods by which the preceding data can be used, several typical examples are assumed and their solutions calculated according to the procedure recommended. A representation of all conditions typical of the field is impossible within the limited space of this chapter. The problems chosen represent simple cases, although the fundamentals illustrated provide a clear background for the calculation of more involved applications.

Example 1. Heating a Solid Magnetic Bar

Assume that the ends of steel bars 1 in. in diameter are to be heated for 6 in. The initial temperature is 70 F and the bars are to be heated to 1200 F. To satisfy the production rate required, each piece must be heated in 30 seconds. A frequency of 450 kc is to be used.

The physical properties of the metal, selected from Table 14.5 are as follows:

Density — 0.285 lb per cubic in.
Specific heat (average) — 0.118 Btu per pound per degree Fahrenheit
Resistivity — 6.75 × 10⁻⁶ ohm-in. at 70 F
• Temperature coefficient of resistance — 0.0024 per degree Fahrenheit

1. THERMAL POWER

$$\text{Volume of metal enclosed by coil} = \frac{6\pi(1)^2}{4} = 4.71 \text{ cu in.}$$

$$\text{Rate of heating} = \frac{4.71 \times 0.285}{0.5} = 2.68 \text{ lb per minute}$$

$$P = (17.6)(2.68)(0.118)(1200-70) \tag{8}$$

$$= 6310 \text{ watts}$$

2. RADIATION, CONVECTION, AND CONDUCTION LOSS

Radiation and convection, from Fig. 14.7a =	5	watts per square inch
Conduction loss, from Fig. 14.7b	= 800	watts per square inch
Total radiation surface = $\pi(1)(6)$	= 18.9	sq in.
Conduction surface = $0.7854(1)^2$	= 0.79	sq in.
Radiation and convection loss = 5(18.9)	= 95	watts
Conduction loss = 0.79(800)	= 632	watts
Total	727	watts

3. POWER DENSITY

$$PD = \frac{\text{watts input to work piece}}{\text{volume of metal in coil}} = \frac{6310 + 727}{4.71} \tag{10}$$

$$= 1495 \text{ watts per cubic inch}$$

4. PEAK MAGNETIZING FORCE

The peak magnetizing force is found by eq 11 applying to a solid magnetic cylinder:

$$H = \left(\frac{PD \times d}{0.438\sqrt{f\rho}}\right)^{\frac{2}{3}}$$

The value of ρ corresponding to the average temperature, 600 F, is first determined by

$$\rho_{600} = 6.75 \times 10^{-6}[1 + 0.0024(530)]$$
$$= 15.3 \times 10^{-6} \text{ ohm-in.}$$

$$H = \left(\frac{1495 \times 1.0}{0.438\sqrt{450\,000 \times 15.3 \times 10^{-6}}}\right)^{\frac{2}{3}}$$
$$= 118 \text{ oersteds}$$

The validity of eq 11 is then checked by (11a):

$$d\sqrt{\frac{\mu f}{\rho}} \geqq 13\,400$$

where

$$\mu = \frac{32\,400}{H} = \frac{32\,400}{118} = 275 \tag{7}$$

Then,

$$1.0\sqrt{\frac{(275)(450\,000)}{15.3 \times 10^{-6}}} = 9.0 \times 10^6$$

This is greater than 13 400, and eq 11 is valid.

5. ASSUMED COIL DESIGN

Assume the coil to be wound of 1/4-in.-outside-diameter copper tubing, three turns per inch, 6.0 in. long, 18 turns, 1.75-in. pitch diameter or 1.50-in.-inside diameter.

$$\text{Spacing between coil inside diameter and work piece} = \frac{1.5 - 1.0}{2} = 0.25 \text{ in.}$$

$$\text{Ratio } \frac{\text{length}}{\text{spacing}} = \frac{6.0}{0.25} = 24$$

6. COIL CURRENT

From Fig. 14.15, if we use ratio $\dfrac{\text{length}}{\text{spacing}} = 24$, the coil current factor, K_1, is 1.05. The coil current, by eq 19 is

$$I_c = \frac{1.43(118)}{3.0} \times 1.05 = 59.0 \text{ amperes} \tag{19}$$

7. COIL VOLTAGE

(a) *Voltage due to Flux in the Air Space*

Coil cross-sectional area $= 0.7854(1.5)^2 = 1.76$ sq in.
Work piece area $\quad= 0.7854(1.0)^2 = 0.79$ sq in.
Area of air space $\qquad\qquad\qquad\quad 0.97$ sq in.

$$E_a = 28.6(450\,000)(18)(118)(0.97) \times 10^{-8} \tag{21}$$
$$= 266 \text{ volts}$$

(b) *Voltage due to Flux in Work Piece*

$$\delta_f = 17.6\sqrt{\frac{H\rho}{f}} \tag{23}$$

Where resistivity ρ is at maximum temperature

$$\rho_{1200} = 6.75 \times 10^{-6}[1 + 0.0024(1200 - 70)]$$
$$= 25.1 \times 10^{-6}$$

$$\delta_f = 17.6\sqrt{\frac{(118)(25.1 \times 10^{-6})}{0.450 \times 10^6}} = 0.00143 \text{ in.}$$

$$E_w = 0.0162(1.0)(450\,000)(18)(0.00143) \tag{24}$$
$$= 188 \text{ volts}$$

(c) *Voltage due to Coil Resistance and Flux in Turns*

Length of tubing in coil $= \pi 1.75 \times 18 = 99.0$ in.
Length of tubing in leads to coil $\qquad\quad 8.0$ in.
Total $\quad 107.0$ in.

From Table 14.3,

A-c resistance of tubing $= 785 \times 10^{-6}$ ohm per inch
A-c resistance of coil $\quad = (785)(107)10^{-6} = 0.084$ ohm

$$E_{ir} = (59)(0.084) + j(59)(0.084) \tag{26}$$
$$= 4.95 + j4.95$$
$$= \sqrt{(4.95)^2 + (4.95)^2}$$
$$= 7.0 \text{ volts}$$

(d) *Total Coil Voltage*

1. Due to flux in air space $\quad$ 266 volts
2. Due to flux in work piece $\quad$ 188 volts
3. Due to coil resistance $\qquad$ 7 volts
Total, E_c $\quad$ 461 volts

8. COIL COPPER LOSS

$$\text{Copper loss} = (59)^2(0.084) \tag{28}$$
$$= 292 \text{ watts}$$

9. TOTAL POWER LOAD

Thermal power input to work piece	6310 watts
Radiation, convection, and conduction loss	727 watts
Coil copper loss	292 watts
	7329 watts

10. TOTAL VOLT-AMPERES

$$\text{Load volt-amperes} = (461)(59) = 27\ 200 \text{ va}$$
$$\text{Ratio} \frac{\text{load volt-amperes}}{\text{load watts}} = \frac{27\ 200}{7\ 329} = 3.72$$

11. GENERATOR RATING

Required power output	7.3 kw
Required radio-frequency current	59 amperes
Required volt-amperes	27.2 kva

These values are all conservatively available by selecting a 10-kw 450-kc radio-frequency generator. No modification of the coil design is required, because all values are within the rating of a standard 10-kw unit.

The relatively small coil loss requires only a small water flow for adequate cooling, and the required water pressure does not need further consideration.

Example 2. Heating a Hollow Nonmagnetic Cylinder

Assume that lengths of brass tubing (cartridge brass 70–30) are to be heated continuously at a rate of 30 ft per minute, starting at a temperature of 75 F to a maximum temperature of 425 F. The tubing is 0.75 in. outside diameter with 0.03125-in. wall thickness. A frequency of 450 kc is to be used. What rating of radio-frequency generator is required, and what coil design will satisfy these requirements?

The physical properties of the metal, selected from Table 14.5 are as follows:

Density	0.308 lb per cubic inch
Specific heat (average)	0.092 Btu per pound per degree Fahrenheit
Resistivity	2.51×10^{-6} ohm-in. at 70 F
Temperature coefficient of resistance	0.00086 per degree Fahrenheit

1. THERMAL POWER

$$\text{Cross-sectional area of tubing} = 0.7854[(0.75)^2 - (0.6875)^2]$$
$$= 0.0707 \text{ sq in.}$$
$$\text{Weight per linear foot of tubing} = (12)(0.0707)(0.308) = 0.262 \text{ lb}$$
$$\text{Rate of heating} = (0.262)(30) = 7.86 \text{ lb per minute}$$
$$\text{Thermal power} = (17.6)(7.86)(0.092)(425 - 350) \tag{8}$$
$$= 4460 \text{ watts}$$

2. RADIATION AND CONVECTION LOSS

Radiation, convection, and conduction losses are negligible.

3. POWER DENSITY

The power density of a hollow cylinder is calculated as though the cylinder were solid. It is then necessary to assume the volume of metal heated at any particular instant. For this, assume the coil to be one foot long, then:

Volume of metal in coil $= 0.7854(0.75)^2(12) = 5.30$ cu in.

Power density, $PD = \dfrac{4460}{5.30} = 842$ watts per cubic inch

4. PEAK MAGNETIZING FORCE

The peak magnetizing force required for a thick-wall hollow nonmagnetic cylinder is found by the use of eq 15. But, for this procedure to be valid, the wall thickness must be greater than the depth of current penetration, eq 15b. Penetration is greatest at maximum temperature, corresponding to the greatest value of resistivity.

$$\rho_{425} = 2.51 \times 10^{-6}[1 + 0.00086(425 - 70)]$$
$$= 3.28 \times 10^{-6} \text{ ohm-in.}$$

$$\delta = 3170 \sqrt{\frac{3.28 \times 10^{-6}}{450\,000}} = 0.00857 \text{ in.}$$

$$t_w = 0.03125 \text{ in.}$$

The wall thickness is greater than the depth of current penetration and eq 15 applies, providing eq 15a is satisfied.

$$0.75 \sqrt{\frac{450\,000}{3.28 \times 10^{-6}}} = 278\,000$$

which is greater than 13 400, required for the validity of eq 15.

The value of resistivity used for calculating the peak magnetizing force is at the average temperature; hence

$$\rho_{213} = 2.51 \times 10^{-6}[1 + 0.00086(213 - 70)]$$
$$= 2.82 \times 10^{-6} \text{ ohm-in.}$$

$$H = \sqrt{\frac{(842)(0.75)}{2.59 \times 10^{-3}\sqrt{(450\,000)(2.82 \times 10^{-6})}}} \tag{15}$$

$$= 465 \text{ oersteds}$$

5. COIL DESIGN

Assume the coil to be wound of 3/16-in.-outside-diameter copper tubing, four turns per inch, 12 in. long, 48 turns, $1\frac{1}{16}$-in. pitch diameter or 0.875 in. inside diameter.

Spacing between coil inside diameter and work piece $= \dfrac{0.875 - 0.750}{2} = 0.0625$

$$\text{Ratio} \dfrac{\text{length}}{\text{spacing}} = \dfrac{12.0}{0.0625} = 193$$

6. COIL CURRENT

From Fig. 14.15 factor $K_1 = 1.0$

$$I_c = \dfrac{1.43(465)}{4.0} \times 1.0 = 166 \text{ amperes} \qquad (19)$$

7. COIL VOLTAGE

(a) *Voltage due to Flux in Air Space*

    Coil cross-sectional area $= 0.7854(0.875)^2 = 0.600$ sq in.
    Work piece area $= 0.7854(0.75)^2 \ = \underline{0.443}$ sq in.
                Area of air space 0.157 sq in.

$$E_a = 28.6(450\,000)(48)(465)(0.157) \times 10^{-8} \qquad (21)$$
$$= 454 \text{ volts}$$

(b) *Voltage due to Flux in Work Piece*

$$P = Q = \dfrac{6310}{0.75\sqrt{\dfrac{450\,000}{3.28 \times 10^{-6}}}} \qquad (22a)$$
$$= 0.0234$$

$$E_w = (28.6)(450\,000)(48)(465)[0.443(0.0234 - j0.0234)] \times 10^{-8} \qquad (22)$$
$$= 29.8 - j29.8 \text{ volts}$$

(c) *Voltage due to Coil Resistance and Flux in Turns*

    Length of tubing in coil $= \pi 1.0625 \times 48 = 161$ in.
    Length of tubing for leads $=$ $\underline{10}$ in.
                     Total 171 in.

From Table 14.3, a-c resistance of 3/16-in. tubing $= 1050 \times 10^{-6}$ ohm per inch. A-c resistance of coil $= (171)(1050 \times 10^{-6}) = 0.180$ ohm

$$E_{ir} = (166)(0.18) + j(166)(0.18) \qquad (26)$$
$$= 29.9 + j29.9 \text{ volts}$$

(d) *Total Coil Voltage*

    1. Due to flux in air space, E_a 454 $+ jo$
    2. Due to flux in work piece, E_w $29.8 - j29.8$
    3. Due to coil resistance, E_{ir} $\underline{29.9 + j29.9}$
               Total $513.7 + j0.1$

$$E_c = 514 \text{ volts}$$

8. COIL COPPER LOSS

$$\text{Copper loss} = (166)^2(0.18) \tag{28}$$

$$= 4950 \text{ watts}$$

9. TOTAL POWER LOAD

Thermal power input to work piece 4460 watts
Coil copper loss   4950 watts

Total 9410 watts

10. TOTAL VOLT-AMPERES

$$\text{Load volt-amperes} = (514)(166) = 85\ 400 \text{ va}$$

$$\text{Ratio} \frac{\text{load volt-amperes}}{\text{load watts}} = \frac{85\ 400}{9\ 410} = 9.08$$

11. GENERATOR RATING

Required power output   9.4 kw
Required radio-frequency current 166   amperes
Required volt-amperes   85.4 kva

12. MODIFICATION OF LOAD

To match the generator of the afore-mentioned requirements, the power and kilowatt-amperes can be satisfied by the use of a standard 10-kw generator. However, the radio-frequency current exceeds the rating of a 10-kw unit, and some modification is necessary. Proceeding in the preferred order of modifications ·

(a) The radio-frequency current could be reduced by increasing the coil turns. But closer spacing is impractical, and reduction to a smaller diameter tubing would undoubtedly result in difficulty in cooling the coil by the necessary water flow.

A preferable arrangement is to use two coils of the same design, connected in series, such as illustrated by Fig. 14.21. Two tubes are passed simultaneously through the coils at one-half the original speed. The total production of the pair is unchanged, although the *power density* of each coil is reduced to half the former value, the total *thermal power* remaining the same.

The peak magnetizing force, H, becomes $1/\sqrt{2}$ of its former value. The new coil current is reduced by this same proportion and becomes $166/\sqrt{2} = 118$ amperes. The voltage of *each coil* is likewise reduced, and the total for the two coils in series becomes $514 \dfrac{2}{\sqrt{2}} = 730$ volts. The coil current is now reduced to within the rating of a 10-kw generator, and the application is satisfactory.

(b) The afore-mentioned modification, using two coils in series, is the least costly arrangement and is usually satisfactory. However, circumstances do not always allow the simultaneous heating of two pieces. This application could be

Fig. 14.21. Two multiturn coils are connected in series to anneal these cartridge cases. Cases are placed in a fixture which automatically moves into position when ready to start the heating cycle. One station is loaded while the other is heating.

(*Courtesy Induction Heating Corporation*)

satisfied by the use of external series capacitors. If such a modification is chosen, only one coil being used as formerly, the approximate value of current through the capacitor should be the generator current rating subtracted from the coil current. Thus, $166 - 135 = 31$ amperes. The value of capacitance required,

$$C = \frac{31}{(2\pi)(450\,000)514} \times 10^6 \qquad (30)$$

$$= 0.0213 \text{ microfarad}$$

A capacitor of 0.0213 microfarad rated at 31 ampers, 450 kc, connected across the coil would satisfy the application.

13. WATER FLOW REQUIRED FOR COOLING THE COIL

If it is assumed that two coils are connected in series as in modification (*a*), the total coil copper loss is 4950 watts. If they are cooled by 70 F water, and the outlet temperature is to be 150 F or less, the flow required is

$$Q = 1.57 \frac{4950}{150 - 70} \tag{31}$$

$$= 97 \text{ cu in. per minute}$$

The total length of copper tubing for two coils $= \dfrac{2 \times 171}{12} = 28.5$ ft.

From Fig. 14.18 the friction drop expected through 3/16-in. tubing coiled to a small diameter is 3.5 lb per foot of tubing. Total drop through two coils in series $= (28.5)(3.5) = 100$ lb.

This is too high for most cooling systems. By the use of insulating tubing of the proper length for the water connections to each coil, the electric connections can be made in series while the water flow for the two coils is made in parallel. The flow required to carry away the loss of each coil is also cut in half, resulting in a friction drop of 1.0 lb per foot, Fig. 14.18, or 14.3 lb for each coil. In addition, an approximate pressure drop of 0.5 lb can be anticipated through each reducing fitting from 1/4-in. pipe size to the tubing, Fig. 14.20.

Example 3. Heating Nonmagnetic Strip

Assume that nonmagnetic stainless-steel strip 3 in. wide by 1/16 in. thick is to be heated continuously at 10 ft per minute from a temperature of 75 to 800 F. A frequency of 450 kc is to be used. What rating of radio-frequency generator is required for the application?

The physical properties of the metal, selected from Table 14.5, are as follows:

Density   0.280 lb per cubic inch
Specific heat (average)   0.120 Btu per pound per degree Fahrenheit
Resistivity 11.4×10^{-6} ohm-in. at 70 F
Temperature coefficient of resistance   0.0015 per degree Fahrenheit

1. THERMAL POWER

Cross-sectional area of strip $= (3)(0.0625) = 0.1875$ sq in.
Weight per linear foot $= (12)(0.1875)(0.280) = 0.631$ lb
Rate of heating $= 10 \times 0.631 = 6.31$ lb per minute
Thermal power $= (17.6)(6.31)(0.120)(800 - 75) \tag{8}$
                              $= 9670$ watts

2. RADIATION, CONVECTION, AND CONDUCTION LOSS

Radiation, convection, and conduction losses are negligible.

3. POWER DENSITY

Assume that the coil will be 12 in. long; then

Volume of metal in coil $= (12)(0.1875) = 2.25$ cu in.

Power density, $PD = \dfrac{9670}{2.25} = 4300$ watts per cubic inch

4. PEAK MAGNETIZING FORCE

The peak magnetizing force is found by eq 13 applying to a nonmagnetic strip. The resistivity used should correspond to the average temperature.

$$\rho_{400} = 11.4 \times 10^{-6}[1 + 0.0015(400 - 70)]$$
$$= 17.0 \times 10^{-6} \text{ ohm-in.}$$

Then,

$$H = \sqrt{\frac{(4300)(0.0625)}{1.30 \times 10^{-3} \sqrt{(450\,000)(17.0 \times 10^{-6})}}} \tag{13}$$

$$= 273 \text{ oersteds}$$

The validity of the equation is checked by

$$0.0625 \sqrt{\frac{450\,000}{17.0 \times 10^{-6}}} = 10\,200 \tag{13a}$$

This is greater than 9500, as required for eq 13 to be valid.

5. COIL DESIGN

Assume the strip is to be passed through the coil guided over rollers spaced some distance away from the coil. Experience has shown that considerable clearance is required between the coil and strip to prevent flashover. For this reason, a rectangular coil 1.0 in. (mean) thickness by 5.0 in. (mean) width is chosen. The coil is to be wound of 1/4-in.-outside-diameter copper tubing, two turns per inch, 24 turns, 12 in. long.

Internal area of coil = $(0.75)(4.75)$ = 3.56 sq in.

Spacing between coil and work piece = $\dfrac{0.75}{2} - \dfrac{0.0625}{2} = 0.344$ in.

Ratio $\dfrac{\text{length}}{\text{spacing}} = \dfrac{12}{0.344} = 34.8$

6. COIL CURRENT

From Fig. 14.15, factor $K_1 = 1.0$

$$I_c = \frac{1.43(273)}{2} \times 1.0 = 196 \text{ amperes} \tag{19}$$

7. COIL VOLTAGE

(a) *Voltage due to Flux in Air Space*

Internal area of coil = $(0.75)(4.75)$ = 3.56 sq in.

Area of work piece = $\dfrac{(0.0625)(3)}{}$ = 0.19 sq in.

Air space = 3.37 sq in.

$$E_a = 28.6(450\,000)(24)(273)(3.37) \times 10^{-8} \tag{21}$$
$$= 2850 \text{ volts}$$

(b) *Voltage due to Flux in Work Piece*

The resistivity at maximum temperature is required for use in eq 22b

$$\rho_{800} = 11.4 \times 10^{-6}[1 + 0.0015(800 - 70)]$$

$$= 23.9 \times 10^{-6} \text{ ohm-in.}$$

$$P = Q = \frac{8000}{0.0625\sqrt{\dfrac{450\,000}{23.9 \times 10^{-6}}}} \tag{22b}$$

$$= 0.935$$

$$E_w = 28.6(450\,000)(24)(273)[0.19\,(0.935 - j0.935)] \times 10^{-8} \tag{22}$$

$$= 150 - j150 \text{ volts}$$

(c) *Voltage due to Coil Resistance and Flux in Turns*

Length of tubing in coil = $(1 + 5)(2)(24)$ = 288 in.
Length of tubing for leads   =   10 in.
                                Total   298 in.

From Table 14.3, the a-c resistance of 1/4-in-outside-diameter copper tubing is 785×10^{-6} ohm per inch for coils *of circular cross section*. This value is derived from eq 27 wherein the factor $K_2 = 3.25$ (Fig. 12.16) is used. For coils of rectangular cross section an approximate value of $K_2 = 2.5$ should be used. Therefore, the a-c resistance of 1/4-in.-outside-diameter copper tubing, for a rectangular coil, is $\dfrac{2.5}{3.25}$ $(785 \times 10^{-6}) = 604 \times 10^{-6}$ ohm per inch, at a frequency of 450 kc.

$$\text{A-c coil resistance} = (298)(604 \times 10^{-6}) = 0.18 \text{ ohm}$$

$$E_{ir} = 196(0.18) + j196(0.18) \tag{26}$$

$$= 35.3 + j35.3$$

(d) *Total Coil Voltage*

1. Due to flux in air space, E_a 2850 $+ j0$
2. Due to flux in strip, E_w 150 $- j150$
3. Due to coil resistance, I_{ir} 35.3 $+ j35.3$
                        Total 3035.3 $- j114.7$

$$E_c = \sqrt{(3035)^2 + (115)^2}$$

$$= 3040 \text{ volts}$$

8. COIL COPPER LOSS

$$\text{Copper loss} = (196)^2(0.18) \tag{28}$$

$$= 6920 \text{ watts}$$

9. TOTAL POWER LOAD

> Thermal power input to strip   9670 watts
> Coil copper loss   6920 watts
>   Total 16 590 watts

10. TOTAL VOLT-AMPERES

$$\text{Load volt-amperes} = (3040)(196) = 596\ 000 \text{ va}$$

$$\text{Ratio} \frac{\text{load volt-amperes}}{\text{load watts}} = \frac{596\ 000}{16\ 590} = 36.0$$

11. GENERATOR RATING

> Required power output   16.6 kw
> Required radio-frequency current 196   amperes
> Required volt-amperes   596   kva

12. MODIFICATION OF LOAD TO MATCH THE GENERATOR

The preceding requirements and Table 14.1 show that the power load can be supplied by a 20-kw generator, but both the radio-frequency current and kilovolt-amperes exceed the ratings of a 20-kw unit. Modification of the coil to include more turns would reduce the radio-frequency current but would not change the required kilovolt-amperes. Because of this, it is necessary to effect a reduction of coil voltage in addition to the change in coil current.

Assume that by improvement in the method of guiding the strip through the coil its internal area can be reduced such that a new coil is designed having a thickness (mean) of 7/8 in. width (mean) of $4\frac{1}{4}$ in., 30 turns or $2\frac{1}{2}$ turns per inch. The following changes result:

> Internal area of coil = (0.625)(4.0) = 2.50 sq in.
> Area of work piece   = 0.19 sq in.
>   Air space = 2.31 sq in.

The increase in coil turns to 2.5 turns per inch reduces the required current to

$$196 \times \frac{2.0}{2.5} = 157 \text{ amperes.}$$

The calculation of coil voltage, paragraph 7, shows that with reasonable accuracy the new coil voltage is

$$\text{Original voltage} \times \frac{\text{new coil turns}}{\text{original coil turns}} \times \frac{\text{new air space}}{\text{original air space}} \quad \text{or}$$

$$3040 \times \frac{30}{24} \times \frac{2.31}{3.37} = 2600 \text{ volts}$$

Because of the change in coil design, the coil copper loss is modified:

Length of tubing in coil = $2(0.875) + (4.25)30 = 306$ in.

Length of tubing for leads　　　　　　　= $\underline{10\text{ in.}}$

　　　　　　　　　　　　　　Total　　316 in.

A-c coil resistance = $(316)(604 \times 10^{-6}) = 0.185$ ohm

Copper loss　　　= $(157)^2(0.185) = 4550$ watts

The new load requirements are:

Load power　　　　　= $9670 + 4550 = 14\,220$ watts

Radio-frequency current = 157 amperes

Load volt-amperes　　= $(2600)(157) = 408\,000$ va

These conditions are now within the rating of a 20-kw generator. In fact, it would be possible to utilize the full 175 amperes of the generator rating and obtain a somewhat greater production rate.

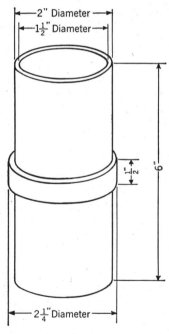

FIG. 14.22.　Dimensions of piece for example 4.

13. WATER FLOW REQUIRED FOR COOLING THE COIL

The water flow required for cooling the coil, if 70 F inlet and 150 F outlet temperatures are allowed, is

$$Q = 1.57 \frac{4550}{150-70} = 90 \text{ cu in. per minute} \quad (31)$$

From Fig. 14.19, the approximate friction drop is 0.5 lb per foot of 1/4-in. tubing.

$$\text{Total friction drop} = (0.5)\left(\frac{316}{12}\right) = 13.2 \text{ lb};$$

hence, the coil is cooled without difficulty.

Example 4.　Brazing a Nonmagnetic Cylinder

Assume that a brass (red 80–20) ring $2\frac{1}{4}$-in. outside diameter by 2 in. inside diameter by 1/2 in. long is to be brazed to the outside of a hollow tube 6 in. long of the same material, Fig. 14.22. The tube is 2 in. outside diameter by $1\frac{1}{2}$ in. inside diameter. The ring is located at the center of the tubing. A temperature of 1350 F is required. The initial temperature is 70 F. To meet the production rate necessary, each piece must be brazed in one minute. A frequency of 450 kc is to be used. What equipment is required?

The physical properties of the metal, selected from Table 14.5, are as follows:

Density	0.313 lb per cubic inch
Specific heat (average)	0.097 Btu per pound per degree Fahrenheit
Resistivity	2.08×10^{-6} ohm-in. at 70 F
Temperature coefficient of resistance	0.000 83 per degree Fahrenheit
Thermal conductivity	973 Btu per hour per square foot per degree Fahrenheit per inch

1. THERMAL POWER

Cross section to be heated = $0.7854[(2.25)^2 - (1.5)^2]$
                           = 2.22 sq in.
Volume of metal heated   = $(2.22)(0.5)$
                           = 1.11 cu in.
Rate of heating   = $1.11(0.313)(1.0) = 0.348$ lb per minute
Thermal power   = $17.6(0.348)(0.097)(1350 - 70)$ (8)
                           = 762 watts

2. CONDUCTION, RADIATION, AND CONVECTION LOSS

To estimate the conduction loss assume that a section $1\frac{1}{2}$ in. each side of the area heated remains at the initial temperature, 70 F. The area of the metal face through which this heat flows is

$$0.7854[(2.0)^2 - (1.5)^2] = 1.37 \text{ sq in.}$$

The average conduction loss, for each is

$$P_k = 2.03 \times 10^{-3} \frac{(973)(1.37)(675 - 70)}{1.5} \qquad (9)$$

= 1090 watts for each side
= 2180 watts total

The loss by radiation and convection is negligible.

3. POWER DENSITY

Thermal power input to work piece   762 watts
Conduction input to work piece   2180 watts
Total input to work piece   2942 watts

$$\text{Power density, } PD = \frac{2942}{(0.7854)(2.25)^2(0.50)} \qquad (10)$$

= 1480 watts per cubic inch

4. PEAK MAGNETIZING FORCE

The peak magnetizing force is found by eq 15, which applies to a thick-wall hollow nonmagnetic cylinder. Calculation of the depth of current penetration is unnecessary, because, by inspection, it is less than the wall thickness. The resistivity of the metal at average temperature is

$$\rho_{675} = 2.08 \times 10^{-6}[1 + 0.000\ 83(675 - 70)]$$
$$= 3.13 \times 10^{-6} \text{ ohm-in.}$$

$$H = \sqrt{\frac{(1480)(2.25)}{2.59 \times 10^{-3}\sqrt{(450\ 000)(3.13 \times 10^{-6})}}} \qquad (15)$$

$$= 1045 \text{ oersteds}$$

The validity of eq 15 is checked by

$$2.25 \sqrt{\frac{450\ 000}{3.13 \times 10^{-6}}} = 850\ 000 \qquad (15a)$$

which is greater than 13 400, and eq 15 is valid.

5. COIL DESIGN

Assume the coil to be wound of 1/4-in.-outside-diameter copper tubing, two turns closely spaced, approximately 1/2 in. long (4 turns per inch) 2.375 in. inside diameter, 2.625 in. mean diameter.

Spacing between coil inside diameter and work piece $= \dfrac{2.375 - 2.25}{2} =$
0.0625 in.

$$\text{Ratio} \frac{\text{length}}{\text{spacing}} = \frac{0.50}{0.0625} = 8.0$$

6. COIL CURRENT

From Fig. 14.15, factor $K_1 = 1.20$

$$I_c = 1.43 \frac{1045}{4.0} \times 1.20 \qquad (10)$$

$$= 448 \text{ amperes}$$

7. COIL VOLTAGE

(a) *Voltage due to Flux in Air Space*

Internal area of coil $= 0.7854(2.375)^2 = 4.43$ sq in.
Area of work piece $= 0.7854(2.25)^2 = 3.98$ sq in.
Area of air space $= 0.45$ sq in.

$$E_a = 28.6(450\ 000)(2)(1045)(0.45) \times 10^{-8} \qquad (21)$$
$$= 121 \text{ volts}$$

(b) *Voltage due to Flux in Work Piece*

The resistivity at maximum temperature is

$$\rho_{1350} = 2.08 \times 10^{-6}[1 - 0.000\ 83(1350 - 70)]$$
$$= 4.28 \times 10^{-6} \text{ ohm-in.}$$

$$P = Q = \frac{6310}{2.25\sqrt{\dfrac{450\ 000}{4.28 \times 10^{-6}}}} \tag{22a}$$

$$= 0.008\ 62$$

$$E_w = 28.6(450\ 000)(2)(1045)[3.98(0.008\ 62 - j0.008\ 62)] \times 10^{-8} \tag{22}$$
$$= 9.2 - j9.2 \text{ volts}$$

(c) *Voltage due to Coil Resistance and Flux in Turns*

Length of tubing in coil $= \pi(2.625)(2) = 16.5$ in.
Length of tubing for leads   8.0 in.
                              Total $= \overline{24.5}$ in.

From Table 14.3, the a-c resistance of 1/4-inch tubing is 785×10^{-6} ohm per inch and

A-c coil resistance $= (24.5)(785 \times 10^{-6}) = 0.0192$ ohm

$$E_{ir} = 448(0.0192) + j448(0.0192) \tag{26}$$
$$= 8.6 + j8.6 \text{ volts}$$

(d) *Total Coil Voltage*

1. Due to flux in air space $121 \quad + j0$
2. Due to flux in work piece $9.2 - j9.2$
3. Due to coil resistance $\underline{8.6 + j8.6}$
                  Total $\overline{138.8 - j0.6}$

$$E_c = 139 \text{ volts}$$

8. COIL COPPER LOSS

$$\text{Copper loss} = (448)^2(0.0192) \tag{28}$$
$$= 3850 \text{ watts}$$

9. TOTAL POWER LOAD

Thermal power   762 watts
Conduction loss 2180 watts
Coil copper loss $\underline{3850}$ watts
       Total $\overline{6792}$ watts

10. TOTAL VOLT-AMPERES

$$\text{Load volt-amperes} = (139)(448) = 62\ 300 \text{ va}$$

$$\text{Ratio } \frac{\text{load volt-amperes}}{\text{load watts}} = \frac{62\ 300}{6\ 792} = 9.18$$

11. GENERATOR RATING

Required power output   6.79 kw

Required radio-frequency current 448   amperes

Required volt-amperes   62.3 kva

12. MODIFICATION OF THE LOAD TO MATCH THE GENERATOR

The preceding requirements indicate that the power output and kilovolt-amperes are within the rating of a 10-kw radio-frequency generator. However, the radio-frequency current considerably exceeds the rating of a 10-kw unit, Table 14.1. Therefore, some method to match the load must be found to utilize a 10-kw generator.

FIG. 14.23. Rear view of multiple-position work table with panels removed to show current transformers, double-throw transfer switch and water connections. Each coil is permanently connected to each transformer secondary winding, switching being done on the primary side of the transformer. Water connections are in series with cooling water circulating continuously through all transformers. The resistance of water connections between transformers is sufficient to allow switching without interfering with water circulation.   (*Courtesy Induction Heating Corporation*)

(a) The coil design cannot be appreciably modified, because its design is limited by the shape and dimensions of the work piece. Several coils may be connected in series to heat several pieces simultaneously at a lower rate (see

FIG. 14.24. Plastic preforms are rapidly heated before being placed in the press mold by dielectric heating between electrodes connected to this 10-kw 30-mc radio-frequency generator. (*Courtesy Westinghouse*)

example 2). However, in this case the greater portion of load results from conduction and the time for heating would be increased such that the solution is unsatisfactory.

(*b*) Capacitors connected in parallel with the coil could be applied, but their cost would be prohibitive

(*c*) A current transformer interposed between the generator and coil is the most economical solution for this application. When this is done, the total power load is increased by the amount of copper loss in the transformer. The exact value of the loss depends upon the transformer design, although it can be estimated as being equal to the coil copper loss. For this example, the total power load would then be increased to the approximate full rating of a 10-kw generator.

13. COOLING THE COIL

Inspection of Fig. 14.19, and eq 31 indicates the coil will be adequately cooled. However, if a current transformer is used, both its primary and secondary winding must also be water-cooled.

DIELECTRIC HEATING

The applications of dielectric heating already form a spectacular list that includes nearly every industry. Yet the possibilities are barely uncovered. Dielectric heating is used by the plastics industry for both curing of the plastic and preheating of the material before placing it in the molds. Plastic preforms, as they are called, heated just below the curing temperature before they are placed in the mold allow closing of the press in a shorter time and reduce wear of the mold, both factors reducing the ultimate cost.

FIG. 14.25. Rear view 2-kw 30-mc unit showing single-phase phanotron rectifier (lower right); blower for air-cooled oscillator tube (center); control (lower left); with oscillator tube, tank circuit and tuning network in the top compartment.

(*Courtesy Westinghouse*)

Dielectric gluing seems to possess no limit of possibility, and the applications range from the manufacture of thick sections of plywood to the manufacture of aircraft panels and even to spot gluing of small sections. Here, the chief virtue of dielectric heating is its ability to heat uniformly the entire thickness. The maximum section is limited only by the cost of the equipment required.

The principle can also be applied for drying lumber, textiles, or paper. Here there is considerable question of economics because of the relatively large amount of energy required to evaporate the water content. Some balance using partial drying by dielectrics appears to lend a hopeful solution to such problems, and doubtless much will be accomplished in the near future.

The twist of textile yarns is effectively "set" by dielectric heating. Here, the wound package of yarn is treated within the high-frequency field, and the twist of the yarn afterwards retains its original coiling.

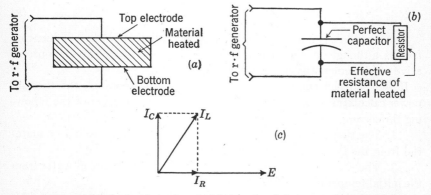

FIG. 14.26. Dielectric heating of material (a) placed between electrodes becomes electrically equivalent (b) to a perfect capacitor, shunted by a resistor. Heating is then accomplished by current flowing through the effective resistance of the material.

Fabrics of synthetic plastics or synthetic rubber are "stitched" without thread by passing the seam through an electronic "sewing machine" that brings successive closely spaced spots to the thermosetting temperature instantly, thereby permanently joining the layers.

The frequencies used for dielectric heating lie above those employed in induction heating. They begin at about two million cycles, and extend upward even above 100 mc. Most dielectric-heating work is done at a frequency between 10 and 30 mc.

When a material is heated by the dielectric process, it is placed between flat plates or *electrodes*, with each plate connected to the radio-frequency generator as the source of high voltage and high frequency, somewhat as indicated in Fig. 14.26a. The material itself then forms the dielectric, and the electrodes are the plates of a capacitor. This actually is an imperfect capacitor because of the losses within the dielectric.

An equivalent circuit, Fig. 14.26b and vector diagram, Fig. 14.26c, show a reactive current I_c through an equivalent perfect capacitor, and an in-phase current I_R flows through a resistor in which the losses of the imperfect capacitor can be considered to reside. The dielectric then becomes heated in proportion to I^2R, where R represents the resistive component of the dielectric loss.

Computing the Radio-Frequency Generator Requirements

The first step in determining the rating of a radio-frequency generator is to determine the thermal power required to raise the materials at the specified rate through the required temperature range. This is done by the same formula given for induction heating and repeated here for convenience.*

$$P = 17.6Mc\Delta T \text{ watts} \tag{8}$$

Equation 8 does not allow for any loss by radiation or other influencing factors, although an over-all allowance of 20 percent usually yields conservative results unless the circumstances are abnormal.

If the material contains water that must be evaporated, the thermal power calculation must be modified to become a summation of the following three components:

1. The thermal power required to raise the temperature of dry material from the starting to the final temperature.

2. The thermal power required to raise the temperature of water from the initial temperature to 212 F.

3. The thermal power required to evaporate the water, calculated by

$$P = 18\ 000M' \text{ where } M' = \text{pounds of water vaporized per minute}$$

Once the thermal power is determined, the first approximation of frequency chosen, the dimensions of the material known, and the loss factor of the material known or selected from Table 14.6, the required voltage gradient across the electrodes can be obtained using the following relation*:

$$PD = 1.41 \left(\frac{E}{t}\right)^2 fe'' \times 10^{-12} \tag{33}$$

Voltage Limitations

The power input to the material is, according to eq 33, proportional to the square of the *voltage gradient* through the material. It would appear that an effective method of increasing the power input to the material would be to raise the voltage across electrodes. However, practical considerations limit the voltage across electrodes to about 15 000 volts. Considerable difficulty is encountered at a higher voltage because of corona and arc-overs. While it is possible to increase this limit by careful design, economics seldom shows such a solution to be satisfactory. If the first solution to a problem shows an exceedingly high voltage required to comply with the demand for a given rate of heating, it may be possible to increase the frequency.

*See Table 14.4 for explanation of the units used in formula.

It is sometimes necessary to allow an air space between the material being heated and the top electrode. In such cases, the voltage distribution between the material and air space is not equal and must be refigured by*

$$V = \frac{E}{1 + \dfrac{e'g}{h}} \tag{34}$$

An alternate form of eq 34 is sometimes more convenient to use:

$$\frac{V}{h} = \frac{E}{h}\left(\frac{1}{1 + \dfrac{e'g}{h}}\right) \tag{34a}$$

The voltage gradient across the air space should also be checked, because this is more frequently the limiting factor in determining the maximum voltage possible between electrodes.

Frequency Limitations

Aside from the greater complication of designing and adjusting radio-frequency generators to operate at extremely high frequency, for a given electrode size, the higher the frequency the greater is the probability of unequal voltage distribution over the area caused by standing-wave effect. Although there are several ways of minimizing this effect, conservative application requires that the maximum distance from the high-voltage connection to the furthest edge of electrode does not exceed 1/16 of the wave length. To comply with this limitation, the operating frequency should not exceed

$$f' = \frac{750}{l\sqrt{e'}} \tag{35}$$

where f' = limiting frequency (megacycles)
   l = distance, connection to furthest edge of high-voltage electrode (inches)
   e' = dielectric constant of material

Impedance Matching

Radio-frequency generators designed for dielectric heating include tuning equipment (such as shown in Fig. 14.25) for matching the impedance of the electrode circuit with the generator output. Data specifying the maximum and minimum impedance of the electrode circuit that can be

*See Table 14.4 for explanation of the units used in formula.

Fig. 14.27. Electrode heating assembly built into the top of a 2-kw 27.4-mc radio-frequency generator with wire-mesh lid interlocked with the generator control for protection of the operator. The mesh lids affords safety, prevents radio interference, and allows the escape of gases released during heating, without shielding the work from view. Two infrared lamps prevent cooling of the work surfaces by the surrounding air.

(*Courtesy RCA*)

used with any particular radio-frequency generator are obtainable from the manufacturer. With such information, one can compute the load impedance by first calculating the capacitance of the electrode as though it were a parallel-plate capacitor:

$$C = 0.224e' \frac{A}{t} \times 10^{-12} \qquad (36)$$

Fig. 14.28. This electronic sewing machine "stitches" a hem in thermoplastic-coated fabric such as used in the manufacture of raincoats, balloons, food wrappings and similar commodities. By using extremely high frequency connected to the machine electrodes, watertight seams are joined by instant thermoplastic setting of the materials.

(*Courtesy RCA*)

where
C = capacity (farads)
A = electrode area (square inches)
t = distance between electrodes (inches)
e' = dielectric constant of material

If the entire area of the electrodes is not covered by material of the same dielectric constant, the electrode area must be proportioned into the areas of dissimilar material and the capacitance of each calculated separately. The over-all capacitance is then the sum of the two equivalent portions.

The reactive impedance of the load is then determined by

$$\text{Reactive impedance, } X_c = \frac{1}{2\pi f C} \text{ ohms} \tag{22}$$

$$\text{Effective resistance } R = X_c e \text{ ohms} \tag{23}$$

where
$$e = \text{power factor} = \frac{\text{loss factor}}{\text{dielectric constant}} = \frac{e''}{e'}$$

These constants for a few of the materials commonly heated are given in Table 14.6.

Sometimes the radio-frequency generator cannot be tuned to a particular load because of too low an impedance of the electrode circuit. In such cases, several pieces of the material to be heated can be stacked together so as to increase the electrode impedance. With some thought devoted to the best stacking of material, it is usually possible to load the equipment efficiently and keep within the range of adjustment provided for the tuning equipment.

TABLE 14.1. TYPICAL RADIO-FREQUENCY GENERATOR RATINGS

Power Ratings	Load, Radio-Frequency Current	Load Kva
5	110	165
10	135	400
20	175	525
50	300	1350
100	425	2150
200	600	3600

TABLE 14.2. LIST OF SYMBOLS FOR INDUCTION HEATING

P = thermal power input to work piece (watts)
P_k = power by conduction through the material (watts)
W = power input to work piece (watts per square inch)
PD = power density (watts per cubic inch)
M = rate of material heating (pounds per minute)
ΔT = temperature rise (degrees Fahrenheit)
c = specific heat of material (Btu per pound per degree Fahrenheit)
d = diameter of cylindrical work piece (inches)
t_w = wall thickness of hollow cylinder (inches)
A_a = cross-sectional area of cylinder (square inches)
w = width of strip or slab (inches)
t = thickness of strip or slab (inches)
A_s = cross-sectional area of strip or slab (square inches)
T_c = total number of turns in coil
N = coil turns per inch of length
l_c = length of coil (inches)
d_c = inside diameter of coil (inches)
A_c = cross-sectional area inside coil (square inches)
I_c = coil current (rms amperes)
E_i = "internal" coil voltage (rms volts)
E_c = voltage across coil (rms volts)
ϕ_o = total flux inside coil (peak value)
f = frequency (cycles per second)
ρ = electrical resistivity (ohm-inches)
H = peak magnetizing force at the surface of the piece to be heated (oersteds)

μ = effective magnetic permeability of material
R_c = effective a-c resistance of coil at frequency used
α = temperature coefficient of resistance per degree Fahrenheit
K = thermal conductivity (Btu per hour per square feet per degree Fahrenheit per inch), see Table 14.5
K_1 = coil current factor (see Fig. 14.15)
K_2 = empirical resistance factor from Fig. 14.16.

TABLE 14.3. EFFECTIVE A-C RESISTANCE OF COPPER TUBING COIL OF CIRCULAR CROSS SECTION AND CLOSELY SPACED TURNS

Frequency = 450 000 cycles, Temperature = 100 deg F

Tubing, Outside Diameter (In.)	Resistance, Ohms per Inch
$\frac{1}{8}$	1600×10^{-6}
$\frac{3}{16}$	1050×10^{-6}
$\frac{1}{4}$	785×10^{-6}
$\frac{5}{16}$	628×10^{-6}
$\frac{3}{8}$	498×10^{-6}

TABLE 14.4. LIST OF SYMBOLS FOR DIELECTRIC HEATING

P = thermal power input to material heated (watts)
M = rate of material heating (pounds per minute)
M' = rate of water evaporation (pounds per minute)
ΔT = temperature rise (degrees Fahrenheit)
c = specific heat of material (Btu per pound per degree Fahrenheit)
PD = power density (watts per cubic inch)
A = cross-sectional area of electrodes (square inches)
R = resistive component of material heated (ohms)
X_c = reactive component of material heated (ohms)
C = capacitance between electrodes (farads)
f = frequency (cycles)
f' = limiting frequency (megacycles)
E = voltage between electrodes (volts)
t = spacing between electrodes (inches)
V = voltage across material heated (volts)
h = thickness of material heated (inches)
g = thickness of air space above material (inches)
l = distance, point of high-voltage connection to farthest edge of electrode (inches)
e = power factor of material at frequency used
e' = dielectric constant of material at frequency used
e'' = loss factor of material at frequency used.

TABLE 14.5. PHYSICAL CONSTANTS OF METALS

Material	Resistivity, Ohm-Inches at 70 F	Temperature Coefficient of Resistance, F	Average Specific Heat, Btu per Pound per Degree F			Thermal Conductivity, Btu per Hour per Sq Ft per Inch per Degree F	Weight, Pounds per Cubic Inch
			70 F	200 F	1200 F		
Aluminum							
Alcoa 2S (soft)	1.10×10^{-6}	0.00220	0.214	0.230	0.274	1392	0.098
Alcoa 3S (soft)	1.15×10^{-6}					1570	0.098
Alcoa 3S (soft)	1.36×10^{-6}					1310	0.099
Alcoa 3S (hard)	1.66×10^{-6}					1070	0.099
Alcoa 17S (soft)	1.51×10^{-6}					1190	0.101
Alcoa 61S (soft)	1.51×10^{-6}					1190	0.098
Brass							
60–40 (Muntz metal)	2.39×10^{-6}	0.00109	0.092	0.094	0.100	877	0.303
70–30 (cartridge)	2.51×10^{-6}	0.00086	0.092	0.094	0.100	839	0.308
80–20 (red)	2.08×10^{-6}	0.00083	0.092	0.094	0.100	937	0.313
90–10 (bronze)	1.59×10^{-6}	0.00104	0.092	0.094	0.100	1291	0.318
Carbon	$1380. \times 10^{-6}$	0.00050	0.165	0.254	0.445	842	0.128
Chromium	1.02×10^{-6}		0.110	0.112	0.135		0.250
Cobalt	3.82×10^{-6}	0.00366	0.103	0.104	0.106		0.315
Copper	0.679×10^{-6}	0.00218	0.092	0.094	0.110	2668	0.321
Gold	0.961×10^{-6}	0.00189	0.031	0.031	0.032	2030	0.700
Graphite	$315. \times 10^{-6}$		0.170		0.310	35	0.082
Iron — pure	3.86×10^{-6}	0.00361	0.104	0.113	0.210	467	0.282
Iron — cast (average)	$35. \times 10^{-6}$	0.0035	0.118			317	0.255
Lead	8.66×10^{-6}	0.00217	0.029	0.031		241	0.412
Magnesium	1.76×10^{-6}	0.00223	0.222	0.248	0.435	1090	0.063

Mercury	37.7×10^{-6}	0.00049	0.033	0.033		55	0.493
Molybdenum (drawn)	2.24×10^{-6}	0.0622	0.062	0.065	0.075	1005	0.326
Monel metal	16.5×10^{-6}	0.00111		0.127			0.318
Nickel	3.07×10^{-6}	0.00334	0.105	0.113	0.126	415	0.322
Platinum	3.87×10^{-6}	0.00167	0.032		0.034	483	0.774
Silver	0.641×10^{-6}	0.00211	0.056	0.056	0.058	2830	0.380
Steel							
Soft	6.75×10^{-6}	0.0024	0.110	0.114	0.143	334	0.284
Tempered blue	7.95×10^{-6}	0.0013	0.120	0.148	0.150	334	0.284
Tempered hard	18.0×10^{-6}	0.00089	0.120	0.125		334	0.283
Ni 10, C 0.1	11.4×10^{-6}		0.122			334	0.280
Ni 80, C 0.1	32.3×10^{-6}		0.112			334	0.280
Cr 13, C 0.08	24.0×10^{-6}					334	0.280
Invar 35% Ni	31.8×10^{-6}	0.0007	0.095	0.120	0.126	334	0.290
Si 4%	24.4×10^{-6}	0.00045				334	0.278
Steel wire							
E.B.B.	4.1×10^{-6}	0.0028	0.116			334	0.280
B.B.	4.7×10^{-6}	0.0022	0.116			334	0.280
Piano	4.9×10^{-6}	0.0018	0.110			334	0.280
Tantalum	6.11×10^{-6}	0.00172	0.036	0.043	0.043	377	0.587
Tin	4.53×10^{-6}	0.00233	0.054	0.057	0.062	450	0.264
Tungsten	2.17×10^{-6}	0.00261	0.034	0.034		1381	0.688
Zinc	2.26×10^{-6}	0.00206	0.092	0.095	0.105	769	0.257

TABLE 14.6. PROPERTIES OF NONCONDUCTORS

Material	Volume Resistivity, Ohm-Inches	Specific Heat, Btu per Pound per Degree F	Weight, Pounds per Cu In.	Dielectric Constant		Loss Factor		
				1 Mc	30 Mc	1 Mc	10 Mc	30 Mc
Amber	2×10^{16}		0.038	2.9	2.9	0.02		0.06
Celluloid, clear	8×10^{9}		0.049	6.4		0.33		
Fiber, commercial	2×10^{9}	0.25	0.038	5.0		0.25		
Glass								
Commercial plate	8×10^{12}		0.089	6.8	6.6	0.07	0.06	0.06
Flint			0.105	6.4		0.03		
Pyrex "Radio"	5×10^{13}	0.20	0.077	4.0	4.0	0.003	0.004	0.004
Pyrex "Chemical"			0.082	5.2	5.0	0.022	0.030	0.034
Isolantite	1.1×10^{14}			6.1		0.011		
Mica	2×10^{13}	0.206	0.094	5.5	5.5	0.0016	0.0016	0.0016
Mycalex	4×10^{12}	0.20	0.117	7.0	7.0	0.014	0.014	0.014
Nylon	4×10^{12}	0.55	0.014	3.0	3.0	0.06	0.06	0.06
Paper, fullerboard		0.40	0.039	3.5	3.0	0.14	0.16	0.18
Phenolic insulation, laminated								
Nema grade CE	4×10^{11}	0.42	0.049	5.3	5.0	0.26	0.30	0.33
Nema grade LE	4×10^{11}	0.42	0.049	5.0		0.22		
Nema grade X	4×10^{12}	0.42	0.049	6.5		0.45		
Nema grade XX	4×10^{12}	0.42	0.049	5.5		0.25		
Nema grade XXX	4×10^{12}	0.42	0.049	5.5	5.2	0.19	0.25	0.26
Micarta 259		0.42	0.060	5.8	5.7	0.060	0.080	0.11

Material								
Porcelain								
Dry process	2×10^8	0.26	0.083	7.5		0.040	0.044	0.06
Wet process			0.088	7.0		0.060		
Quartz, fused	10^{18}	0.18	0.080	3.8	3.8	0.0008	0.0004	0.0004
Resins								
Bakelite		0.32	0.046	4.5	4.0	0.13		0.12
Beetle		0.40	0.054	5.5	5.2	0.15		0.26
Cellulose acetate		0.35	0.047	4.0	3.5	0.17	0.14	0.13
Durez 11863			0.071	4.5	4.5	0.023	0.023	0.023
Lucite		0.35	0.042	2.7	5.8			0.03
Plaskon		0.32	0.055		2.6			0.26
Polysterene			0.038	2.6	4.3	0.0003	0.0004	0.0005
Resinox 7013			0.067	4.4		0.026	0.040	0.043
Vinylite			0.051	2.9		0.044		
Rosin	2×10^{16}		0.039	2.5				
Rubber								
Natural gum	10^{13} to 10^{15}	0.33	0.041	2.4	2.4	0.005	0.10	0.01
Hard			0.041	3.0	2.5	0.15	1.0	0.08
Synthetic			0.03 to 0.07	2 to 8		0.01 to 0.10		
Shellac	4×10^{15}		0.043	3.5		0.015		
Steatite	10^{14}		0.092	5.9		0.006		
Sulphur	10^{16}	0.14	0.073	4.0				
Varnish								
Insulating				4.8		0.25		
Spar				5.5		0.17		

TABLE 14.6. PROPERTIES OF NONCONDUCTORS (Continued)

Material	Volume Resistivity, Ohm-Inches	Specific Heat, Btu per Pound per Degree F	Weight, Pounds per Cu In.	Dielectric Constant		Loss Factor		
				1 Mc	30 Mc	1 Mc	10 Mc	30 Mc
Varnished cloth								
Yellow			0.045	2.5		0.08		
Black			0.046	2.0		0.04		0.020
Waxes								
Beeswax	4×10^{14}		0.035	2.4	2.3	0.025		
Cerese			0.034	2.3		0.0025		0.0015
Ozokerite	2×10^{14}		0.033	2.3	2.3	0.002		
Parafin	2×10^{18}	0.50	0.031	2.1	2.1	0.0006		0.0006
Parowax	4×10^{15}	0.50	0.031	2.2	2.2	0.0005		0.0005
Wood (dry)								
Ash		0.42	0.023	2.6				
Balsawood			0.007	1.4		0.02		
Birch		0.40	0.022	5.2		0.32		
Maple			0.022	4.4		0.15		
Mahogany	10^{10}		0.024	2.1	2.1	0.06	0.08	
Oak	2×10^{13}		0.025	3.3		0.09		0.08

SUMMARY

In applying radio-frequency generators for induction heating, these ratings of the unit affect its application:

1. The power output (kilowatts).
2. The radio-frequency current (amperes).
3. The volt-ampere output (kva).

The application is engineered by determining:

1. The physical properties of the material.
2. The peak magnetizing force necessary to attain the desired rate of heating.
3. The dimensions — and number of turns of the work coil.
4. The radio-frequency current through the coil.
5. The radio-frequency voltage across the coil.
6. Modification of the coil design and/or the use of accessory equipment may be necessary.
7. The coil must be cooled by adequate flow of cooling water.

In applying radio-frequency generators for dielectric heating these ratings of the unit affect its application:

1. The power output (kilowatts).
2. The range of load impedance to which the unit can be matched without the use of accessory equipment.

The application is engineered by determining:

1. The physical properties of the material.
2. The *voltage gradient* across the material necessary to attain the required rate of heating, for the operating frequency chosen.
3. Any nonuniform voltage gradient resulting from dissimilar materials between electrodes or factors affecting a uniform field must be considered, and the effect of a nonuniform voltage gradient upon the materials is determined for each.
4. The load impedance is calculated and checked against the rating of the radio-frequency generator chosen.
5. If the electrodes are large, the maximum frequency permissible is limited by the allowable variation of voltage along the electrodes, that is, the *standing wave* effect.

REFERENCES

T. P. Kinn, "Vacuum-Tube Radio-Frequency Generator — Characteristics and Application to Induction-Heating Problems," *AIEE Transactions*, Vol 63, 1944, pp 1290–1304.

H. F. Storm, "Surface Heating by Induction," *AIEE Transactions*, Vol 63 October 1944, p 749.

N. R. Stansel, "Induction Heating — Selection of Frequency," *AIEE Transactions*, Vol 63, October 1944, p 755.

C. C. Levy and J. L. Lunas, "Electrical Equipment for Induction Heating," *Westinghouse Engineer*, Vol 2, February 1942, pp 20 and 22.

J. P. Jordan,"Application of Vacuum-Tube Oscillators to Inductive and Dielectric Heating in Industry," *AIEE Transactions*, Vol 61, 1942, p 831.

R. M. Baker, "Heating of Nonmagnetic Electric Conductors by Magnetic Induction — Longitudinal Flux," *AIEE Transactions*, Vol 63, June 1944, p 273.

R. M. Baker and C. J. Madsen, "High-Frequency Heating of Conductors and Nonconductors," *Electrical Engineering*, Vol 64, February 1945, pp 50–7.

George M. Brown, "Efficiency of Induction-Heating Coils," *Electronics*, Vol 17, August 1944, p 124.

Frank W. Curtis, "Coil Design for Successful Induction Heating," *American Machinist*, December 9 and 23, 1943.

Frank W. Curtis, "Tool-Design Principles Apply to Induction Heating," *American Machinist*, March 16 and April 13, 1944.

Frank W. Curtis, "Induction-Heating Advantages Warrant New Design Techniques," *Product Engineering*, April 1944.

H. C. Gillespie, "Surface Hardening of Metals," *Electronics*, Vol 17, July 1944, p 102.

Wesley M. Roberts, "Coupling Methods for Induction Heating," *Electronics Industries*, Vol 3, April 1944.

R. M. Baker, "Induction Heating of Moving-Magnetic Strip," *AIEE Transactions*, Vol 64, April 1945, pp 184–9.

Frank W. Curtis, *High-Frequency Induction Heating*, McGraw-Hill Book Co., New York, 1945.

R. W. Auxier, "Dielectric Heating Speeds Curing of Plastic Laminates," *Product Engineering*, May 1944 (or Westinghouse reprint 4118).

G. W. Scott, Jr., "The Role of Frequency in Industrial Dielectric Heating," *AIEE Transactions*, Vol 64, August 1945, pp 558–62.

Douglas Venable, "Dielectric — Heating Fundamentals," *Electronics*, November 1945, pp 120–4.

Chapter 15

BASIC CIRCUITS OF ELECTRONIC CONTROL

Electronic control refers to the harnessing of some electronic device, usually a vacuum tube, with other electric devices to perform a task frequently distinct from the art of electronics itself. The electronic-control system may be responsive instantly to an impulse as brief as a millionth of a second, or it may be sensitive only to a signal of many seconds duration, or may even delay its own action by a matter of minutes. The control may be responsive to light, or to dark, or to radiation outside the range of human senses. Although electronic devices can be made sensitive to almost any situation and arranged to take appropriate action, the control seldom does more than start, stop, or change a current that passes through a coil, perhaps of a magnetic relay to close a contact or to a motor to affect its velocity.

The number of accomplishments possible with electronic control is limitless. To attempt here to discuss them all would be hopeless. Neither is it necessary. The basic electronic-control circuits are relatively few. By minor variations of these fundamental circuits readily tailored to the occasion, the infinite variety of electronic chores are accomplished. The more important of these basic circuits are explained in this chapter.

D-C Power Supply for Anode and Grid Potentials

VOLTAGE DIVIDERS

The d-c supply for anode and grid-bias potentials is usually obtained from one of the several types of rectifier and filter circuits described in Chapter 9. Frequently several different direct voltages are required for anode and bias circuits. The cost of providing a separate rectifier and filter for each of these potentials is prohibitive, and frequently it is unnecessary. A single rectifier and filter is designed to provide an output voltage totaling the sum of the desired potentials. A resistor is connected across the filter-output terminals with taps located on the resistor so as to divide the total voltage into the desired potentials. Used in this fashion, a resistor is called a *voltage divider*. The total load current of the rectifier and filter circuit equals the sum of the currents in the individual branch circuit plus the current through the voltage-divider resistor acting alone. Although some power is wasted in the voltage divider, its simplicity more than offsets its relatively poor efficiency.

A typical circuit, Fig. 15.1a, supplies the anode and grid-bias potentials for a simple two-stage resistance-coupled amplifier in which it is assumed that tube T_1 requires a bias of -5 volts and an anode supply of $+100$ volts. Assume a load resistance drop of 25 volts, Fig. 15.1b, corresponding to -5

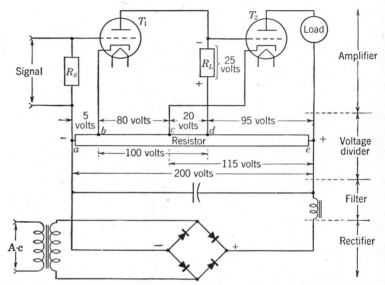

(*a*). A voltage-divider resistor divides the filter output voltage into the several potentials required to operate the two-stage resistance-coupled amplifier.

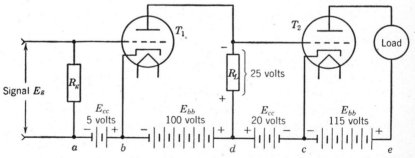

(*b*). A functional circuit replaces the actual circuit of (*a*) with the potentials of voltage-divider taps represented by batteries.

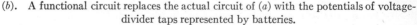

Fig. 15.1

volts applied to the grid of T_1. Tube T_2 requires a bias of -5 volts and an anode supply of $+115$ volts. A voltage-divider resistor $a\text{-}e$ is connected directly across the filter output terminals. Tap b is located to obtain 5 volts

a–b for the grid of T_1, while its anode supply of 100 volts is between taps b–d. When the input signal voltage is zero, the anode current flowing causes a drop of 25 volts across R_L. The voltage across R_L makes the grid of tube T_2 5 volts negative, accomplished by locating tap c 20 volts toward the negative side of tap d. The anode supply for tube T_2 is between c and e, the positive end of the supply. A negative signal voltage to the input reduces the voltage drop across R_L and allows the grid of T_2 to become more positive because of voltage c–d. Anode current of T_2 is thereby increased; that is, load current is raised by a negative signal voltage and vice versa.

The circuit, Fig. 15.1a, is typical of many industrial electronic devices and represents a practical method of obtaining several potentials from a single rectifier and filter d-c supply. Such circuits often become complicated and difficult to follow without close attention to the voltage-divider taps. They are simplified by converting to a functional diagram, Fig. 15.1b, in which the several potentials across the voltage divider are represented as individual batteries, each assigned the potentials of the voltage-divider branch circuits. The practice of substituting a functional equivalent diagram in place of the actual circuit is used throughout this text to clarify the operation of many circuits.

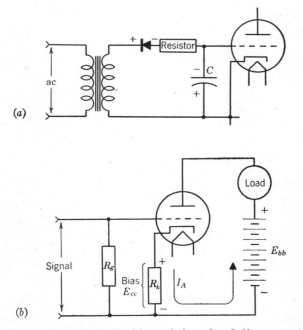

FIG. 15.2 (a). Grid bias is obtained by an independent half-wave rectifier and simple filter; (b) by a cathode bias resistor. Anode current causes voltage across R_k.

GRID-BIAS SUPPLY

Many circuits require the grid-bias potential to be isolated from the anode circuit. In such a case the voltage-divider method of Fig. 15.1a is not suitable. The usual method of isolating grid-bias potential is to use a separate transformer winding with a half-wave rectifier and simple filter consisting of a resistor and capacitor, Fig. 15.2a. Half-wave rectifiers and a simple filter are satisfactory for bias supplies because of the small load current.

Another method, known as *cathode bias* obtains a negative voltage for biasing the grid by connecting resistor R_k, Fig. 15.2b, in the cathode return circuit. Anode current through R_k causes a voltage drop, negative at the grid end of the resistor. The resistance must be so proportioned in relation to the anode current as to result in the desired grid-bias voltage.

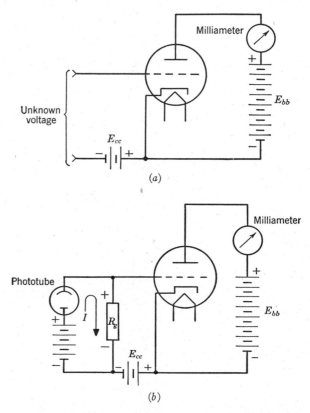

FIG. 15.3. Proportional control of d-c anode current is obtained by (a) varying potential applied to the grid, or (b) varying current through R_g as by the intensity of light on the phototube.

Pliotrons — For Proportional Control of Direct Current

Many industrial applications require the output of an amplifier to be proportional to the magnitude of signal voltage. If the output circuit is energized by a d-c supply, a pliotron is selected for the job. The tube can be a triode, tetrode, or pentode, depending upon the circuit requirement.

A typical example of such an application is the simple vacuum-tube volt-meter,* Fig. 15.3a. An unknown voltage applied to the grid circuit controls the magnitude of anode current through the milliammeter. The output current is proportional to the input voltage, allowing the milliammeter to be calibrated in terms of the input voltage. The device serves as a voltmeter, absorbing only a small amount of power from the unknown source.

Another example is a simple light-intensity meter, Fig. 15.3b, in which a phototube is connected to the input circuit. It is desired that the milliam-meter indication be proportional to the intensity of illumination. Increased phototube illumination passes a greater current through grid resistor R_g, making the grid potential more positive and increasing the anode current through the milliammeter.

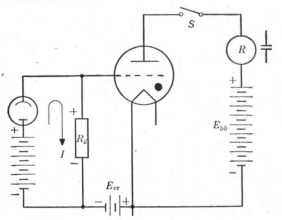

Fig. 15.4. A thyratron connected for instantaneous lock-in energizes relay R instantly when a pulse of phototube illumination fires the tube. The relay remains energized until switch S is opened.

Thyratrons — For Instantaneous Control of Direct Current

The characteristic of thyratrons when their anodes are connected to a d-c supply is discussed in Chapter 8, page 121. As explained, anode current can be stopped only by opening the anode circuit with a switch or by otherwise

*A good discussion of practical vacuum-tube voltmeters will be found in Terman, *Radio Engineers' Handbook*, pp 929–37. See also Reich, *Theory and Applications of Electron Tubes*, pp 597–620.

reducing the anode potential below the arc-drop potential. Industrial applications frequently require a circuit that closes instantly in response to an impulse of short duration and holds the circuit closed after the initiating impulse has passed.

A circuit typifying *instantaneous lock-in* is that of Fig. 15.4. Relay coil R is connected with the thyratron anode and a d-c supply E_{bb}. When switch S is closed, momentary illumination of the phototube cathode sufficient to make the thyratron grid positive fires the tube and energizes the relay coil, immediately closing its contact. Although the illumination of the phototube is brief, the relay remains energized until switch S is opened to interrupt the thyratron anode current

The instantaneous lock-in circuit of Fig. 15.4 is easily modified to any form of grid control in place of the phototube. Industrial electronic devices of this type are used for alarms, high-speed impulse timing, response to delicate contacts inclined to chatter, and numerous photoelectric register devices (see Chapter 17).

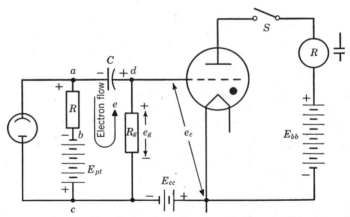

FIG. 15.5. Impulse coupling of the phototube through C to the thyratron grid fires the tube by a sudden increase of illumination.

A modification, Fig. 15.5, of the previous lock-in circuit connects the phototube to the thyratron grid, through capacitor C. This circuit is known as *impulse coupling* of the phototube, responding only to a sudden *change* of illumination on the phototube, and is relatively insensitive to a steady level of illumination. It is employed wherever a phototube is subject to unavoidable illumination from such sources as daylight and lighting fixtures, the intensity of which is variable though the change is relatively slow. Superimposed upon this unavoidable illumination is that from a proper light source, of much greater intensity than the extraneous illumination and controlled for a rapid *change*.

One common example is the scanning of a printed web where reference marks passing a light beam at high velocity suddenly change the beam intensity. Supply E_{pt} excites the phototube and passes current through resistor R. If the phototube is steadily illuminated by extraneous light at a low level, its current is small, and the voltage across R is small. Capacitor C is charged with negative potential at a, nearly the same as b, while the thyratron grid is negative by the bias E_{cc}. If the phototube illumination is suddenly increased, the voltage across R is increased, making the potential of a less negative. The charge voltage of C is then greater than voltage a–c, and C discharges through the grid resistor R_g. Electrons from the discharging capacitor flowing through R_g instantly make the grid terminal d positive to fire the thyratron. The tube remains conducting until switch S is opened. A slow change in phototube illumination alters the voltage across R and affects the voltage to which C is charged, although the thyratron is fired by the rapidly discharging current of C through R_g and, hence, does not depend greatly upon the capacitor charge voltage.

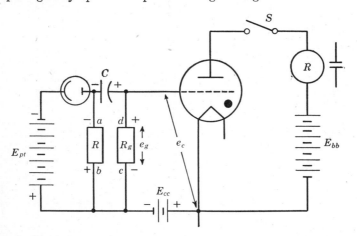

Fig. 15.6. Impulse coupling of the phototube fires the thyratron by a decrease in illumination. The normally bright phototube passes current through R. Voltage a–b across R charges C, as shown. Decreasing illumination reduces voltages across R, discharging C through R and R_g. Positive potential at d fires thyratron.

Operation of the circuit is reversed, Fig. 15.6, so as to fire the thyratron by a sudden decrease in phototube illumination as shown in the figure. Here the normal illumination is intense to cause a large phototube current through R from the supply E_{pt}. Voltage a–b is then relatively large. However, voltage c–d across R_g is small because of the negligible grid current drawn by the thyratron while nonconducting. Capacitor C is charged nearly to the voltage across R with the polarity indicated in the figure.

When phototube illumination is suddenly decreased, current through R and the voltage across it suddenly decrease. The charge voltage of C then exceeds the voltage $a–b$ across R. The capacitor discharges rapidly by its electrons flowing from terminal a to terminal d. Electron flow through R_g manifests a voltage $c–d$ with the polarity indicated. Voltage $c–d$ exceeds bias E_{cc} to render the thyratron grid potential positive. The tube conducts instantly and continues to remain conducting until switch S is opened.

Thyratrons—For Proportional Control of Alternating Current

Many industrial-control devices make use of the proportional control of anode current manifest by connecting an a-c source to the thyratron anode. As explained in Chapter 8, once the thyratron becomes conducting, conduction continues until anode voltage is below the arc potential. With alternating current for the anode source, electrode potential is zero twice for each

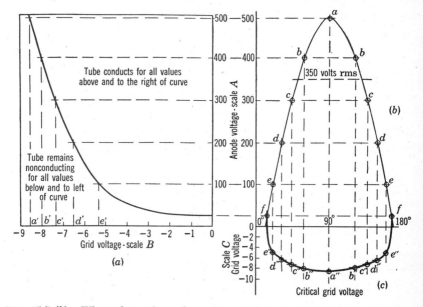

FIG. 15.7 (b). When alternating voltage is applied to the thyratron anode, (a) the tube fires at various grid voltages, corresponding to the instantaneous anode potential, and (c) a critical grid-voltage curve is derived by plotting the grid voltage directly under the points of anode potential.

cycle of applied voltage. Thus, anode current stops flowing at the end of each positive half-cycle of a-c anode voltage. No control of current termination is possible. However, the starting point of current initiation is subject to control by grid potential. In this way the *average* anode current flowing is controlled by the thyratron grid and a basis for proportional control of anode current is established.

An understanding of such control is facilitated by Fig. 15.7, which shows a typical thyratron control characteristic (a) and one positive half-cycle of anode voltage (b). As illustrated by the control characteristic (a), conduction ensues for any given anode potential if the instantaneous grid potential is less negative than a corresponding amount read from the characteristic. Thus, as anode voltage increases from zero to maximum, the negative grid potential required to hold off conduction increases in a like proportion. As the anode voltage rises from zero, conduction cannot begin, regardless of grid voltage, at less voltage than f, the minimum arc drop. For each anode voltage from f to a, there is a corresponding grid voltage 0 to a' at which the tube fires. The values are symmetrical about a as a maximum. These grid voltages projected back to the anode-voltage curve lead to points f to a'', Fig. 15.7c. A curve passing through these points is known as the *critical grid voltage* for the thyratron with a-c anode voltage applied. The scale of anode voltage (a) ususally differs from the scale of grid voltage (c) so as to obtain a more legible critical-voltage curve.

The critical-voltage curve, Fig. 15.7c, means that any instantaneous grid voltage lying above the curve for a corresponding instantaneous anode voltage allows the tube to conduct. The tube remains nonconducting as long as its instantaneous grid voltage is below the curve for the corresponding magnitude of anode voltage.

If alternating potentials are applied to both the anode and grid circuits, the phase relations between them can be shifted. By this means the point at which the actual grid voltage intersects the critical grid voltage can be shifted from nearly zero to 180 degrees (of the anode-voltage positive half-cycle), Fig. 15.8. Assume that the load circuit is a pure resistance, such that anode current can rise and fall immediately. If the grid voltage E_g lags the anode voltage by 45 degrees, Fig. 15.8a, E_g crosses the critical potential at a. E_g is more negative than the critical value to the left of a, and the tube is nonconducting during the first 45 degrees of anode voltage. To the right of a, E_g is less negative than the critical value, instantly establishing anode current. Anode current then continues in sinusoidal fashion for the remainder of the half-cycle or until the applied anode voltage becomes less than the tube arc drop.

As the grid voltage is further shifted to 90 degrees or 135 degrees lag with respect to the anode voltage, Figs. 15.8b and c, conduction is further delayed until E_g crosses the critical curve at b and c respectively.

The *average* anode current is decreased by lagging the grid voltage behind the anode voltage, as inspection of the shaded areas of Fig. 15.8 shows.

No delay of conduction is possible if the grid voltage leads the anode voltage, Fig. 15.8d, because, regardless of the angle of lead, the grid voltage is positive at the beginning of the anode voltage wave, and conduction begins as soon as the positive anode voltage rises to slightly more than the arc-drop voltage.

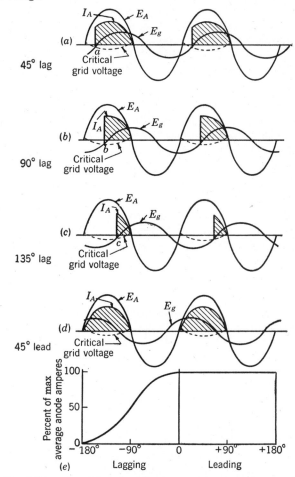

FIG. 15.8. By shifting the phase of grid voltage with respect to anode voltage from 0 to 180 degrees lagging, the thyratron fires for all or none of the positive half-cycle. No control of firing is possible if the grid voltage leads the anode voltage.

By shifting the phase of grid voltage, with respect to anode voltage, from nearly zero to 180 degrees lagging, Fig. 15.8e, the average anode current can be controlled from almost zero to maximum.

If the load (anode) circuit contains inductance, the conditions are considerably altered, Fig. 15.9. If the inductance is large in comparison with the resistance, current through the inductance lags the voltage across its

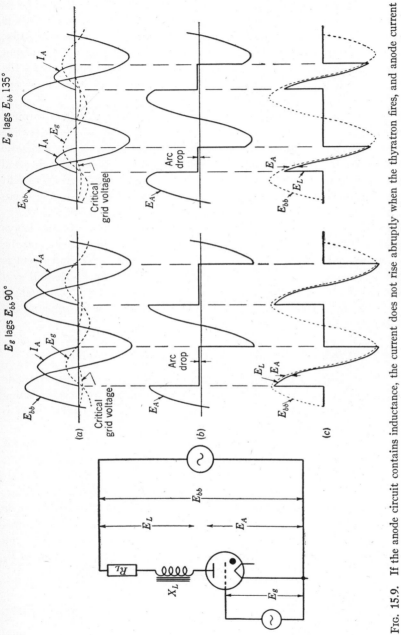

FIG. 15.9. If the anode circuit contains inductance, the current does not rise abruptly when the thyratron fires, and anode current continues to flow after the anode voltage passes through zero.

terminals by approximately 90 degrees. The anode current rises slowly as E_g crosses the critical grid voltage, Fig. 15.9a, to fire the tube. The rate of current rise depends on the inductance. The voltage across the tube, Fig. 15.9b, decreases instantly from the high value existing before current flow to the arc-drop voltage when the tube fires. The voltage across the load circuit (c) instantly rises to the anode-circuit supply voltage except for the tube arc-drop voltage.

Anode current continues after the anode supply voltage passes through zero because of the load inductance. The tube continues to conduct while load current is maintained by the return of energy stored in the magnetic field of the inductance. Meanwhile the anode supply voltage has reversed polarity as does the inductive-load voltage, Fig. 15.9c. When anode current stops, the inverse voltage across the tube immediately rises to the open-circuit anode supply voltage, and the load-circuit voltage drops to zero.

Lagging the grid voltage further with respect to the anode voltage delays thyratron firing and reduces both the amplitude of anode current and the conducting cycle of anode current. The average value of anode current is controlled by adjusting the lagging phase angle between anode and grid voltages, the same as for a resistance load. Control curves similar to Fig. 15.8e can be constructed, although the problem is more complex,† because a separate curve is required for each value of L/R.

Circuits for Shifting the Phase of the Grid Voltage

Circuits, designed to alter the phase relation between grid and anode voltages, are called *phase-shift circuits*. Many schemes for accomplishing this result are used, although the fundamentals of all of them are reduced to the few basic methods described herewith.

The phase-shifting circuit of Fig. 15.10a, consisting of a center-tapped transformer winding, fixed capacitor, and variable resistor, is compact, inexpensive, and simple to design. Inphase voltages E_1 and E_2 are connected to R and C in series. Voltage E_{bb} typifies the anode supply voltage, which can be obtained either from a winding on the same transformer or from a separate source. The capacitor current through the resistor assures that the voltage drop across R leads the voltage across C. However, the vector sum of these two voltages must always total the constant sum of E_1

†For data concerning this effect see:

MIT staff, *Applied Electronics*, pp 283–7.

Vedder and Puchlowski, "Theory of Rectifier — D-C Motor Drive," *AIEE Transactions*, Vol 62, 1943, pp 863–9.

Chin, "Gaseous Rectifier Circuits," *Electronics*, April 1945, pp 138–44 and May 1945, pp 132–7.

Puchlowski, "Voltage and Current Relations for Controlled Rectification with Inductive and Generative Loads," *AIEE Transactions*, Vol 64, May 1945, pp 255–60.

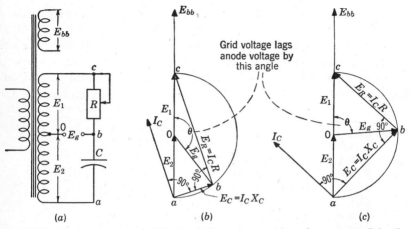

FIG. 15.10. A capacitor phase-shift circuit depends upon the voltage across R leading the voltage across C. Grid voltage E_g is constant in magnitude, but shifted in phase with respect to anode voltage E_{bb} by varying R.

and E_2, and they are always 90 degrees apart. Hence, the junction between capacitor and resistor voltages, point b, follows the path of a semicircle with a and c as limits. This is indicated in Fig. 15.10b. The magnitude of grid voltage $0–b$ remains constant, although its angle with respect to E_{bb} is changed by the adjustment of variable resistor R. If R is large, E_g lags E_{bb} by a relatively large angle, Fig. 15.10b. Decreasing R brings E_g more nearly in phase with E_{bb}, Fig. 15.10c.

Similar phase-shift control is obtained by using a reactor L and resistor R, Fig. 15.11. In this case, the voltage across reactor L leads the voltage

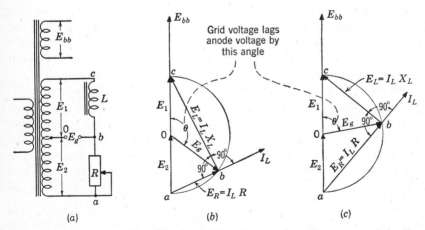

FIG. 15.11. A reactor phase-shift circuit depends upon the voltage across L leading the voltage across R. Grid voltage E_g lags E_{bb}, the angle varied by the value of R.

across R. Increasing the magnitude of R decreases the angle of lag between E_g and E_{bb}.

The circuit of Fig. 15.11 is sometimes modified to use a fixed resistor and variable reactor. One useful circuit of this type, Fig. 15.12, employs a *saturating reactor*‡ L having a-c windings b–c connected in the phase-shifting circuit and a d-c winding e–f. The effective reactance is altered by the

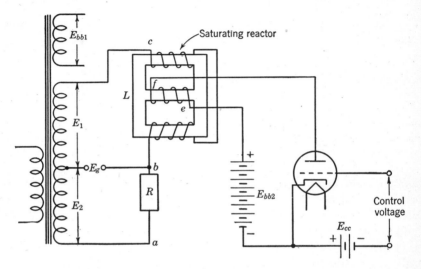

FIG. 15.12. A saturable-reactor phase-shift circuit controls the lagging angle of E_g by the magnitude of current through d-c winding e–f.

current through d-c winding e–f. The larger this direct current, the lower the effective a-c reactance b–c. One method of varying the d-c saturating current employs a pliotron with its anode current proportional to the controlling grid potential. The circuit of Fig. 15.12 permits the control of a relatively large amount of power through the thyratron by a small amount of power input to the pliotron constituting one type of power amplifier.

Another phase-shifting scheme frequently used in connection with polyphase equipment employs a phase-shifting transformer, similar in construction to a slip-ring type of three-phase motor having a three-phase wound stator and either a single- or three-phase rotor. If the mechanical position of the rotor is varied with respect to the stator, the phase angle of secondary or rotor voltage is changed in relation to the stator voltage. The thyratron anode voltage is usually in phase with the stator supply and the rotor cir-

‡See Wentz, "Saturable-Core Reactors Now Smaller, More Capable," *Westinghouse Engineer*, November 1943, pp 115–7; also, Harry Holubow, "D-C Saturable Reactors for Control Purposes," *Electronic Industries*, March 1945, pp 76–9.

cuit connected to the thyratron grid. Mechanical variation of the shaft position controls the thyratron firing angle by the shifting phase position or rotor voltage.

Peaking Transformers

If one of the afore-mentioned phase-shift methods is used to effect grid control, as discussed in connection with Fig. 15.8, a variation of the firing angle sometimes results from several uncontrolled variables. For example, a change in line voltage affects the magnitude of the grid voltage, which then alters the exact position at which the grid voltage crosses the curve of tube critical grid voltage. The firing angle of the thyratron is changed slightly by this effect. Also, the tube critical-grid-voltage characteristic changes slightly with ambient temperature variation, contributing to a change of firing angle.

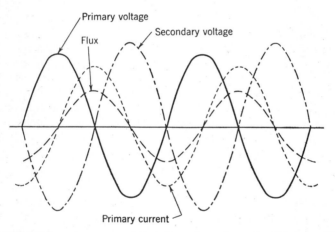

FIG. 15.13.   Voltage, current, and flux alternations of a conventional transformer.

Some applications require more accurate control of the firing point than is obtained by using any of the previous phase-shifting circuits. The control for resistance welding, for example, requires precise control of the firing angle and exact repetition from one cycle to another.

To review the conditions present in a conventional transformer design, Fig. 15.13, the primary no-load or magnetizing current lags the primary voltage 90 degrees, and transformer flux follows the alternations of primary current. Maximum secondary voltage is induced corresponding to the *greatest rate of change* of flux and, therefore, lags the alternating flux by 90 degrees. Secondary voltage is thus 180 degrees lagging the primary voltage.

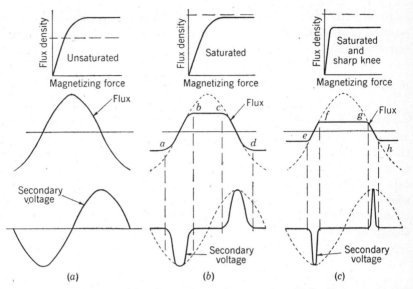

FIG. 15.14 (*a*). Flux and secondary voltage alternate sinusoidally if the core is not saturated. (*b*) Saturation flattens the flux alternations, and the secondary voltage becomes peaked. (*c*) The choice of core material narrows the secondary-voltage peaks.

If the transformer is designed so as to operate below the knee of the core saturation characteristic, Fig. 15.14a, both the flux and secondary voltage alternate sinusoidally. If the cross section of the core material is reduced, the iron becomes saturated, Fig. 15.14b, and the flux starts to increase but cannot rise beyond *b*, the saturation point. The flux remains constant to *c* as the primary current declines. Secondary voltage is induced only by a *changing* flux. Hence, a peak of secondary voltage occurs as the flux changes *a* to *b* and once again, *c* to *d*.

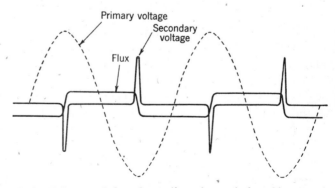

FIG. 15.15. Voltage and flux alternations of a typical peaking transformer.

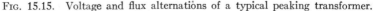

These peaks of secondary voltage are made still narrower by selecting a core material of which the saturation characteristic manifests a sharp knee, Fig. 15.14c. The core becomes saturated early in the primary-current cycle, and the *changing* flux is restricted to *e–f* and *g–h*. In this way, the peaks of secondary voltage are kept narrow and accurately coincide with the point where primary current passes through zero. Transformers of this design are known as *peaking transformers*, with a typical characteristic, Fig. 15.15, exhibiting narrow peaks of secondary voltage lagging the primary voltage 180 degrees.

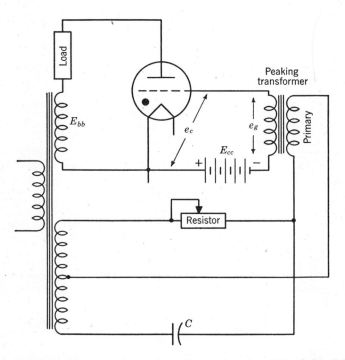

FIG. 15.16. The peaking transformer is used in conjunction with a hold-off bias and phase-shifting circuit to fire the thyratron at each positive secondary-voltage peak.

Peaking Transformer for Thyratron Control

A peaking transformer connected in the thyratron grid circuit, Fig. 15.16, accurately controls the firing point. The instantaneous grid voltage e_c is the algebraic sum of negative bias voltage E_{cc} often called the *hold-off bias*, and the peaking transformer secondary voltage E_g. The transformer primary winding is phase-shifted by any one of the previous schemes as

Fig. 15.10. The hold-off bias E_{cc} is made sufficiently negative, Fig. 15.17, so that it is well below the thyratron critical grid voltage, and no anticipated variations in either the bias voltage or firing characteristic will cause the tube to fire extraneously. A positive peaking transformer secondary voltage makes the thyratron grid potential positive — well above the critical grid voltage such that definite conduction of the thyratron is assured.

As shown by Fig. 15.17, the tube fires at the instant the peaked voltage crosses the critical grid voltage. Changes in the d-c bias, magnitude of peaked voltage, or the tube firing characteristic affect the firing angle negligibly. By a shift in the phase of the peaked voltage with respect to the anode voltage, the firing angle can be adjusted over a wide range as previously explained.

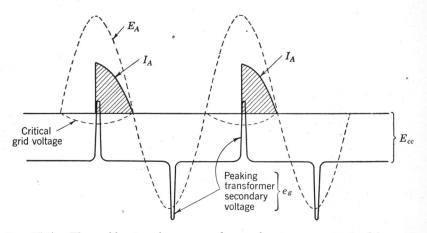

FIG. 15.17. The peaking transformer secondary peaks assure an accurate firing angle and is undisturbed by normal variation of line voltage or tube temperature.

Inverse-Parallel Connection of Thyratrons for Control of Alternating Current

Thyratrons (and ignitrons) are half-wave rectifiers, although, by the use of two tubes in an *inverse-parallel* connection, Fig. 15.18, the pair controls alternating current through the load circuit. Tubes used in this connection are sometimes spoken of as "electronic contactors," because their action is similar to that of a switch. As a circuit to control alternating current, these devices possess the advantage of incredible speed, are capable of repeated closings of the circuit at any desired point on the voltage wave, and always open the circuit at the zero of supply voltage (actually, neither the thyratron nor the ignitron can open a circuit; by control of its grid, it can be rendered nonconducting on the next positive wave of anode voltage).

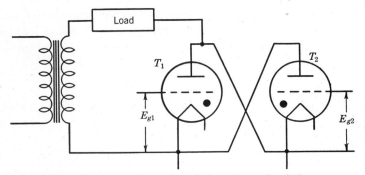

FIG. 15.18. Alternating current is conducted through a pair of thyratrons arranged in an inverse-parallel connection.

A pair of thyratrons in inverse-parallel connection allows passage of alternating current, Fig. 15.19, by conducting positive half-cycles through T_1 and negative half-cycles through T_2. In this way, the full a-c wave passes through the load circuit. (The grid voltage of Fig. 15.19 is purposely shown leading the anode voltage to render the tubes conducting for their full half-cycle.) By the use of one of the phase-shifting circuits previously described

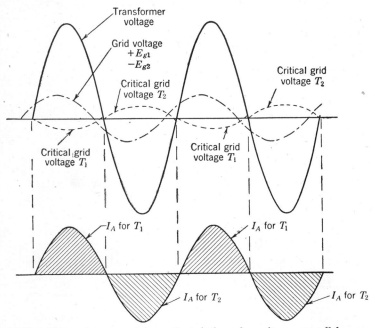

FIG. 15.19. Alternating current is conducted through an inverse-parallel connection of thyratrons by tube T_1 conducting positive half-cycles and T_2 conducting negative half-cycles.

conduction can be delayed through both tubes and the rms alternating load current is reduced to less than the maximum. One use for such a circuit is electronic heat control of resistance welders, discussed further in Chapter 16, page 416.

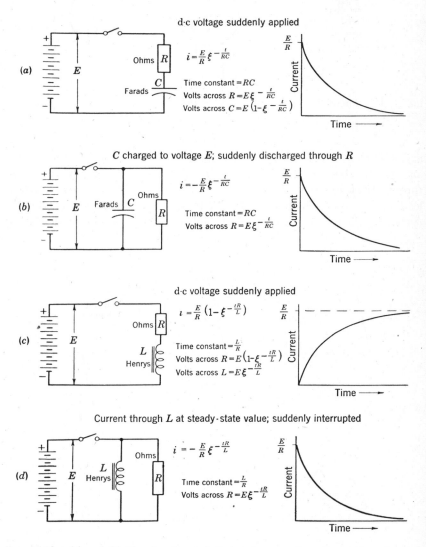

Fig. 15.20.　(a) and (b), the charging and discharging capacitor current through a resistor decreases exponentially, the rate depending upon the time constant or product of resistance and capacitance. (c) and (d), the charging and discharging current of inductance and resistance in series depends upon the ratio L/R.

Circuits for Electronic Timing

If a d-c potential is suddenly applied to a capacitor and resistor in series, Fig. 15.20a, the initial current neglects the presence of the capacitor. All of the battery voltage appears across the resistor, and none across the capacitor. As electrons flow into the capacitor, the voltage across C increases and decreases across R. Ultimately, C becomes fully charged, the current is zero, and the full battery voltage appears across C.

A similar action is obtained when the capacitor is discharged into the resistor, Fig. 15.20b. In this case, C is fully charged to the battery voltage and the switch opened.

Similar circuits combining a resistor with a reactor, Figs. 15.20c and d are sometimes used as time-delay circuits, with characteristics as illustrated. In all data of Fig. 15.20, R is expressed in ohms, C in farads, and L in henrys, and ϵ is the base of natural logarithms, or 2.718.

The time constant of a circuit is a useful yardstick by which the performance of the circuit can be judged. For example, assume the discharge connection, Fig. 15.20b is used in a circuit wherein the d-c potential is 100 volts, R is one megohm, and C is one microfarad. The time constant is 1 second, that is, $(1 \times 10^6)(1 \times 10^{-6}) = 1$ second. As shown in Fig. 15.21a, 1 second after initiation of the discharge cycle the voltage *remaining* across the capacitor is $1/2.718$ of the original voltage, or 37 volts, approximately. At the end of another interval equal to the time constant the voltage is reduced by another multiple of $1/2.718$, or to 13.5 volts.

If the resistor is increased to 10 megohms, Fig. 15.21b, the time constant is now 10 seconds, which means that 10 seconds are required to discharge the voltage down to 37 volts. Changing the value of resistance and capacitance without changing the magnitude of their product does not change the time constant and does not alter the performance of the circuit. This is demonstrated in Fig. 15.21c.

The time constant of any circuit is a useful factor of merit. It provides the simple rule that approximately 37 percent voltage of a *discharging* circuit remains for each elapsed interval equal to the time constant. If the circuit is *charging* a capacitor in series with a resistor, then 37 percent voltage remains out of the capacitor for each elapsed time-constant interval.

The timing circuits of Fig. 15.20 are basic. They are combined into electronic circuits in several ways. Sometimes the voltage across a charging circuit resistor is connected to the grid of either a pliotron or a thyratron. In other schemes, the voltage across a charging capacitor is more useful, and frequently the voltage across a discharging capacitor circuit is used. Electronic circuits, combining these fundamentals to obtain electronic timing, are discussed more in detail in Chapter 16.

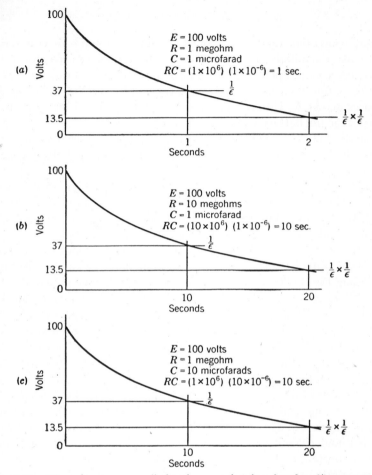

Fig. 15.21. The voltage across a discharging capacitor is reduced to 37 percent of the original voltage for each interval equal to a multiple of the circuit time constant.

Circuits for Regulating Current and Voltage

Some electronic circuits require a current or potential held constant to within closer tolerance than is possible by deriving the circuit power directly from an available source. As examples, cathodes heated directly from a storage battery are subject to a current variation as the battery voltage declines because of discharging, or grid potential derived from a rectified a-c supply varies in proportion to fluctuations in the a-c source potential. These conditions are improved by using one or all three devices.

Current is held reasonably constant throughout variations in applied potential by means of a *ballast tube* connected in series with the circuit.

A ballast tube consists of a filament of small cross section, enclosed in a glass envelope containing a gas at low pressure for the conduction of heat from the filament to the enve-lope. The filament temperature coefficient of resistivity is such that as the voltage across it varies within the normal range of operation, Fig. 15.22, the current through the circuit remains appreciably constant. Ballast or current-regulator tubes are man-ufactured in a variety of ratings from approximately 4 to 50 volts with a current rating from 200

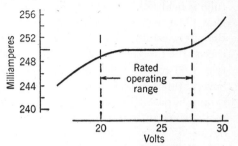

Fig. 15.22. Characteristic of a typical current regulator tube. Within the rated voltage operating range the current remains nearly constant.

milliamperes to 2 amperes. Because the control characteristics of these tubes depend upon the temperature of a wire filament, they do not respond rapidly and are intended to regulate for slow changes of source voltage.

A source of constant d-c *potential* is obtained by using a *voltage-regulator tube*, Fig. 15.23, connected in series with a resistor across the varying input voltage as Fig. 15.24. They

Fig. 15.23. A typical voltage-regulator tube consists of two electrodes in a gas-filled envelope. If current is within the region of normal glow (see Fig. 5.9) the voltage across the tube remains constant. Illustration approximately two-thirds size. (*Courtesy RCA*)

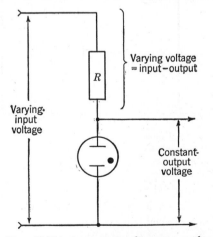

Fig. 15.24. A constant voltage across the voltage-regulator tube is obtained, providing the value of series resistance is chosen to assure the tube current is within the rated operating range.

are cold-cathode two-electrode glow-discharge gas tubes. Their characteristics are discussed in Chapter 5, page 71. A constant voltage across the tube is held only as long as the discharge current remains within a normal glow. The series resistance must be chosen to assure a minimum current definitely establishing the glow; the maximum discharge current must not exceed the tube rating. Voltage-regulator tubes are available for ratings between 60 to 150 volts and for a current not exceeding 30 milliamperes. Several tubes can be connected in series to regulate for a higher voltage, but cannot be paralleled for a higher current. For this reason, they are of greatest use as constant-reference voltage sources and are not regarded as a power device.

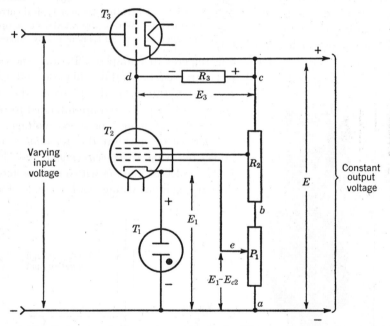

Fig. 15.25. Constant reference voltage E_1, obtained from voltage regulator tube T_1 is used to control the pentode amplifier T_2 and power triode T_3 to regulate output voltage E.

One method used to provide a constant potential source at a somewhat greater power level is that shown in Fig. 15.25. A power tube T_3 is connected between the varying-input direct voltage and constant-output. Regulator tube T_1 holds the cathode of T_2 constant at E_1 volts above the negative supply terminal. Portion $e-a$ of the regulated voltage across potentiometer P_1 is fed to the grid of T_2. The values are chosen such that $e-a$ is equal to voltage E_1 of the regulator tube less E_{c2}, the negative grid voltage of T_2. Any variation of d-c output voltage E affects the grid potential of T_2 because of a variation of the portion e–a of output voltage as compared to the constant reference E_1. The anode current of T_2 through resistor R_3, establishes the grid voltage c–d of power tube T_3. A rise in input voltage tending to increase the output E makes the grid of T_2 less negative (that is, the positive potential e–a increases) increasing its anode current through R_3, making the grid of T_3 more negative, and raising the cathode–anode voltage across T_3. The rise in voltage across T_3 is equal to the rise in supply potential (nearly) such that a constant-output voltage is maintained.

Circuits of this type are constructed of tubes readily available to obtain a d-c output of several hundred volts and 500 milliamperes for which the voltage is held constant within 1 volt. These regulators are used for laboratory instrument and some radio applications requiring a constant d-c power supply from 50 to 250 watts.

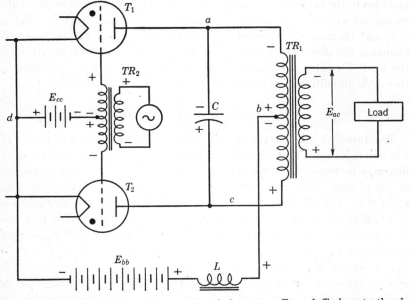

Fig. 15.26. A parallel inverter consisting of thyratrons T_1 and T_2 inverts the d-c supply E_{bb} to alternating current through the load by alternate conduction through the transformer winding a–b and b–c.

Thyratron Inverters from Direct to Alternating Current

The principal elements of a parallel-type thyratron inverter, Fig. 15.26, for inversion of a d-c supply E_{bb} to an alternating voltage E_{ac} are thyratrons T_1 and T_2, capacitor C, and transformer TR_1. A small source of alternating potential§ excites the grid transformer TR_2, alternately driving the grids of T_1 or T_2 positive. Assume the grid of T_1 to become positive, firing T_1. Electrons then flow from the anode of T_1, through the primary a–b of TR_1, and also to terminal a of the capacitor. The changing flux of TR_1 induces a voltage b–c in the transformer winding equal to that across a–b, and C is charged to a voltage of about $2E_{bb}$ with negative polarity at a. The changing transformer flux also induces a secondary voltage TR_1 and current flows through the load circuit. A half-cycle later the alternating grid voltage makes the grid of T_2 positive, instantly firing T_2. At this moment both T_1 and T_2 are conducting, with T_2 virtually connecting C across T_1. The cathode–anode potential across T_1 immediately changes to the charge voltage of C minus the small arc drop of T_2 with the negative capacitor terminal connected to the anode of T_1. A strong negative voltage is thus suddenly applied to the anode of T_1, immediately extinguishing it. Electrons then flow from the anode of T_2, through transformer winding c–b, back to E_{bb}, and also to the bottom terminal of C. Capacitor C is rapidly discharged and recharged with opposite polarity by a flow of electrons through winding a–b, and then to E_{bb}. Current through the primary of TR_1 is reversed, changing the direction of induced secondary voltage and current through the load. Thyratrons T_1 and T_2 are alternately fired and extinguished by this cycle and alternating current flows through the load circuit.‖

Thyratron-Circuit Details

The function of a thyratron grid is discussed in Chapter 8, page 121, wherein it is shown that the grid current, once the tube becomes conducting, may increase to a harmful degree because the grid becomes immersed in the plasma. This must be prevented by connecting a current-limiting resistor R_g, Fig. 15.27, in series with the thyratron grid. The magnitude of this resistance is calculated to limit the maximum grid current to a safe amount after the tube becomes conducting. The resistance differs for various thyratrons, 100 000 ohms being a figure frequently used.

The current-limiting grid resistor is inherently a part of every control in which thyratrons are used. The resistor is not included in many of the basic circuits of this text, because these circuits are descriptive of function only. They are usually included in most working thyratron circuits.

§This may either be an external source of low power or can be taken directly from the a-c output terminals of the inverter itself.

‖The wave form of current through the load is greatly influenced by the load constants and the value of capacitor C. For further details on this and other types of inverter circuits see Dow, *Fundamentals of Engineering Electronics*, pp 527–34; also, C. F. Wagner, "Parallel Inverter with Inductive Load," *AIEE Transactions*, Vol 55, September 1936, p 970, and Reich, *Theory and Applications of Electron Tubes*, pp 477–502.

Another detail frequently associated with a thyratron is the connection of a small capacitor directly between the thyratron grid and its cathode, such as C_g, Fig. 15.27. This capacitor is used to prevent *shock-over* of the tube when a positive potential is suddenly applied to the anode. Shock-over is a tendency for the grid to assume a positive polarity at the instant when positive potential is applied to the anode, even though a negative bias voltage is applied to the grid circuit. This effect is caused by momentarily altering the voltage distribution from anode–grid–cathode within the tube because of the interelectrode capacitance of the tube elements. C_g prevents the tube from

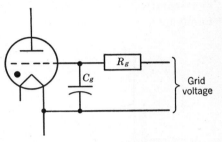

FIG. 15.27.   Details of thyratron circuits frequently include grid-current-limiting resistor R_g and a capacitor C_g to prevent shock-over when positive voltage is suddenly applied to the tube anode.

accidentally firing when positive anode potential is applied. The value of C_g depends upon the particular thyratron used; 0.005 microfarad being average for three-electrode tubes and 0.001 microfarad for some shield-grid thyratrons.

THYRATRON SWEEP CIRCUITS

Many electronic functions utilize a voltage increasing linearly with time. One illustration of this principle is the timing reference voltage used to move the trace of a cathode-ray oscilloscope across the viewing screen at a uniform rate. But this is only one part of the problem. Once the trace has been traversed to one extreme position, it must be returned as rapidly as possible to the original starting point to repeat the cycle.

The principle is illustrated by Fig. 15.28, wherein it is assumed that an electron beam is positioned to the extreme left of the screen by voltage zero¶ and is moved to the extreme right position by voltage m. As motion starts, the beam is traversed from left to right at a constant rate by the uniformly increasing voltage 0–a. Upon reaching the right-hand limit corresponding to voltage m, the beam is rapidly returned to the left-hand position by instantly decreasing the voltage from a to b. The cycle is immediately repeated by uniformly increasing the voltage from b to c and again returned by the rapidly decreasing voltage c–d. The beam is thereby trav-

---

¶Deflection of an electron beam by voltage applied to deflecting plates of a cathode-ray tube is explained in Chapter 4, p 42. For greater detail, refer to MIT staff, *Applied Electronics*, pp 19–36.

ersed across the screen at a uniform rate represented by the time interval
0–b, b–c, etc., and returned by a–b, c–d, etc.

Circuits for performing this function are known as *sweep circuits* and the
representative curve is called a *saw-tooth* curve. The time required for uniformly increasing the voltage 0–a is the *sweep time* and determines the *sweep*

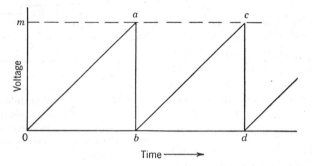

FIG. 15.28.   An ideal saw-tooth curve for electronic sweep circuits increases the voltage
from zero to maximum uniformly, as 0–a then instantly returns to zero a–b. The cycle
immediately repeats b–c–d, etc.

frequency. The interval required for the voltage to decrease rapidly from a
to b is the *retrace time* and must be a very small fraction of the sweep time
for the circuit to be of practical value. The saw-tooth curve of Fig. 15.28
represents the ideal to be approached as near as possible, although practical
circuits never attain these hypothetical characteristics.

One simple type of sweep circuit, Fig. 15.29a, employs a thyratron T and
capacitor C charged by source E_{bb} through resistor R_1. As the capacitor is
charged through R_1, the voltage across its terminal increases exponentially
with the polarity indicated. At some predetermined voltage, the thyratron
cathode–anode voltage becomes sufficient to start conduction of the tube.
The capacitor then rapidly discharges through the thyratron, and the discharge current continues until the voltage across C is reduced below the
arc-drop of the tube. The thyratron is then extinguished, and the charging
cycle once more repeats.

The characteristic is manifest by Fig. 15.29b. Voltage across the capacitor
rises exponentially, and for this rea on the straight sides of the idealized
saw-tooth curve, Fig. 15.28, can never be equaled by the practical circuit.
However, if the thyratron is fired at a voltage corresponding to a small
fraction of voltage E_{bb}, only the reasonably linear part of the exponential
curve is used. As the capacitor is rapidly discharged through the thyratron,
voltage decreases according to the curve a–b. By the proper choice of circuit

constants* the time interval required for this discharge is short, although it is never zero, as indicated by the straight vertical side of the idealized saw-tooth curve, Fig. 15.28.

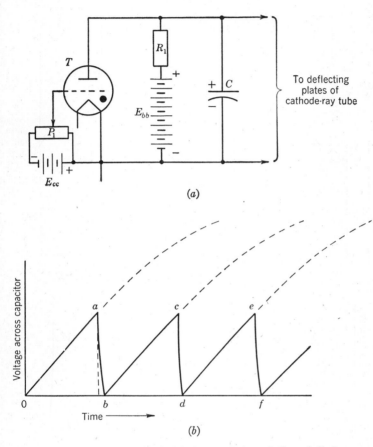

(a)

(b)

FIG. 15.29.   A practical sweep circuit (a) charges C through R_1 and discharges rapidly through thyratron T. The saw-tooth curve (b) is reasonably straight 0–a by firing T at voltage peaks a, c, e, restricted to a small portion of charging voltage E_{bb}. The capacitor is rapidly discharged a–b.

An improved sweep characteristic is obtained using the circuit of Fig. 15.30a, by which capacitor C is charged from source E_{bb} through pentode T_2. In this circuit, T_2 charges the capacitor at a constant-current rate. The features of the pentode that afford this characteristic are discussed in

*See Neustadt, "Thyratron Linear Time Axis for Cathode-Ray Oscillograph," *Electronics*, April 1945, pp 198–9.

Chapter 7. If the capacitor charging current is held constant through T_2, the voltage across its terminals rises uniformly with respect to time, as Fig. 15.30b shows. The voltage across C is also impressed across thyratron

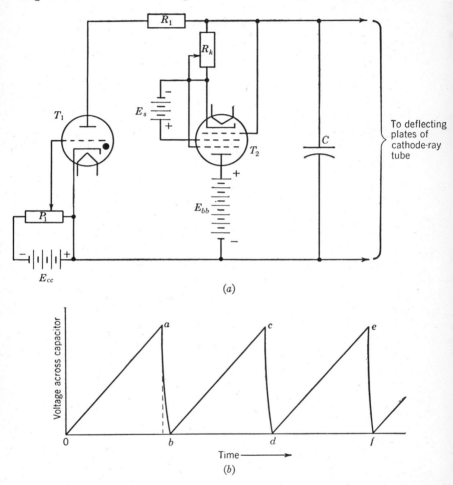

(a)

(b)

FIG. 15.30. An improved sweep circuit (a) charges C through pentode T_2, adjusted for constant anode current. The saw-tooth curve (b) is then straight 0–a while charging C and the discharge a–b through thyratron T_1 and resistor R_1 is rapid.

T_1, which fires at a predetermined cathode–anode voltage, and the capacitor is rapidly discharged through T_1, resistor R_1 limiting the discharge current. In this way, the voltage across C, Fig. 15.30b increases uniformly with respect to time and is decreased rapidly. The saw-tooth curve thus generated approaches the ideal to a reasonable degree.

The sweep frequency, or time required for building up the voltage across C to fire thyratron T_1, is adjusted by control of the control-grid bias of pentode T_2 and/or adjustment of the thyratron grid bias. The range of frequency required of practical apparatus demands further adjustment of the circuit by the selection of several values for capacitor C, usually accomplished by the inclusion of a multicircuit selector switch to change the value of C over a wide range of adjustment.

SUMMARY

The *basic circuits* of Chapter 15 illustrate how components are connected to achieve some specific result, one or more being interconnected to harness an electronic device to perform a task usually distinct from the art of electronics itself.

Voltage dividers are employed to divide the output of a single d-c source into two or more potentials, each serving as an individual source.

Cathode bias is derived from anode current flowing through a resistor connected in the tube cathode lead.

Proportional control of direct current is afforded by proportional variation of grid potential applied to a pliotron.

Instantaneous control of direct current is afforded by thyratrons, using a d-c anode-voltage source with grid bias either gradually or suddenly reduced. Once conducting, anode current continues until interrupted by external means.

Instantaneous lock-in circuits respond suddenly to an impulse applied to a thyratron grid. Although the duration of grid impulse is but a few microseconds, anode current continues until interrupted by external means.

Impulse control of grid potential responds only to a rapid change of the controlling medium, such as a sudden change of phototube illumination.

Proportional control of alternating current is afforded by thyratrons with the anode source alternating current and grid potential controlled to start conduction, corresponding to a variable angle of the anode-voltage phase.

Critical grid voltage denotes the least negative thyratron grid potential required to prevent conduction as a-c anode voltage changes from zero to maximum to zero of the applied positive half-cycle

By phase-shifting the relation of thyratron-applied a-c grid potential to a-c anode potential average anode current through the tube (and load) is controlled. A reduction of load current to less than the circuit maximum is achieved only when grid potential lags the applied anode voltage. When the phase of grid voltage leads the anode voltage, load current manifests a constant maximum, regardless of the leading angle.

Phase-shift circuits, of many types, are used to control the phase angle between thyratron grid and anode potential for the proportional control of load current.

Peaking transformers afford most accurate control of thyratron firing angle by virtue of their peaked secondary-voltage characteristic, thus affecting grid potential by strong pulses constant in angular relation to the applied anode voltage.

The *inverse-parallel* connection of two thyratrons (or ignitrons) affords electronic conduction of alternating current. Load current is started or stopped, or its magnitude can be varied by control of tube grid voltage.

Timing circuits are based on these characteristics:

(a) Voltage across a capacitor charged in series with a resistor (from a d-c source) rises exponentially in proportion to elapsed time.

(b) Voltage across a capacitor, previously charged from a d-c source, then discharged through a resistor, decreases exponentially in proportion to elapsed time.

(c) Voltage across a reactor in series with a resistor and d-c source is a maximum as the circuit is closed and then decreases exponentially in proportion to elapsed time.

(d) Voltage across a reactor paralleled by a resistor, with current previously established through the reactor, decreases exponentially in proportion to elapsed time after current through the reactor is interrupted.

Constant current through a circuit is achieved by using a *ballast* regulator tube.

Constant potential of a d-c source is achieved by using a two-element gas-filled *voltage-regulator* tube.

Inversion of direct to alternating current is achieved by connecting two thyratrons in an inverter circuit. Alternate conduction of the tubes make possible the alternations of transformer current necessary for a-c load current.

Sweep circuits, used as the timing base for cathode-ray oscillographs, depend upon the timing principles previously summarized with special emphasis to attain (a) linearity of voltage increase in proportion to time and (b) very rapid collapse of the voltage thus linearly attained at the desired magnitude of potential.

REFERENCES

MIT Electrical Engineering Staff, *Applied Electronics*, John Wiley & Sons, New York, 1943, pp 7–55 and 283–7.

Jacob Millman and Samuel Seely, *Electronics*, McGraw-Hill Book Co., New York, 1941, pp 419–32.

Herbert J. Reich, *Theory and Applications of Electron Tubes*, McGraw-Hill Book Co., New York, 1944, pp 505–53.

W. G. Dow, *Fundamentals of Engineering Electronics*, John Wiley & Sons, New York, 1937, pp 56–96 and 522–34.

F. E. Terman, *Radio Engineers' Handbook*, McGraw-Hill Book Co., New York, 1943, pp 929–37.

W. D. Cockrell, *Industrial Electronic Control*, McGraw-Hill Book Co., New York, 1944, pp 80–7 and 129–49.

C. B. Stadum, "Basic Electronic Circuits for Industrial Functions," *Product Engineering*, February 1944.

P. T. Chin and E. E. Moyer, "Principles of Grid Control for Thyratrons," *AIEE* Technical Paper 45–62, presented January 1945.

P. T. Chin, "Gaseous Rectifier Circuits," *Electronics*, April 1945, pp 138–43, and May 1945, pp 132–7.

K. P. PUCHLOWSKI, "Voltage and Current Relations for Controlled Rectification with Inductive and Generative Loads," *AIEE Transactions*, Vol 64, May 1945, pp 255–60.

HARRY HOLUBOW, "D-C Saturable Reactors for Control Purposes," *Electronic Industries*, March 1945, pp 76–9.

E. H. VEDDER and K. P. PUCHLOWSKI, "Theory of Rectifier — D-C Motor Drive," *AIEE Transactions*, Vol 62, 1943, pp 863–9.

E. C. WENTZ, "Saturable-Core Reactors Now Smaller, More Capable," *Westinghouse Engineer*, November 1943, pp 115–17.

H. NEUSTADT, "Thyratron Linear Time Axis for Cathode-Ray Oscillograph," *Electronics*, April 1945, pp 198–9.

AUGUST HUND, *High-Frequency Measurements*, McGraw-Hill Book Co., 1933, pp 136–61.

Chapter 16

INDUSTRIAL APPLICATION OF
ELECTRONIC CONTROL

Beginning about 1930, industrial plants gradually came to accept the steadily increasing parcels of industrial electronic-control equipment, sometimes reluctantly, at other times because no other method of accomplishing the desired results existed. In those early days, electronic devices were given such nonvital tasks as opening doors, or signaling upon interruption of a light beam, and other functions that mattered little if electronics should fail. Gradually, their reliability increased until the operation of an entire machine, even the production of an entire plant now may depend upon the unfailing response of an electronic tube. From among the many industrial electronic devices, a few of the most frequently encountered have been chosen for discussion here.

Electronic Timing

The varied application of electronic timers is almost without limit. For industrial use the timing interval may range from $1/120$ second to several minutes. Short intervals, $1/120$ to 1 second, are commonly applied to resistance welding where current flows through the metals joined for a brief period, or else the heat flowing by conduction away from the weld may raise the temperature of metal adjacent to the weld to higher than an acceptable limit. More general applications usually require a timing interval of a few seconds to several minutes. In either case, electronic timing is measured by capacitor charge or discharge, as explained in Chapter 15. For both, the popularity of electronic timing is largely a result of the ease with which the timing is adjusted, often remote from the tubes themselves, and the accuracy with which electronic circuits repeat the measurement of each interval.

One timing circuit frequently employed for industrial application, Fig. 16.1, uses a single thyratron, a control relay CR, and the circuits energized by an a-c supply.* The complete diagram, Fig. 16.1a, shows the tube nonconducting and control relay de-energized while time-initiating switch

---

*For other timing devices similar to the one described see Cockrell, *Industrial Electronic Control*, pp 177–83.

S is open. With S open, only the grid circuit is energized, as Fig. 16.1b shows. Following this circuit from L_1 to L_2, resistors R_1, R_2, and potentiometer P_1 divide the supply voltage, such that, during the half-cycles when terminal L_1 is positive, voltage ce is connected across the tube grid-to-cathode. Positive terminal c of this circuit connects to the thyratron grid. Cathode k connects to e through R_4. The tube then functions as a diode, the grid acting as a small anode to rectify voltage ce and charge capacitor C_1 with the polarity shown in the figure.

When switch S is closed, Fig. 16.1c, the cathode is connected directly to L_1 and the anode to L_2. The tube is energized and ready to conduct. Resistor R_4 is shunted across the a-c supply. The grid circuit is represented by the dotted section of the diagram. Inspection of the grid circuit shows that voltage to it comprises the instantaneous sum of alternating voltage a–c of the potentiometer circuit together with the direct voltage c–f across capacitor C_1, charged during the "off" interval while S is open. The conditions found upon closing S are more clearly indicated by Fig. 16.2 from which it is evident that a large negative voltage derived from the capacitor charge is placed on the grid and the tube does not fire. The charge of C_1 gradually diminishes by discharging through R_3 (Chapter 15, page 374) and the instantaneous sum of a-c and d-c potential approaches zero with each cycle. Eventually, at the instant of the greatest positive potential at c, the instantaneous grid voltage crosses the thyratron-critical-grid-voltage curve and the tube immediately conducts, as during the seventh cycle, Fig. 16.2. Relay coil CR is energized, and its contacts are operated. From here on the part played by the contacts of CR does not concern the electronic circuit.

The tube is nonconducting with negative anode voltage applied, as between the seventh and eighth cycle. To prevent the relay coil current from dropping to zero (which would cause the contacts to chatter) capacitor C_2 is connected across the coil, and some of the electrons stored in the capacitor while the thyratron is conducting pass through CR coil to sustain current while the tube anode is negative. During the eighth and all succeeding cycles, the thyratron conducts to send current through CR coil and replenish the charge on C_2.

Relay CR remains energized as long as S is closed, but is de-energized instantly when S is opened. Capacitor C_1 is recharged by the grid, Fig. 16.1b and the relay is reset. A predetermined interval is required to recharge C_1 and this timing circuit is not instantaneously reset. The time required to recharge C_1 fully is usually 10 percent of the interval by which the operation of CR is delayed, thus requiring a pause between successive periods one tenth the delay interval.

The purpose of R_5 and C_3 are described in Chapter 15, page 381.

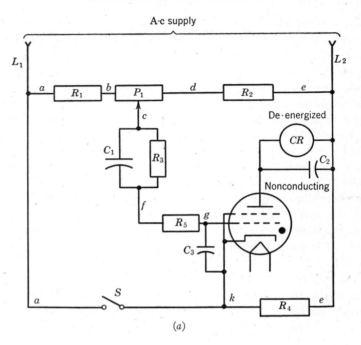

(a)

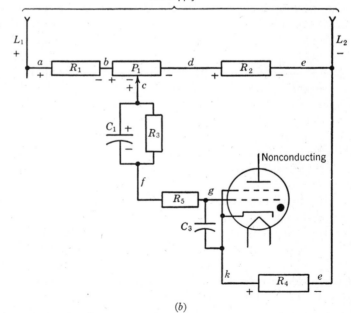

(b)

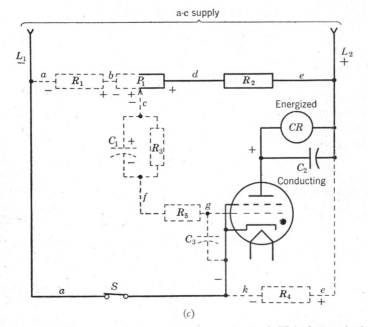

FIG. 16.1. (a) With S open the tube is nonconducting, and CR is de-energized. Capacitor C_1 is charged (b) with the grid acting as the anode of a diode rectifier. With S closed, the thyratron is ready to conduct, (c), but is blocked by the negative charge on C_1 until C_1 is discharged through R_3.

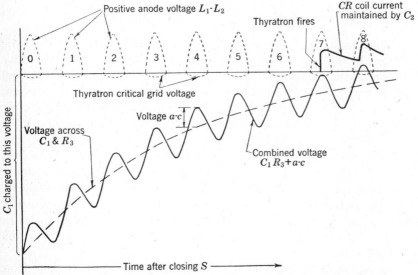

FIG. 16.2. As C_1 discharges through R_3, successive peaks of the alternating voltage component become less negative until one peak intersects the critical grid voltage curve, as during the seventh cycle of the figure. Timing is adjusted by P_1 which determines the direct voltage to which C_1 is charged.

391

Photoelectric Relays

Photoelectric relays are manufactured in a variety of forms, differing chiefly in their sensitivity to light and their speed of response. One of the simplest units requires a light intensity of 40 foot-candles applied for approximately 0.05 second, whereas units have been built with sufficient sensitivity to operate from the light of a remote star or to respond to an impulse of illumination lasting for only five microseconds. With such a variety to choose from, one must carefully consult the manufacturer's data before selecting a photoelectric relay to meet any particular requirement.

Photoelectric relays operate by variation in the *quantity* of light impinging on the phototube cathode. For convenience, the manufacturer's data usually express the rating of a photoelectric relay in terms of foot-candles, or *light intensity*. These intensity ratings are based on the assumption that the entire phototube cathode area, or in some cases the lens area, will be covered with light of the expressed intensity. If the area is partially restricted, the intensity of illumination must be proportionately increased to maintain the required quantity of light. Partial obstructions, such as smoke, fog, and sleet, reduce the light-source intensity, and such losses must be allowed for.

The operation of photoelectric devices is initiated by light reaching the phototube in any of several ways:

1. Transmission.   3. Refraction.
2. Reflection.   4. Radiation.

Transmitted light is the most common manner of operating photoelectric devices. In this, light from the source falls directly on the light-sensitive surface. Reflected light is of two forms: direct specular reflection and diffused reflection. The former follows the laws of the familiar mirror principle, whereas the latter responds only to the light scattered by the irregularity of the reflecting surface. Diffused reflection is usually preferred for applications wherein the reflecting surface is moving (such as paper running over guide rolls), because the operation is less affected by variation in alignment of the optical system or in the material being scanned. An example of operation by radiated light is the indication of temperature of a hot body. Photoelectric devices give an excellent indication of temperature above 1200 F, although the phototube temperature must not be allowed to exceed 150 F, either through conduction or radiation from a hot body.

The phototube should be mounted close to the first amplifier tube. Some of the simple relays, using only one tube, frequently restrict the maximum length of phototube lead to 10 ft and use a special cable having low capacitance and high leakage resistance. To meet situations requiring longer leads, scanners (see Fig. 17.4) consisting of a compact assembly of phototube and one amplifier tube are available. Output of the amplifier can then be connected to other component parts of the circuit located in a remote chassis.

Fig. 16.3.   Westinghouse type-RQ phototroller using one thyratron and small control relay (cover removed).   (*Courtesy Westinghouse*)

One example of a photoelectric relay operated directly from alternating current is the Westinghouse type *RQ* phototroller,† Fig. 16.3 and Fig. 16.4. This unit is comparatively insensitive, requiring an operating level of 40 ft-candles. However, it is widely used for many applications where ample illumination is available. Its schematic diagram, Fig. 16.5 illustrates how all circuits are energized directly from the transformer secondary winding.

†For other photoelectric relay circuits operated from alternating current see Cockrell, *Industrial Electronic Control*, pp 183–8; also Gulliksen and Vedder, *Industrial Electronics*, pp 63–86.

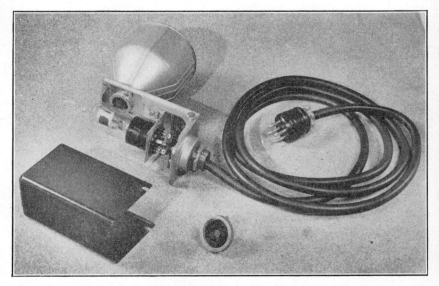

FIG. 16.4.   When space is limited, the phototube is mounted in an extended housing equipped with a receiving lens.   Plug attached to end of cable fits phototube socket in Phototroller chassis.   (*Courtesy Westinghouse*)

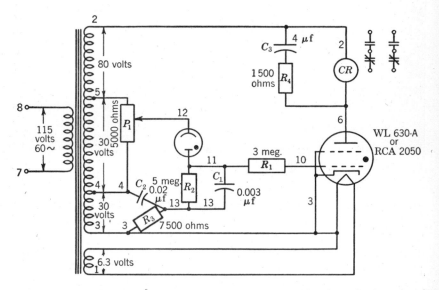

FIG. 16.5.   Circuit of the RQ phototroller. Thyratron grid voltage is the sum of alternating voltage across R_3 and direct voltage across C_1. If the phototube is illuminated, it rectifies to charge C_1, negative at terminal 11, and blocks conduction of the thyratron.

This circuit is designed to energize the relay coil CR when the phototube is dark and de-energize CR when the phototube is lighted, the predominating condition encountered with simple photoelectric applications. Explanation of this circuit is aided by the voltage relations shown in Fig. 16.6. Thyratron

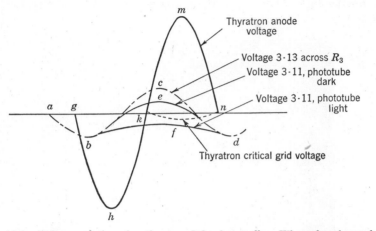

FIG. 16.6. Voltage relations for the type-RQ phototroller. When the phototube is dark, positive grid voltage c fires the thyratron during each half-cycle. Brilliant illumination of the phototube causes the grid voltage ·to follow a-b-f-d and prevents conduction.

grid voltage 3–11 consists of a phase-shifted component 3–13 across R_3 plus the voltage 13–11 across C_1 and R_2. If it is assumed that the phototube is completely dark and nonconducting, the grid voltage follows $abcd$, Fig. 16.6, and the thyratron fires at the beginning of each positive half-cycle, because its grid voltage leads the anode voltage, made possible by the phase-shifting function of C_2 and R_3 (see Chapter 15, page 367). Note that the phototube cathode is connected toward the upper end of the transformer winding as compared to the thyratron cathode terminal 3. Because the phototube conducts only when its cathode 12 is negative, and during this half of the cycle the thyratron anode terminal 2 is also negative, the phototube conducts while the thyratron does not and vice versa. Assume that the phototube is slightly illuminated. During the negative half-cycle of anode voltage ghk, the phototube conducts and, as a diode, rectifies to charge C_1 with negative polarity at the grid terminal 11. During the positive half-cycle of anode voltage kmn, C_1 discharges, but slowly enough for the thyratron grid voltage to follow bed, (instead of bcd, as it does with the phototube dark.) The thyratron still fires at the beginning of each half-cycle, for the grid voltage is positive at k, the beginning of the anode cycle. If the phototube illumination is increased to charge C_1 to nearly the peak b

of negative grid voltage, the discharge of C_1 during the positive-anode half-cycle follows *bfd*, and the curve of grid voltage 3–11 does not cross the thyratron critical grid voltage. The thyratron does not fire, and relay CR remains de-energized if the phototube is sufficiently bright. Potentiometer P_1 provides for adjustment of the operating level of illumination of the phototube.

Fig. 16.7. The RX-1 phototroller consists of a phototube, one d-c amplifier, thyratron (in shield) and control relay. (*Courtesy Westinghouse*)

The purpose of phase-shifting circuit C_2R_3 is to assure that the thyratron fires early in the anode-voltage half-cycle to prevent relay chatter. Chattering is further eliminated by capacitor C_3 to maintain CR coil current while the thyratron is nonconducting (during the negative half-cycle). The resistor R_4 is needed to limit the maximum charging current of C_3 while the thyratron is conducting; otherwise the anode current may exceed the allowed maximum.

Sensitive photoelectric relays usually employ one amplifier tube in addition to the phototube and thyratron. Their circuits operate on direct current obtained from a rectifier and filter. One example is the Westinghouse type RX–1 phototroller,‡ Fig 16.7. The phototube is shown mounted. in the relay chassis although it can be removed and enclosed within a remote phototube housing, such as Fig. 16.4, connected to the relay chassis by an extended cable.

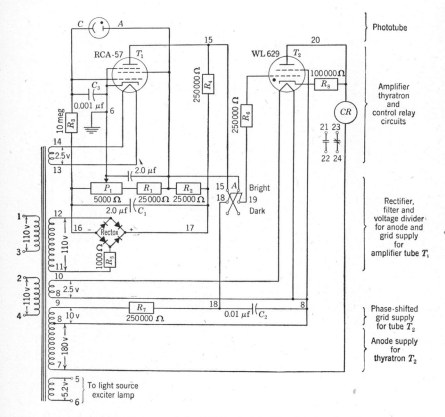

FIG. 16.8.   Schematic diagram of the RX-1 phototroller showing Rectox copper-oxide reactifiers with filter and voltage divider for the source of d-c potentials.

The schematic wiring diagram, Fig. 16.8, shows this unit to consist of a phototube, pliotron, thyratron, and Rectox copper-oxide full-wave rectifier. A two-pole double-throw toggle switch is provided in the front of the chassis (above dial, Fig. 16.7) so that this unit can be operated to energize the control relay CR either when the phototube is illuminated or when it is dark.

‡For other circuits operating according to entirely different principles see Cockrell, *Industrial Electronic Control*, pp 158–66.

The functional diagram, Fig. 16.9, illustrates how the actual schematic diagram of Fig. 16.8 is redrawn to aid the study of circuit operation. Increasing the phototube illumination increases the current through R_3, making the grid of T_1 more positive and raising its anode current. The

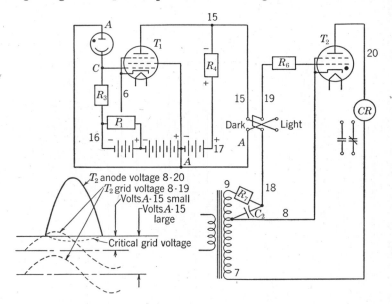

FIG. 16.9.   Functional schematic diagram of the RX-1 phototroller illustrating how the actual diagram is redrawn to include features essential to operation.

voltage across R_4 is thus increased by greater illumination of the phototube Voltage A–15 is the difference between direct voltage A–17 and voltage 17–15 across R_4, because these polarities are opposed. Hence, increased illumination of the phototube causes voltage A–15 to decrease. If it is assumed that the two-pole double-throw switch is closed to the right (or upward in Fig. 16.8), A is connected to the thyratron grid, and the unit operates by increasing the phototube illumination.

The thyratron-grid voltage consists of a phase-shifted a-c component across capacitor C_2 plus a d-c component A–15. (The phase-shifting circuit C_2R_7 is used for the same purpose as previously described in connection with the type-RQ phototroller.) If it is assumed that the phototube is dark, terminal A is negative relative to 15, and the a-c grid voltage is displaced negatively (downward in the figure) relative to the thyratron cathode potential, sufficient to prevent firing of thyratron T_2. As the phototube illumination increases, voltage A–15 is reduced, and the a-c grid voltage moves upward, ultimately allowing the curve of grid voltage to intersect the thyratron-critical-grid-voltage curve. Thyratron T_2 then conducts to energize control relay CR.

If the selector switch is reversed, connecting 15 to the thyratron grid, potentiometer P_1 is adjusted with the phototube brightly illuminated so that the voltage across R_4 exceeds the direct voltage $A-17$. The thyratron-grid voltage is then negative, preventing conduction, but, as the phototube illumination decreases, terminal 15 becomes less negative, and T_2 is fired by reduced phototube illumination.

Fig. 16.10.   The light source used to excite the RX-2 phototroller projects a pulsating light beam by the perforated motor-driven disk between the lamp and lens. An infrared filter (right) is mounted before the lens when an invisible beam is required.

(*Courtesy Westinghouse*)

When the light source and phototube are widely separated, it becomes necessary to operate at a low level of light intensity. For these applications, the ratio of illumination from the bona fide light source to that from extraneous light decreases as the lamp is further removed from the phototube. Some means must be devised to separate the effects of extraneous light from those of the desirable excitation.

One solution is employed in the Westinghouse type $RX-2$ phototroller. Appearance of the amplifier cabinet is the same as that shown in Fig. 16.7, although the circuit is designed so that the phototube responds only to rapidly fluctuating light. A reasonable amount of extraneous light of either steady or slowly changing intensity has but little effect upon operation. A special light source, Fig. 16.10, is required to actuate this equipment. A perforated disk located between the exciter lamp and the projecting lens is driven by a small synchronous motor. Thus, the light is interrupted or "chopped" 540 times per second. The pulsating beam is projected to the phototube where its amplifying circuit responds to the rapidly fluctuating intensity and is relatively insensitive to a uniform or slowly changing extraneous light.

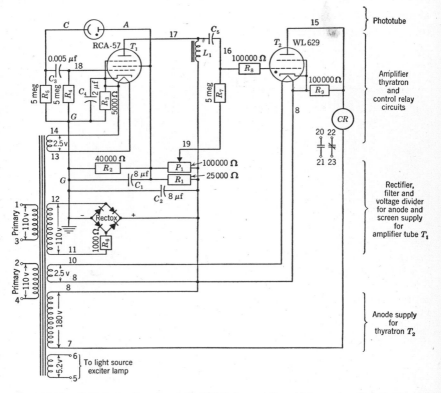

FIG. 16.11. Schematic diagram of the RX-2 phototroller which consists of a phototube, one amplifier impedance-coupled to a thyratron and control relay. Rectox copper-oxide rectifiers are used to obtain the necessary d-c potentials.

The type-RX-2 phototroller circuit, Fig. 16.11, consists of a phototube connected to a pliotron (pentode) amplifier, T_1, through a capacitor-coupling circuit C_3, the output of which is impedance-coupled to the grid of thyratron T_2. Capacitor-coupling the phototube to the first amplifier together with impedance-coupling to the thyratron grid eliminates the effects of steady extraneous illumination on the phototube, because these effects result in d-c components and do not pass through the coupling circuits. Amplifier T_1 is operated from a d-c supply consisting of a full-wave rectifier and voltage-divider circuit, whereas thyratron T_2 is operated with an a-c anode supply.

A functional diagram, Fig. 16.12, shows the operation of this circuit more clearly. Rapid fluctuations of the phototube illumination result in rapid charging and discharging of capacitor C_3. As the intensity of phototube illumination rises, the voltage across R_5 is increased because of the phototube current through it. Capacitor C_3 is charged by this voltage, the charging current flowing through R_4. Voltage across R_4, because of this current, manifests a positive polarity at the grid terminal, thereby increasing the

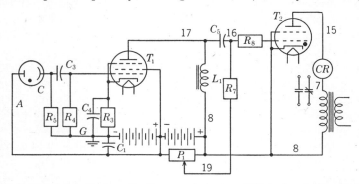

Fig. 16.12. Functional schematic diagram of the type RX-2 phototroller. Pulsating illumination of the phototube results in an alternating voltage amplified by T_1 which appears across R_7 to fire thyratron T_2 and energize relay CR.

anode current of T_1. As the intensity of phototube illumination falls, the voltage across R_5 is reduced. Capacitor C_3 then discharges, because its potential is then greater than the voltage across R_5. The discharging current through R_4 manifests a negative potential at the grid terminal, and T_1 anode current is decreased. Thus, the anode current of T_1 responds to a rapid fluctuation of phototube illumination. A steady illumination of the phototube has no appreciable effect upon the grid potential of T_1, because C_3 is not alternately charged and discharged. The grid bias of T_1 is obtained by a cathode resistor R_3 (see page 357), and C_4 by-passes the a-c component of anode current around R_3. The purpose of C_1 is explained in Chapter 7, page 103. The a-c component of T_1 anode current causes a large alternating voltage across reactor L_1, which is transferred to an alternating voltage across R_7 without appreciable attenuation through C_5. The design of L_1, C_5, and R_7 are co-ordinated to be most responsive to the 540-cycle frequency of light-source pulsations. If the phototube is illuminated by a pulsating light of proper frequency, peaks of the amplified voltage across R_7 which are positive at 16 exceed the negative bias 8–19 and cause thyratron T_2 to conduct. Control relay CR is energized, closing its contact. Interruption of the modulated light beam cuts off the alternating voltage across R_7, leaving the bias 8–19 to render thyratron T_2 nonconducting, de-energizing CR. This phototroller operates reliably with an illumination of only 0.1 ft-candle (referring to the intensity of light received from the modulated light source). By employing a condensing lens in front of the phototube the intensity required for operation is proportionately reduced.

Resistance-Welding Controls

Resistance welding has achieved its present stature as a fabricating method largely because of the electronic tube and the precision it makes possible. Many of the early tasks assigned to resistance welding were satisfactorily performed by magnetic contactors. But these tasks were usually confined to the welding of relatively thick sections of mild steel, requiring a long duration of current for each weld, and no unusual degree of accuracy was necessary for the timing of each weld interval. With the advent of welding nonferrous metals, accurate timing immediately became more and more essential.§ The duration of current for each weld shrank from many cycles to sometimes only a single cycle and not always all of that. Magnetic contactors, no matter how skillfully designed, cannot start and stop welding current in the extremely short intervals required, nor can they repeat their performance with the precision demanded. Thus, the ignitron tube became the logical answer to the problem. The ignitron finds no difficulty in starting current at any precise portion of a voltage cycle, it can be depended upon always to stop the current at the end of each conducting cycle, it has no moving parts, and it easily performs this duty millions of times without wear.

Ignitron tubes, used for the control of welding current, are always employed in pairs, connected in the inverse parallel circuit discussed in Chapter 15, page 373. In this way, the flow of alternating current to the welding transformer primary winding is controlled. Ignitrons so used are frequently called *ignitron contactors*. Electronic control for resistance-welding applications can be divided into three distinct parts or basic units: (1) the ignitron contactor, (2) synchronous timing control equipment, and (3) heat control. Any or all of these basic functions can be obtained by the interconnection of as many units as desired, or one complete assembled equipment purchased to include as many of these functions as a particular welding job requires. Because these functions are independent, they are discussed separately to avoid the confusion of attempting to illustrate all of them in one single diagram.

§For information in regard to the technique of welding ferrous and nonferrous metals, see *Resistance Welding Manual*, Resistance Welder Manufacturers' Association, Philadelphia, Pa.

THE IGNITRON CONTACTOR

A typical ignitron contactor is illustrated in Fig. 16.13. Two ignitron tubes are mounted in the cabinet together with two copper-oxide rectifiers, control relay, and fuse mounted on the door. The circuit diagram is given in Fig. 16.14. The ignitrons are connected in an inverse-parallel circuit

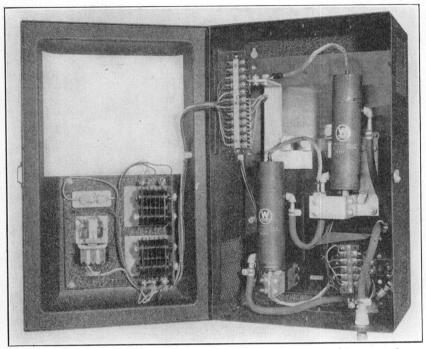

FIG. 16.13.   A Weldotrol or ignitron contactor for resistance-welding control
(*Courtesy Westinghouse*)

(Chapter 15, page 373) and control the current through the welding transformer primary-winding. Rectifiers R_1–R_2 and R_3–R_4 direct the current through the ignitors by their valve action. Between the mid-terminals of each rectifier are connected a water-flow switch, a control contact, and a fuse. The water-flow switch‖ prevents conduction through the ignitrons,

‖One type of *water-flow* switch, sometimes called a *thermostatic* switch, functions by passing current (usually low-voltage from a transformer secondary winding) through a short section of metal tubing through which the water also flows. The tubing is heated by the current through it, and its temperature is measured by a thermostatic element. A water rate equal to or greater than the predetermined rate for adequate ignitron cooling cools the tubing sufficiently to prevent opening of the thermostatic contacts. A reduction in the water flow results in a higher temperature of the tubing, and the contacts open. Momentary fluctuations of the water flow do not cause the contacts to open because of the thermal time lag of the device.

unless the flow is sufficient for adequate cooling of the tubes. The fuse protects the ignitors against a damaging current. The control contact can be any form of switch, either manual or automatic to time the duration of welding current. Electronic timers of the type described earlier in the chapter are frequently used. One typical illustration is that of Fig. 16.15. Other circuits manifesting greater accuracy are described in the following pages.

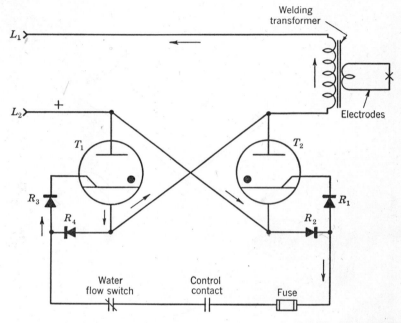

FIG. 16.14. The ignitron contactor, basic unit for any resistance-welding control, consists of two ignitrons connected in an inverse parallel connection with the welding transformer primary winding.

Closure of the control contact starts the weld, and opening it stops the welding current. If the water-flow switch and the control contact are closed, Fig. 16.14, assume L_2 to be of positive polarity. Current then flows through R_2, through the fuse, control contact, and water-flow switch, through R_3, through the ignitor of T_1, then through the transformer primary winding to L_1. The flow of ignitor current fires T_1, and the conduction thus started immediately transfers between the mercury pool and the anode. The power current then flows to the anode and no longer flows through the ignitor or copper-oxide rectifiers. These rectifiers are used as valves to block reversed-current flow from L_2 upward to the pool of T_2 and thence, in the wrong direction, through the ignitor of T_2. During the opposite half-cycle when L_1

becomes positive, ignition current flows through the welding transformer through rectifiers R_4 and R_1, the ignitor of T_2, and thence to L_2. Ignitron T_2 then conducts for its half-cycle, while rectifiers R_3 and R_4 prevent undesired current through the ignitor of T_1.

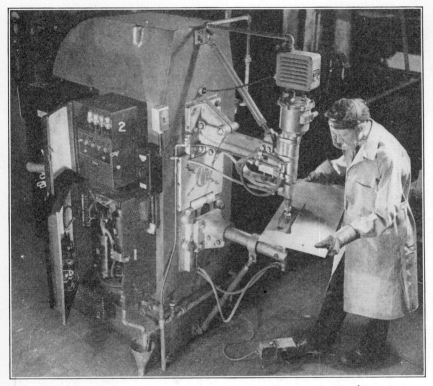

Fig. 16.15.   This spot-welding machine is electronically controlled by (1) an ignitron contactor in the lower cabinet and (2) thyratron timing in the upper cabinet for the weld duration and the sequence of the complete welding cycle.   (*Courtesy Westinghouse*)

The ignitron contactor is a basic component part for the control of welding current. It is frequently used alone for duties not requiring the complications of precise timing. In this case, the control contact is manually opened and closed by the operator, and the duration of welding time is controlled by the operators' judgment.

Ignitrons for welding service are applied on an intermittent basis and conduct a high current for a short interval of time. The rating of all apparatus on any intermittent basis requires a study of two considerations, (1) the duty cycle and (2) the time interval over which the intermittent load is averaged.

The duty cycle of a periodically repeated intermittent load is familiar in all forms of engineering and merely expresses the ratio of the time during which the ignitrons conduct to the total time interval.

Averaging time is an expression, usually confined to electronic tubes, although it applies equally well to the more familiar types of electric equipment. As an explanation of the meaning of averaging time, consider a 100-kva transformer, rated on a continuous basis. This transformer will safely

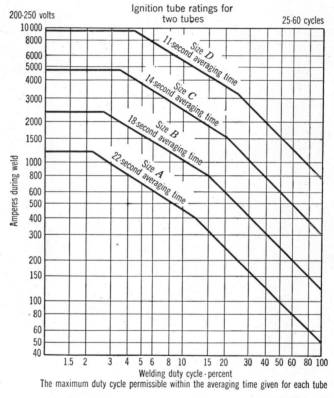

FIG. 16.16.   Ignitron ratings for 230-volt welding service.

carry 100-percent overload for one minute without exceeding a safe temperature rise. Then, assume this transformer carries 200-kva for one minute followed by no load for three minutes. Under this condition, the duty cycle is 25 percent over an *averaging time of 4 minutes*. The transformer can carry this load without difficulty. However, if that same transformer were loaded at 200 kva for one day, followed by a no-load period of three days, the duty cycle would remain at 25 percent over an *averaging time of 4 days*, although it is quite obvious that the transformer could not carry this load without exceeding its normal temperature rise.

The same reasons that make it impossible to apply the transformer on the basis of 100-percent overload for 24 hours apply equally well to electronic tubes. The only difference is that transformers, motors, and generators contain so much copper and iron that a relatively long time is required for their temperature to rise to an unsafe limit. On the other hand, electronic tubes contain relatively little such material and the rate of temperature rise is much higher than for other types of electric equipment. For this reason, they reach their maximum safe temperature rather quickly, and the averaging time must be proportionately reduced.

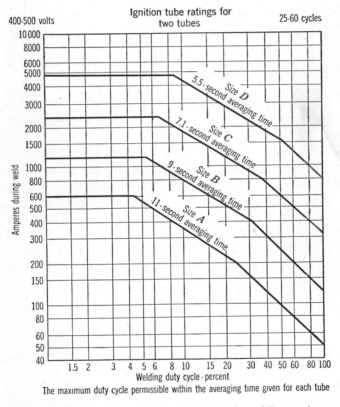

FIG. 16.17.   Ignitron ratings for 460/550 volts welding service.

Ignitrons designed for resistance-welding control are classified into four sizes known as sizes A (the smallest), B, C, and D (the largest). Each has a different averaging time, which, furthermore, depends upon the voltage of the welding transformer primary winding used with the control. The averaging time, together with current ratings for intermittent-load applications, are given in Fig. 16.16 and 16.17 for 230- and 460-volt service, respectively.

To illustrate the use of these rating curves, assume that a manufacturer is welding parts requiring six spots per piece, the current flowing for five cycles for each spot; 1 second is required to shift the piece, and 4 seconds required to change pieces. The weld requires a current of 800 amperes, and the power source is 440 volts, 60 cycles, single phase. A graphical representation of the problem is shown in Fig. 16.18. One must first decide upon the

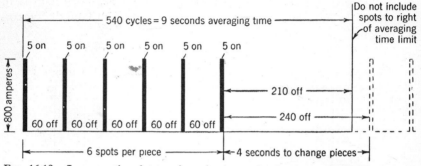

FIG. 16.18. In computing duty cycle, only the conducting intervals within the limit of averaging time are included.

probable size of ignitrons. If we refer to Fig. 16.17, it appears likely that size-B tubes are satisfactory, for which the averaging time is 9 seconds. All time units must be converted either to seconds or cycles, the conversion to cycles being preferred, Fig. 16.18. A line is then drawn on the figure to measure off the averaging time of the ignitron tubes, and the total cycles of conduction within the averaging time limit are counted. In this example, six spots can be made within the averaging limit, but the beginning of the next piece is not included. The percent duty cycle, calculated *within the averaging time limit* is

$$\frac{6 \times 5}{540} \times 100 = 5.6 \text{ percent}$$

For a 5.6-percent duty cycle size-B tubes are allowed to carry about 1200 amperes, which is adequate margin above the 800 amperes required. Hence, size-B tubes are satisfactory for the application.

Suppose that by improvement in technique the spots can be made with only 2/3 second idle time between spots and the pieces changed in 3 seconds. The new conditions are graphically represented by Fig. 16.19. The first piece with six spots, together with three spots of the second piece are now included within the averaging time limit of 540 cycles, and the new duty cycle becomes

$$\frac{9 \times 5}{540} \times 100 = 8.4 \text{ percent}$$

Size-B tubes are still satisfactory for the new conditions, although they are now loaded more nearly to their capacity. Any further improvement in manufacturing technique requires replacement of the tubes by a larger size. The percent duty cycle must then be recalculated on the basis of including the number of spots welded within the new averaging time limit of 426 cycles, which becomes the new basis when size-C ignitrons are employed.

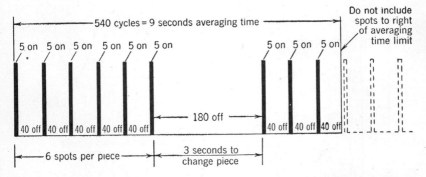

FIG. 16.19.   If the technique for welding the same parts is improved, more welds are made within the averaging time limit, and the duty cycle for the tubes is increased. Larger ignitrons may be required in such cases.

SYNCHRONOUS PRECISION-WELDING CONTROL

The electronic-welding unit just described is classified as a nonsynchronous control, because welding current starts to flow at any point on the alternating-voltage wave when the initiating contact closes. The effect of random closing of the starting contact is illustrated by Fig. 16.20. At (a) the voltage and current waves of a conventional inductive circuit show a, the point of zero current to lag the voltage. The point a is referred to as the *natural power-factor angle* of the inductive circuit. If conduction of the ignitron contactor starts at a, the first positive half-wave of current is equal to each succeeding current loop, and there is no distortion of the current wave form. If the ignitron contactor should commence firing at b, Fig. 16.20b, the first positive half-wave of current is greater than the normal steady-state value, and the current flows for several consecutive cycles before resetting to the steady-state condition. If firing of the ignitron contactor is delayed, Fig. 16.20c, current begins at c, and the first positive half-wave of current is smaller than the steady-state value. The amount of heat (that is, I^2R) developed in the weld is influenced by these unequal current loops exhibited by the conditions of either Fig. 16.20b or c. Welds during the first few cycles of current flow are not uniform. Because of the effects caused by random firing, which is characteristic of nonsynchronous control, this type is undesirable for application to welds of only a few cycles duration unless the material being welded will tolerate some variation of welding heat.

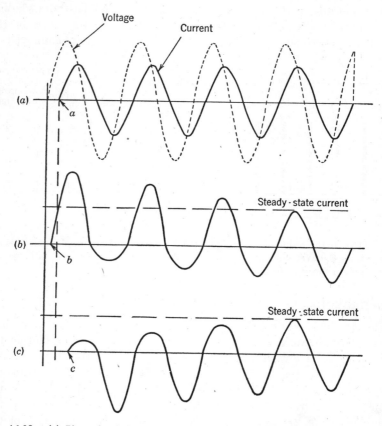

Fɪɢ. 16.20. (*a*) If conduction begins at *a*, the natural power-factor angle of the inductive load, all half-cycles of welding current are uniform. If conduction is started earlier, (*b*), the first half-cycle of current exceeds the steady-state current. If conduction is delayed, (*c*), the first half-cycle of current is less than the steady-state value.

The first duty of synchronous-precision-welding-control equipment is to initiate the firing of each weld at a point coinciding with the natural power-factor angle of the welding transformer, as Fig. 16.20a, to assure the elimination of transient currents. The heating value at each loop of current is then equal, and all welds are uniform (if the effects uncontrolled by the ignitron are neglected).

A second duty of synchronous-control equipment is to assure that each weld begins with a current polarity opposite to the polarity of the last current loop in the preceding weld. Assume that a weld ends with a negative current loop, Fig. 16.21a and that a second weld also begins with a negative current loop, such as may occur when nonsynchronous equipment is used. The transformer core has been left with some residual flux from the previous weld. The first half-cycle of negative current flow in the next

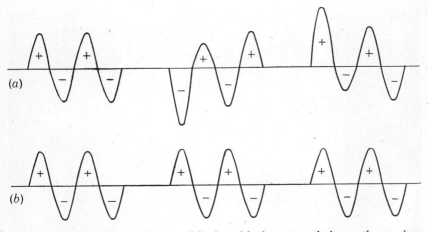

FIG. 16.21. If a second weld interval begins with the same polarity as the previous interval ended (a) magnetic saturation of the transformer core causes the first half-cycle of current to exceed the steady-state value. Synchronous welding control (b) assures that all welds begin with a polarity opposite to the previous ending and eliminates saturation of the transformer core.

weld finds the current increasing in the direction of residual flux. As a result a transient current causes unequal heating in the second weld, although the current may start to flow at the natural power-factor angle in both cases. Synchronous welding control assures that all welds begin and end at opposite polarities, Fig. 16.21b, and the transient characteristic of magnetic saturation of the transformer core is eliminated.

A third duty of synchronous precision-welding control is to time the duration of each weld for an accurately predetermined number of cycles. Methods by which this function is accomplished are discussed in Chapter 15, page 375.

A functional diagram, Fig. 16.23, of a Westinghouse type $SP-11B$ illustrates the principles of one type¶ of synchronous equipment with only the essential components of the circuits included. Ignitrons, T_3 and T_5 conduct the power current through the welding transformer primary winding and

¶For an excellent description of other types of synchronous precision-welding equipment see G. M. Chute, *Electronic Control of Resistance Welding*, pp 184–99.

are fired by thyratrons T_2 and T_4. Thyratron T_1, known as the *starting tube*, must fire before T_2 and ignitron T_3 can conduct. Upon closure of the initiating contact, control relay CR is energized from the a-c supply, closing contact CR_a and opening contact CR_b. Direct voltage is then applied to the anode of T_1 with voltage E_1 used as the source. The grid of T_1 is biased

Fig. 16.22. Synchronous precision timing together with heat control (of the type diagramed by Fig. 16.26) is contained in the cabinet (right). Complete sequence of the spot-welding machine (left) is controlled by thyratron timing in the small cabinet (center).   (*Courtesy Westinghouse*)

negative by d-c source E_2 and does not immediately conduct. A positive grid voltage to fire T_1 is obtained from the secondary winding of peaking transformer TR_1 whose primary is phase-shifted by transformer TR_3, potentiometer P_2, and reactor L. The phase-shifting network is adjusted to make the positive peaked voltage of TR_1 coincide with the natural power-factor angle of the welding-transformer inductive load. Thus, thyratron T_1 fires at the desired point on the positive half-cycle of a-c supply voltage.

For the purpose of explanation, resistors R_1 and R_2 are assumed equal with 100 volts drop across each. Before T_1 is fired, thyratron T_2 is biased

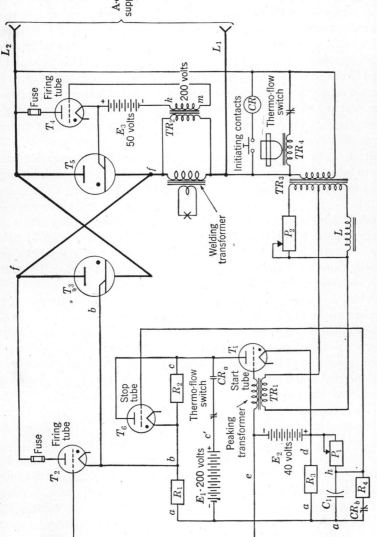

FIG. 16.23. Functional diagram of a Westinghouse SP-11 synchronous welding control.

approximately 140 volts negative by the voltage across R_1, plus d-c source E_2, and cannot conduct until T_1 is fired. When T_1 fires, R_3 is virtually connected across E_1, and, if the arc-drop through T_1 is neglected, the potential of point d becomes 200 volts positive relative to a. At the same time, the voltage across R_1 is 100 volts, making d 100 volts positive relative to b. If the grid circuit of T_2 is traced from its cathode at b, point d is 100 volts positive relative to the cathode. When the 40 volts of E_2 are subtracted, the grid terminal e instantly becomes 60 volts positive. This potential is applied to the grid of T_2 causing it to fire. This occurs at an instant when L_1 of the a-c supply is positive and current flows through the welding transformer primary winding to f, through T_2 to the ignitor b of ignitron T_3, through the cathode pool to L_2. Ignitron T_3 is then fired at the desired point on the alternating-voltage wave by the starting thyratron T_1.

Ignitron T_5 is fired by thyratron T_4 for conduction of negative half-cycles to be explained on page 415. Electronic timing of the weld duration is achieved by a capacitor charging circuit consisting of R_3, C_1, P_1, and thyratron T_6. If we remember that virtually all of the 200-volt source E_1 is instantly applied across R_3 when T_1 fires, the voltage drop across R_3 becomes a source by which C_1 is charged, the rate being determined by the value of charging resistance P_1. Thyratron T_6, known as the *stopping tube*, is initially biased 100 volts negative, because terminal a of R_1 is 100 volts negative relative to b and because the initial voltage across C_1 is zero.

Terminal h, connected to the grid of T_6 is 100 volts negative to b as timing begins. As C_1 charges through resistor P_1, the voltage a–b across C_1 increases (Chapter 15) with positive polarity at h. This increasing charge voltage across C_1 opposes the initial bias voltage a–b across R_1 such that the negative potential at h decreases relative to b. At the expiration of the desired interval h, the grid potential of the stopping thyratron T_6 becomes so small that the tube fires. Adjustment of the time interval is by the resistance setting of P_1.

If the arc drop of thyratrons T_1 and T_6 is neglected, both resistors R_1 and R_3 are then connected across d-c source E_1. Points b and d instantly assume the same potential. When the new conditions of grid voltage for thyratron T_2 are traced, terminal d assumes the same potential as the tube cathode b because of the equal voltage across resistors R_1 and R_3. Grid terminal e becomes 40 volts negative because of the source voltage E_2. Thus, thyratron T_2 is given a negative bias and does not conduct the next instant at which L_1 becomes positive, and ignition current for firing ignitron T_3 is blocked. Welding current is stopped by the conduction of thyratron T_6.

Releasing the control switch de-energizes relay CR, opening contact CR_a, removing the d-c supply E_1 from the anodes of T_1 and T_6, closing

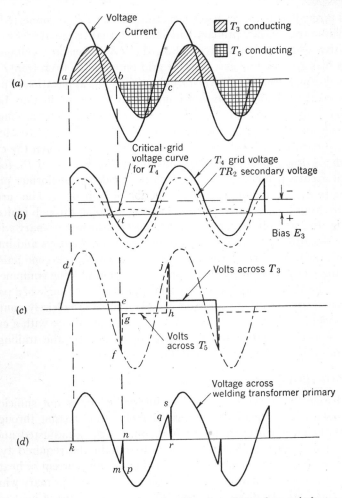

Fig. 16.24.   Current lags the supply voltage because of transformer inductance affording a *trailing-tube* firing circuit for one ignitron. (*c*) Voltage across ignitron tubes and (*d*) voltage across welding transformer primary winding.

contact CR_b, and connecting resistor R_4 across C_1. The capacitor is rapidly discharged and the control reset in preparation for the next welding interval.

Ignitron T_5 and thyratron T_4 are fired for negative half-cycle conduction by a *trailing-tube* circuit consisting of grid transformer TR_2 and d-c bias E_3. Operation of the circuit is illustrated by Fig. 16.24. Conduction starts at a, Fig. 16.24a, by ignitron T_3 and because of inductance of the welding transformer load current continues to flow to b after the alternating voltage has passed through zero and reversed. Grid transformer TR_2 is connected across the welding transformer primary winding, such that terminal m, Fig. 16.23, is positive while L_1 is negative. Thus, the TR_2 secondary voltage over-powers bias E_3 and applies a positive grid potential to thyratron T_4, Fig. 16.24b, during the half-cycle when L_2 is positive. The application of positive voltage to the grid of T_4 does not immediately cause conduction, because the arc voltage across T_3, T_5, and T_4 is too low to ionize T_4 for as long as T_3 remains conducting. The voltage across these tubes, Fig. 16.24c, rises instantly from the arc voltage e to the supply voltage f when the current through T_3 drops to zero. Voltage f instantly fires thyratron T_4, followed by ignitor current flow from L_2 through the welding transformer primary winding to L_1, causing immediate conduction of ignitron T_5. The arc volt-age then drops to g, negative current loops continuing through ignitron T_5 to h, Fig. 16.24c. Voltage across the welding-transformer primary winding, Fig. 16.24d, drops m–n as current through ignitron T_3 stops and immedi-ately returns n–p as ignitron T_5 fires for negative half-cycle conduction.

The three requirements of synchronous precision-welding equipment are fulfilled: (1) Welding begins at the natural power-factor angle of a positive half-cycle by the starting thyratron T_1, (2) timing is precisely controlled by the stopping thyratron, T_6, and (3) all welds terminate with a current loop of opposite polarity to the initial conduction by the trailing-tube circuit of grid transformer TR_2 and T_4.

HEAT CONTROL

To change the duration of welding interval alone is not sufficient to obtain welds of good quality. The rms value of current passing through the materials being welded, known as *heat*, must also be adjusted and the combination of time and heat balanced to obtain the required type of weld.* The most common method of adjusting welding current or heat is by changing the position of a tap on the welding transformer primary winding. This method has two disadvantages: (1) Small variations of heat adjust-ment are not possible because of the practical limit of the number of trans-former taps possible, and (2) the tap cannot be shifted while the welder is operating. Electronic heat control overcomes these disadvantages by firing the ignitron contactor at a point in each cycle so that current flows for less than a complete half-cycle when it is desired that the welding heat be reduced below the maximum. The principle of delaying the firing angle to retard conduction is previously discussed in Chapter 15 and reviewed by Fig. 16.25. If the ignitrons are fired at the point in each voltage half-cycle corresponding to the natural power-factor angle of the welding transformer, the primary current flow is continuous, Fig. 16.25a, and the maximum

*See *Resistance Welding Manual*, pp 52–148.

current for full heat is delivered to the welding transformer. If ignitron firing is delayed, Fig. 16.25b, the current flow becomes discontinuous, and the welding heat is proportionately reduced. Electronic heat control is desirable because of the continuous adjustment possible and the convenience afforded by the small controlling devices common to electronic apparatus.

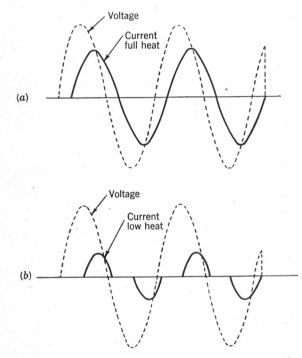

(a)

(b)

FIG. 16.25.   If the ignitrons fire at the natural power-factor angle of the welding transformer, (*a*) current is continuous, and full heat is delivered to the weld. If ignitron conduction is delayed, (*b*) current becomes discontinuous, and the welding heat reduced.

Several systems of electronic heat control are in current use.† The circuit chosen for discussion, Fig. 16.26, is the Westinghouse type *SP–14B*, because this circuit embodies several unique control features, the principles of which are useful to other forms of industrial electronic control. All devices which are shown in both Fig. 16.26 and Fig. 16.23 and bear the same numbers have the same significance in the two diagrams.

The starting thyratron T_1 is fired by the same means described in connection with Fig. 16.23, except that in this case the phase-shifted excitation

†For other circuits showing electronic heat control, see G. M. Chute, *Electronic Control of Resistance Welding*, pp 200–39.

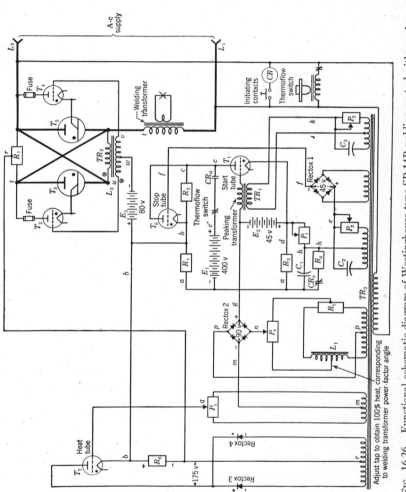

FIG. 16.26.   Functional schematic diagram of Westinghouse type SP-14B welding control with synchronous timing and heat control.

j–k occurs at the beginning of each alternating voltage wave to assure conduction of T_1 before either ignitron is ready to fire.

Thyratron T_2 for firing ignitron T_3 is not fired directly by starting tube T_1 as in the previous case, and, instead, is controlled by the *heat-control* thyratron T_7. Consider the operation of thyratron T_7 alone by first noting its anode voltage to consist of rectified half-cycles obtained from the center-tapped transformer winding, and Rectox rectifiers 3 and 4. Prior to the firing of the starting tube T_1, the grid circuit of T_7 is traced as follows: from its cathode b, through R_1 and R_3, a negative 45-volt bias E_2, a 90-volt bias of Rectox 2, through a small alternating voltage m–q to the grid of T_7. These conditions are represented by Fig. 16.27a, wherein two basic details should be noted. First, the half-wave unfiltered rectifiers, Rectox 3 and Rectox 4 apply *positive anode-voltage peaks for each half-cycle of a-c supply*. Second, the unfiltered voltage across full-wave Rectox 2, with negative polarity toward the grid of T_7, furnishes a source of sharply peaked grid voltage by inverting the rectified voltage such that the greatest magnitude of a-c potential is illustrated by a wave extending below the axis of T_7 cathode potential. The tall peaks occur at the zero point of a-c supply voltage. As long as T_1 remains nonconducting, the voltage across R_1 together with the voltage E_2 depress the peaked voltage of Rectox 2 well below the critical grid voltage for thyratron T_7.

When starting thyratron T_1 fires, the potential of g becomes considerably more positive than b (as described in connection with Fig. 16.23) and the voltage peaks of Rectox 2 are moved upward to intersect the critical grid voltage for thyratron T_7, as Fig. 16.27b. The alternating voltage for supplying Rectox 2 is obtained from a phase-shifting network comprising the center-tapped transformer-winding reactor, L_1, resistor R_5, and potentiometer P_4. This is a conventional phase-shifting circuit previously described in Chapter 15, except that potentiometer P_4 is added for the convenience of obtaining an angular phase shift roughly proportional to the rotation of P_4 slider. By this means, the peaked voltage across Rectox 2 is phase-shifted over a wide range, and these voltage peaks can be adjusted to intersect the critical grid voltage of T_7 at any desired angle of the voltage wave. When adjusted for maximum heat, Fig. 16.27b, these peaks occur early in the anode-voltage cycle, and, when adjusted for low heat, Fig. 16.27c, the peaks are late in each voltage cycle. The significance of the heat-control thyratron T_7 can be appreciated.

To understand how thyratron T_7 alternately fires thyratrons T_2 and T_4, first trace the cathode-grid circuit of T_2 while all tubes are nonconducting. The circuit passes from the cathode of T_2, through the ignitor of T_3, to L_2, then through one half of R_7 to r, through R_6 to b, positive terminal of bias E_3 where -80 volts are supplied to w, the center-tapped grid trans-

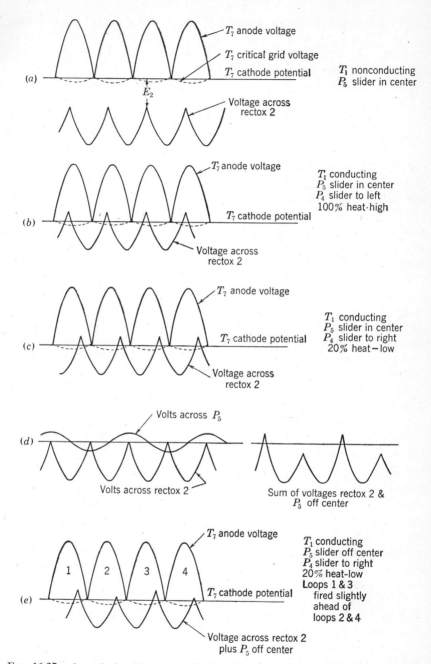

FIG. 16.27. A peaked grid voltage obtained by an unfiltered full-wave rectifier is inverted to utilize the zero points of voltage. Firing is prevented (a), keeping these peaks below the thyratron critical grid potential, the heat controlled (b) and (c) by phase shifting, and tube balance adjusted (d) and (e) by unequal heights of peaks.

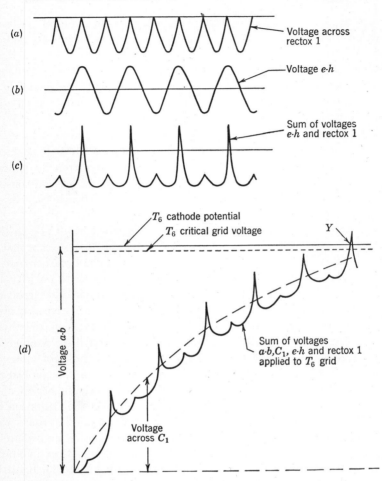

FIG. 16.28. Accurate timing is obtained by combining unfiltered rectified peaks, (a) with an alternating voltage, (b) to obtain the tall peaks, (c) for alternate half-cycles. This peaked wave form is added to a capacitor-charging voltage (d), to obtain accurate intersection Y, with the thyratron critical grid voltage.

former TR_2, then to the grid of T_2. The voltage across one half of R_7 is equal to and opposite to $u–w$, or one half of TR_2 secondary voltage. Because the voltage across one half of R_7 nullifies one half of the TR_2 voltage, the effect of potentials $L_2–r$ and $u–w$ upon the grid circuit of T_2 cancel. The grid circuit of thyratron T_4 is the same except that its circuit is through the ignitor of T_5.

Thyratrons T_2 and T_4 are held nonconducting by bias E_3. When thyratron T_7 conducts, approximately 150 volts appears across R_6 with positive polarity at b. This positive voltage overpowers the bias E_3 and applies a strong positive voltage to the grids of T_2 and T_4. Tubes T_2 and T_3 conduct while L_1 is positive; T_4 and T_5, while L_2 is positive.

Because of slight differences in the firing characteristics of thyratrons and ignitrons, it is necessary to discriminate slightly between the angle of applying ignitor current to ignitrons T_3 and T_5. This is accomplished by the balance potentiometer P_5 acting upon the firing of thyratron T_7. With slider q moved from the center position, the alternating voltage in series with the voltage peaks of Rectox 2, Fig. 16.27d, makes alternate peaks of voltage applied to the grid of T_7 taller. In this way, thyratron T_7, is fired earlier in the alternate half-cycles 1 and 3. Conduction of the ignitrons to obtain exact balance of heat between positive and negative half-cycles is then possible by the adjustment of potentiometer P_5.

Thyratron T_6 performs the function of stopping the current flow in the same manner as previously described, page 414 and Fig. 16.23, except that a circuit detail is added to assure that T_6 fires at the end of a cycle conducted by ignitron T_5 so as to terminate each weld with opposite polarity to that with which it began through T_3. Tracing the cathode-grid circuit of T_6 at the first instant of firing T_1, the voltage across R_1, negative at a, also appears at h because of the zero initial charge of C_1. A phase-shifted alternating voltage e–h is connected in series with an unfiltered direct voltage of Rectox 1, Fig. 16.28a and b, to obtain alternate tall peaks of voltage, Fig. 16.28c, h–f. The sum of voltages across R_1, C_1, and h–f, is applied to the grid of T_6. Contact CR_b of the control relay opens as timing begins, and capacitor C_1 is charged, as explained with Fig. 16.23. At the expiration of the desired number of conducting cycles, a voltage peak intersects the critical grid potential of T_6 as Y, Fig. 16.28d. Stop tube T_6 immediately fires and prevents further conduction of T_7 because of the increased voltage across R_1, as previously explained in connection with Fig. 16.23. Because the tall peaks of voltage across Rectox 1 always occur at the zero voltage of a-c supply, T_6 fires to render T_7 nonconducting at an instant when the T_7 anode voltage is zero and T_7 is blocked from further conduction.

The trailing-tube circuit used in connection with the synchronous precision timing control of Fig. 16.23 is not used with the circuit incorporating heat control.

ELECTRONIC SEAM WELDING

Seam welding is accomplished by passing two pieces to be joined through continuously rotating disk electrodes, Fig. 16.29, while accurately timing the current flow in short pulses with but little lapse between pulses. Seam welding is essentially a rapid succession of spot welds with a predetermined lapse between welds.

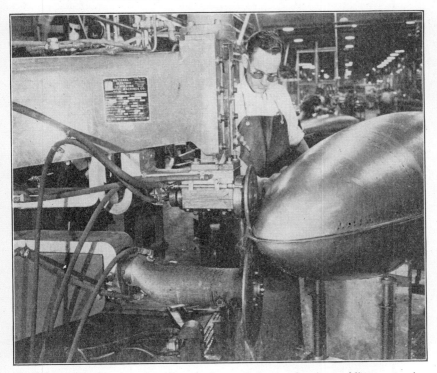

Fig. 16.29.   Tightly welded seams can be made by overlapping welding spots. Accurately timed current pulses are passed through circular water-cooled rotating electrodes.   (*Courtesy Westinghouse*)

An electronic seam-welding circuit consists of an ignitron contactor, together with firing circuits for timing both the duration of current through the weld and the duration of off time between welds. Electronic heat control can be added to the circuit if desired. Two types of seam welding controls are in general use. One type, Fig. 16.30, employs a mechanical device to time the duration of *on* and *off* periods, while another type, Fig. 16.34, uses electronic timing for all functions. The mechanical-timer type is designed specifically for seam-welding applications and is less costly, while the electronic-timing type is used for spot, pulsation, or seam welding by selector switches furnished to afford this flexibility.

On and *off* timing is accomplished in the Westinghouse type *SE–4* seam welder by a disk rotated at 1 revolution per second by a synchronous motor. The disk, Fig. 16.31, is drilled along the periphery with 120 uniformly spaced holes, each hole representing one half-cycle of the a-c supply. Steel pins are screwed in each hole for which one half-cycle of welding current is desired. Thus, a wheel set up to weld two cycles on and three cycles off,

Fig. 16.31a, is arranged with four pins in each group with six holes spaced

between groups. Figure 16.31b illustrates the arrangement for timing 5 cycles on and 55 cycles off. With reference to Fig. 16.32, as each pin (1) passes through the air gap of poles (2) (the lower pole is not visible) the potential of coils (3) is affected by the changing reluctance of the magnetic circuit. The impulse voltage across the coils is used to fire thyratrons which in turn control the conduction of ignitrons passing current to the welding transformer primary winding. Fig. 16.33 illustrates the equipment operating.

A combination spot, pulsation, and seam-welding control, Fig. 16.34, uses thyratron timing circuits to measure the duration of *on* and *off* intervals.‡ The electronic-timing circuits are conveniently adapted to either method of welding by a simple selector switch. The flexibility afforded by complete electronic timing makes this type of control suited to applications where the welding method varies.

ENERGY-STORAGE WELDING SYSTEMS

Energy-storage welding systems are more frequently applied to the welding of aluminum and aluminum alloys than to the welding of steel sheets. Aluminum has high thermal conductivity, high electrical con-

FIG. 16.30.   Firing of ignitrons in this SE-4 seam welder is controlled by a continuously rotating disk driven by a synchronous motor.
(*Courtesy Westinghouse*)

ductivity, and a very rapid softening action with respect to temperature

‡For a detailed description of the circuit function see G. M. Chute, *Electronic Control Resistance Welding*, pp 289–302.

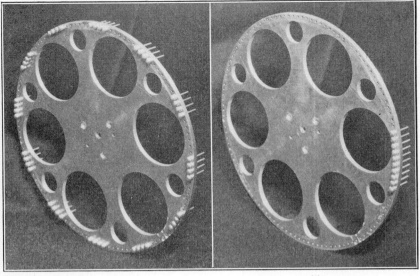

(a)   (b)

FIG. 16.31.   Each pin inserted affects current flow for one-half cycle, each hole left blank renders the ignitrons nonconducting for one-half cycle. Wheel at left is set up for 2 cycles *on* and 3 cycles *off*; wheel at right for 5 cycles *on* and 55 cycles *off*.

(*Courtesy Westinghouse*)

FIG. 16.32.   Pins 1 spaced along the periphery of the wheel passing through the air gap of inductor core 2 induce a voltage in coils 3 to affect firing of the ignitrons. The wheel is set up for 2 cycles *on* and 2 cycles *off*.   (*Courtesy Westinghouse*)

FIG. 16.33.   Seam welding (upper electrode raised to insert work) using the control
shown in Fig. 16.30. Electronic heat control is also included within the cabinet (left).
(*Courtesy Westinghouse*)

at the welding point. Because of these characteristics, satisfactory and con-
sistent welds require that both the magnitude and duration of welding
current be precisely controlled. Aluminum alloys also require a much higher
welding current than a comparable thickness of steel sheets. Such precision
puts the conventional a-c systems of ignitron contactor control at a disadvantage, because, although the duration of welding current is accurately
controlled by synchronous-timing circuits, the magnitude of welding
current varies in proportion to the a-c supply voltage. The relatively high
line current required for operating a-c welding circuits makes the problem
of maintaning a constant welder terminal voltage more difficult, and often
the power input to successive welds may vary more than the tolerable limits.
Energy-storage systems overcome this disadvantage by making the power
input to each weld essentially independent of line-voltage variation (over
any reasonable range.)

A second advantage of the energy-storage system is the reduction in peak line current required to make a weld and the advantage of using a balanced three-phase load. As an example, a job requiring 400-kva single-phase maximum demand, using an a-c welding control can be done using an energy-storage system with a maximum demand of approximately 60 kva balanced three phase.

FIG. 16.34. Ignitron firing of this welding timer is entirely controlled by tube timing circuits. By the positioning of selector switches, the equipment can be set up for spot, pulsation, or seam welding.   (*Courtesy General Electric*)

Two energy-storage systems are in current use. One type, classified as a magnetic system and known as the Sciaky process, employs a rectifier to convert the a-c supply to d-c, a magnetic contactor, and welding transformer of special design. The other type, classified as a capacitor system, employs a rectifier, a capacitor, an ignitron to discharge the capacitor, and a welding transformer.

The principles of the Sciaky process are illustrated by the basic circuit, Fig. 16.35a, and current characteristics, Fig. 16.35b. The material is placed between electrodes of the welding machine, and the electrodes are closed. Welding is initiated by closing the magnetic contactors 1 and 2 to charge the welding transformer primary current with direct current from the rectifier. A relatively small secondary current flows, Fig. 16.35b, to preheat

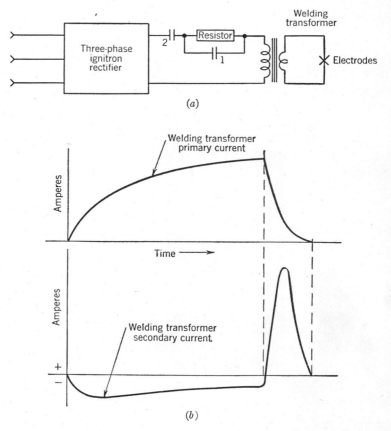

(a)

(b)

FIG. 16.35. The welding transformer core of the magnetic energy-storage system is slowly charged, (b) with direct current and then suddenly discharged by opening contactors, first 1, then 2. High secondary current flows while the stored magnetic energy rapidly collapses.

the material. When sufficient energy is stored in the transformer core, the contactors are opened in sequence, first 1, followed by 2 (actually several contactors may be used in sequence across the resistor). The rapid decay of magnetic flux causes a high secondary current flowing through the electrodes, and the weld is made while discharging the magnetic energy stored in the transformer.

The principles of a capacitor-type energy-storage system are illustrated by Fig. 16.37. A capacitor bank, usually 480 to 2640 microfarads, is charged at a relatively low rate by a three-phase grid-controlled rectifier such that the a-c power demand is kept as low as possible. Material to be welded is placed between electrodes of the welding machine. The welding electrodes

FIG. 16.36.   Interior of capacitor-discharge welding control.

(Courtesy Raytheon)

are closed, followed by discharging the capacitor bank through ignitrons T_1, T_2, and the welding transformer primary winding. The weld is made by the discharge of the energy stored in the capacitor bank through the transformer winding, the result being a high secondary current through the electrodes to heat the material.

The circuit illustrated by the block diagram, Fig. 16.37a, is known as the

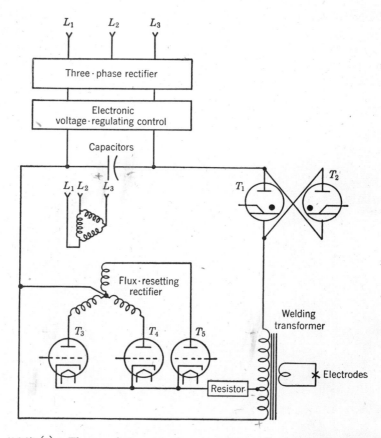

FIG. 16.37 (*a*). The capacitor energy-storage system employs a capacitor charged to a predetermined potential and rapidly discharged through the transformer primary winding.

full-cycle system.§ For all ordinary circumstances, this system is oscillatory in that current through the welding transformer manifests one reversal, first flowing through ignitron T_1 and then through ignitron T_2.

Because the capacitor is always charged with like polarity, current through the transformer winding is initiated in the same direction, making it necessary to reverse the transformer flux after each welding operation. This is done by a relatively small *flux-resetting* rectifier represented by tubes T_3, T_4, and T_5 of Fig. 16.36a. The flux-resetting and capacitor-charging rectifiers are co-ordinated by electronic control of their grids,

§For a complete description of the full-cycle capacitor-discharge system see Bichsel and Hughes, "An Improved Electronic Control for Capacitor-Discharge Resistance Welding," *AIEE Transactions*, Vol 63, 1944, pp 1150–7.

so that each conducts only during the proper portion of the welding cycle.

Operation is depicted by Fig. 16.37b. The capacitor bank is charged by a three-phase power rectifier to a predetermined voltage automatically controlled by an electronic-voltage-regulating circuit. The electronic voltage control performs three important functions: (1) It regulates the voltage to which the capacitor bank is charged, (2) by trickle charging, it accurately maintains the capacitor charged to the desired predetermined voltage until ready to make a weld, and (3) it blocks conduction of the charging rectifier while the capacitor bank is discharging.

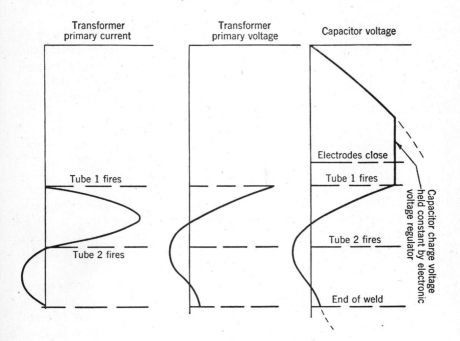

FIG. 16.37 (b).   Secondary welding current flows as the capacitor is rapidly discharged.

A weld is made by discharging the capacitor bank through the welding transformer allowing a full cycle of current through ignitrons T_1 and T_2. Following this, the welding electrodes are opened, the material removed, and the flux-resetting rectifier is controlled to reverse the magnetization of the welding-transformer core to a predetermined degree.

Capacitor-discharge equipment of this type is now used for welding aluminum sheets approximately 0.016 inch thick at a speed of 200 spots per minute. Welding of material up to 0.25 inch thick is possible at a reduced speed. Fig. 16.36 is typical of commercial equipment.

Electronic Motor Control

The trend of industrial processes has been to greater production and higher quality of goods, factors frequently demanding a wider range of operating speed and requiring that the speed be held close to the desired value. These considerations often lead to the choice of either motor–generator sets driving machines by an adjustable-voltage d-c system or, more recently, an electronic drive to attain a wide operating range of speed. The application of a motor–generator-set adjustable-voltage drive satisfies many such drives and under certain conditions may be preferred. In other cases, which are increasing in number, electronic motor control provides the best or only method of fulfilling the demands of machine designers.

A basic functional circuit of the Westinghouse type MRF–11 Mototrol, Fig. 16.40, illustrates the principles of control with only the essential components shown. All tubes are shown as triodes, although pentodes are used in the actual working circuits. The source of d-c potentials E_1 and E_2 are actually obtained by a full-wave kenotron, filter, and voltage divider. Voltages E_3, E_4, and E_5 are obtained by Rectox copper-oxide rectifiers and filters.

Before we attempt to co-ordinate the complete circuit functions, the grid and anode circuits for each tube will be explained independently.

ARMATURE THYRATRONS T_1 AND T_2

Thyratrons T_1 and T_2 comprise a center-tapped single-phase full-wave rectifier for supplying power to the motor armature. Magnetic contactors F and R provide for reversal while their normally closed contacts afford dynamic braking. A primary winding of current transformer TR_2 is connected in the anode circuit of each thyratron.

The basic grid circuit of these thyratrons consists of an a-c component from the secondary winding of grid transformer TR_3 and a d-c component. The latter extends from the center of TR_3 and is the summation of voltages across resistor R_3, source E_2, a reference voltage which is a part of potentiometer P_1, and a voltage drop across resistor R_1. The circuit is then completed to the cathodes of T_1 and T_2. Momentarily neglecting the effect of R_3 and E_2, note that the voltage across R_1 is proportional to the motor-armature voltage (or speed) and is opposed by the reference voltage across the active section of P_1. Thus, a rise in motor speed is manifest by a high negative potential at b, making the grids of T_1 and T_2 more negative to reduce conduction of the thyratron and prevent a rise in motor speed. The motor operating speed is increased by moving P_1 slider toward terminal d to increase the reference-voltage magnitude. (For steady operation, reference voltage b–e is approximately opposed by an equal voltage a–b across R_1.)

FIG. 16.38.   Mototrol equipment consists of an electronic-control cabinet, anode transformer (left), and pushbutton station with speed-control rheostats (right). These parts together with a shunt-wound d-c motor affords operation over a wide speed range powered from an a-c supply.   (*Courtesy Westinghouse*)

MOTOR SHUNT-FIELD EXCITATION

The motor shunt field is excited by a half-wave rectifier consisting of thyratron T_3 and transformer winding. Because of the inductance of the motor-field winding, the shunt-field current flow is maintained essentially constant by the phanotron T_4, which conducts during that part of the cycle when T_3 is nonconducting.

ANODE CIRCUIT OF T_5 CURRENT-LIMIT TUBE

The source of anode potential E_2 returns to the T_5 cathode by way of the reference voltage across P_1 through R_1 and R_4 to the cathode. Because the reference voltage across P_1 and voltage across R_1 are approximately equal and opposite, this circuit virtually reduces to E_2 with R_4 as a load resistor for tube T_5.

FIG. 16.39. Rear view of Mototrol with chassis lowered for accessible adjustments.
(Courtesy Westinghouse)

GRID CIRCUIT OF T_5 CURRENT-LIMIT TUBE

That portion of the grid bias E_3 that appears across P_3 is applied to T_5 grid in series with the voltage g–h across R_5 and a part of P_4. A double keno-tron T_6 rectifies the voltage across secondary winding TR_2 such that a volt-age across P_4 and R_6 bears direct relation to the output of TR_2. Also, because both TR_2 primary windings are connected in the anode circuit of armature thyratrons T_1 and T_2, this rectified direct voltage g–h is always directly proportional to the motor load current.

GRID CIRCUIT OF T_6 LOAD-COMPENSATION TUBE

From cathode j, the grid circuit passes through P_5, voltage g–h, to bias E_5 and to the grid. Increasing motor-armature current makes the T_6 grid more positive at h, causing the voltage across its anode load resistor P_6 to be increased.

ANODE CIRCUIT OF T_7 CONTROL TUBE

The negative terminal of anode source E_2 is connected to the cathode terminal e and the positive terminal k is connected to R_3. The other end of

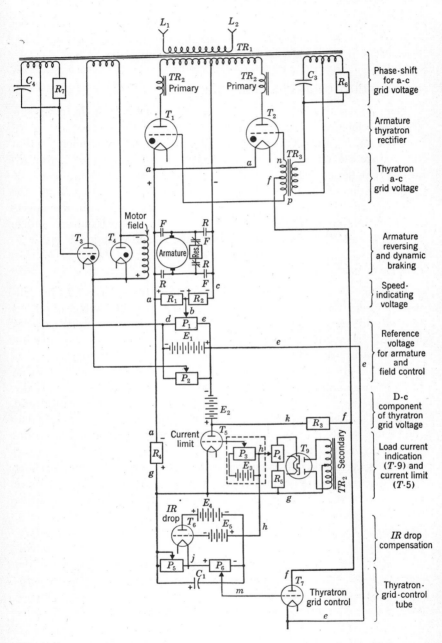

Fig. 16.40. Functional schematic diagram of Westinghouse type MRF-11 Mototrol.

R_3 is connected to the anode terminal f. Thus, R_3 is the load resistor for control tube T_7. Increasing T_7 anode current raises the voltage drop across R_3 with negative polarity at terminal f.

GRID CIRCUIT OF T_7 CONTROL TUBE

The grid circuit of T_7 control tube passes from the cathode terminal e, through reference voltage e–b across P_1, through the voltage across R_1, through R_4, P_5, and a part of P_6 to grid terminal m. If we remember that the voltage e–b across P_1 is essentially opposed by voltage a–b across R_1, we see that these virtually cancel, and the grid voltage of T_7 is affected by a combination of the three voltages: (1) the voltage a–g across R_4, (2) the voltage across P_5, and (3) the voltage j–m across P_6. These three effects are a summation of (1) the current-limit tube T_5, (2) antihunting voltage across P_5, and (3) load compensation by tube T_6 and voltage across P_6.

CONTROL FUNCTION

The principle of controlling the firing of thyratrons T_1 and T_2 for full-wave rectification is shown by Fig. 16.41. The alternating voltage of center-tapped grid transformer TR_3 is connected to the thyratron grids in series with a d-c component, summarized by the circuits from a to f. If this d-c component is large, Fig. 16.41b, the grid voltage does not cross the thyratron critical-grid-voltage curves until very late in the anode-voltage cycle (TR_3 primary voltage is phase-shifted 90 degrees by C_3 and R_6). If the d-c component is made less negative, Fig. 16.41c, the thyratron critical grid voltage is attained earlier during each half-cycle, and armature current is conducted by thyratrons T_1 and T_2 for a longer portion of the anode-voltage cycle.

Motor speed (for a particular torque load) is raised by moving the slider of the speed-adjusting potentiometer P_1 toward terminal d. The reference voltage b–e is thereby increased in the direction to make e more positive than b. This voltage b–e is a part of the thyratron-grid component a–b. The change by which e becomes more positive also makes b more positive, that is, less negative. The firing angle of thyratrons T_1 and T_2 is immediately advanced, Fig. 16.41c. A greater armature current flows, and the motor speed increases until the higher voltage developed across R_1 (proportional to motor speed) satisfies a balance between the new reference voltage b–e and a–b. The motor speed is lowered by moving the P_1 slider toward terminal e, all of the afore-mentioned effects being opposite.

To summarize the circuit components, T_7 controls the angle of firing thyratrons T_1 and T_2 by its anode current through R_3. The more negative T_7 grid becomes, the less negative is terminal f. The thyratrons then con-

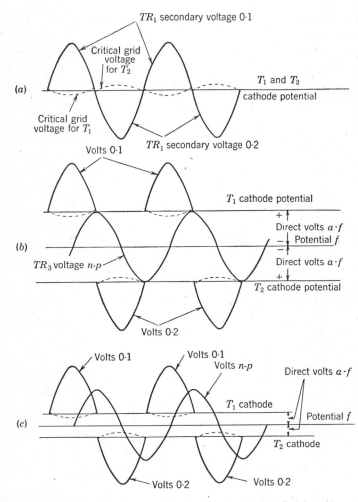

FIG. 16.41. Conduction of the armature thyratrons is controlled by the magnitude of d-c grid voltage connected in each grid circuit. If this direct voltage is large, (b) the thyratrons conduct slightly and the motor speed is very low.   If the direct voltage is small, (c) the thyratrons fire early in the cycle, and maximum motor speed is attained when firing occurs at the peak of the anode voltage wave.

duct for a greater portion of their cycle, as Fig. 16.41c shows. In this way, motor-armature current is increased in response to a demand that it develop a greater torque.

If the motor is operating at light load and a given speed, increasing the load makes T_6 grid more positive and increases the voltage across P_6. Terminal m thereby becomes more negative. Thus, the grid of T_7 is more negative, and the thyratrons are fired earlier in the cycle to conduct an increased armature current required because of the heavier motor load.

Increasing the armature current beyond a predetermined limit makes the grid of T_5 strongly positive at h. Its anode current flowing through R_4 makes g more positive. A positive potential is applied to the grid of T_7 to retard firing of thyratrons T_1 and T_2.

(a)

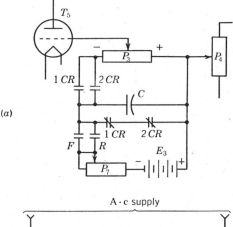

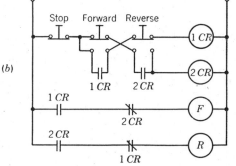

(b)

FIG. 16.42.   Conduction is delayed slightly by forcing the bias of T_5 to increase slowly as C charges through P_7. In the meanwhile, armature contactors close without establishing any current. When the motor is stopped, T_5 bias is removed instantly, and the thyratrons stop conducting before the armature contactors can open.

Adjustment of P_2 controls the firing of the field-excitation thyratron T_3 in a similar manner and affords adjustment of the motor operating speed by changing its shunt-field current. In the actual equipment, the shunt-field excitation circuit is interconnected with the current-limit control so as to assure that the motor is always started with maximum field current and that such is also applied when the armature current exceeds the limit set for tube T_5, although this detail is omitted from the simplified circuit of Fig. 16.40.

ARMATURE CONTACTORS DO NOT MAKE OR BREAK CURRENT

The grid-bias circuit of current-limit tube T_5 shown within the dotted square of Fig. 16.40, is expanded to show details in Fig. 16.42a. Starting the motor either forward or reverse by operation of the pushbuttons as shown in the figure at (b) closes $1CR$ or $2CR$, and bias E_3 is connected

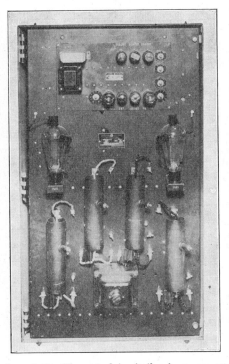

Fig. 16.43. Operation of the Thymotrol is similar in many respects to the circuit described in this text. The principal difference is the method by which the thyratron grids are controlled. (*Courtesy General Electric*)

across P_3 in parallel with capacitor C through resistor P_7. At the first instant, the charge on C is zero, and the bias to T_5 grid is also zero. The current-limit tube then prevents conduction of thyratrons T_1 and T_2 at the first instant of closing the control contactors. As C charges through P_7, the voltage across P_3 gradually rises, and the increasing negative bias on T_5 grid allows conduction of the armature-circuit thyratrons.

When the motor is stopped or reversed, fast acting relays $1CR$ or $2CR$ open rapidly to disconnect P_3 from the bias voltage E_3. The T_5 grid voltage instantly drops to zero and phases the thyratron grids for nonconduction before the armature-circuit contactors open their current-carrying contacts. In this way, the thyratrons operate to relieve the reversing contactors of the necessity of either making or breaking armature current, and the contact life is thereby prolonged.

The General Electric Thymotrol, Fig. 16.43, performs the functions just described, although the circuits for accomplishing the results are quite different. The principal difference between these two circuits is the method by which the firing angle of thyratrons T_1 and T_2 is controlled. The Mototrol employs the combination of a fixed alternating voltage with a variable d-c potential, as explained with Fig. 16.41. The Thymotrol employs a system of saturated reactors to phase-shift the thyratron grid potential according to the principles given in Chapter 15, page 368.‖

SUMMARY

Electronic timing is commonly adapted to resistance-welding technique using a timing range from 1/120 to 1 second. General applications require a range from 1 second to several minutes. In either case, the basic principle depends upon the charge or discharge of a capacitor through a resistor.

Photoelectric relays are built with a sensitivity to light operation ranging from 40 ft-candles to less than 0.1 ft-candle. The less sensitive circuits operate the phototube and amplifier by a-c anode voltages. More sensitive circuits operate with a d-c anode source, obtained by rectification of the a-c supply.

The effects of extraneous light can be minimized by:

(a) Design of the optical system used with the phototube to restrict light reaching the tube cathode to as small an angle in line with the light source as possible.

(b) Use of an impulse-coupling circuit of the phototube to the first amplifier (useful only when the desired light change occurs rapidly).

(c) Use of a circuit designed to respond only to a rapidly fluctuating light together with a light source for projecting a modulated beam.

Ignitron contactors, used for resistance welding, employ two ignitron tubes connected in an inverse-parallel circuit for controlling the flow of welding current.

Ignitrons for welding service are applied on an intermittent basis. In computing the *duty cycle* for these intermittent loads only the number of welds occurring within the *averaging time* for each particular size of ignitron are considered.

Nonsynchronous welding control allows the start of welding current at the

‖For further considerations of electronic motor control see:

E. H. Vedder and K. P. Puchlowski, "Theory of Rectifier — D–C Motor Drive," *AIEE Transactions*, Vol 62, 1943, pp 864–70.

Puchlowski, "Electronic Control of D–C Motors," *AIEE Transactions*, Vol 62, 1943, pp 760–877.

E. E. Moyer and H. L. Palmer, "Thyratron Motor Control," *AIEE Transactions*, Vol 62, 1943, pp 707–12.

K. P. Puchlowski, "Voltage and Current Relations for Controlled Rectification with Inductive and Generative Loads," *AIEE Transactions*, Vol 64, 1945, pp 255–60.

instant of closing the controlling switch. This can occur at any random point of the a-c supply voltage. Transient welding current during the first few cycles is possible using nonsynchronous control.

Synchronous precision-welding control avoids a transient welding current by the following means:

(*a*) Welding current is always started at a point of the a-c supply voltage cycle corresponding to the *natural power-factor angle* of the welding transformer. Closure of the controlling switch only sets up the circuit in readiness to start welding current when the proper instant occurs.

(*b*) All welds begin with polarity of voltage applied to the welding transformer opposite to that by which a previous weld was ended.

(*c*) Timing of the duration of welding current flow is accurately controlled to an exact number of cycles as previously determined by the application.

A *trailing-tube circuit* is used to assure that welding current is terminated by a polarity opposite to that with which it began. This circuit can be used only when the load contains considerable inductance and is not used in conjunction with heat control.

Electronic heat control provides the continuous adjustment of rms welding current flowing by delaying the angle of ignitron conduction beyond the natural power-factor angle of the welding transformer. When firing of the tubes occurs exactly at the natural power-factor angle, current is continuous, and the heat is said to be 100 percent. Delayed firing makes welding current discontinuous, and the heat is less than 100 percent.

Energy-storage welding systems, as compared to the ignitron contactor type, will make a given weld with a lower maximum current from the a-c supply. Also, the heat of each weld is less affected by supply-line voltage change.

The *magnetic energy-storage system* consists of a tube rectifier, a welding transformer of unique design, and control for interrupting the flow of transformer primary current, whereby energy stored within the transformer core is rapidly discharged into its secondary winding, that is, the material being welded.

The *capacitor energy-storage system* consists of a tube rectifier, a capacitor, a welding transformer, and an ignitron circuit for discharging the capacitor into the welding transformer primary winding. Energy stored within the capacitor is rapidly discharged to the welding transformer and through it to the material being welded.

Electronic motor-control systems consist of a grid-controlled thyratron rectifier, a circuit of controlling tubes, and a shunt-wound d-c motor. Either the motor shunt field may be excited at a constant current supplied by a field-excitation rectifier, or the field current can be varied to employ adjustable-speed motor characteristics. The following features of control are provided:

(*a*) Speed control is afforded by adjustment of armature voltage through grid control of an armature-circuit thyratron rectifier.

(*b*) The maximum peak of armature current is limited to within safe capacity of the thyratron tubes by an electronic instantaneous overload circuit.

(*c*) As the motor load increases, thyratron armature voltage rises in proportion to maintain a constant motor speed, accomplished by an electronic load-compensation circuit.

REFERENCES

F. H. GULLIKEN and E. H. VEDDER, *Industrial Electronics*, John Wiley & Sons, New York. 1935, pp 42–106.

W. D. COCKRELL, *Industrial Electronic Control*, McGraw-Hill Book Co., New York, 1944, pp 154–211.

G. M. CHUTE, *Electronic Control of Resistance Welding*, McGraw-Hill Book Co., New York, 1943.

H. J. BICHSEL and E. T. HUGHES, "An Improved Electronic Control for Capacitor-Discharge Resistance Welding," *AIEE Transactions*, Vol 63, 1944, pp 1150–7.

K. P. PUCHLOWSKI, "Electronic Control of D–C Motors," *AIEE Transactions*, Vol 62, 1943, pp 570–77.

E. E. MOYER and H. L. PALMER, "Thyratron Motor Control, *AIEE Transactions*, Vol 62, 1943, pp 707–12.

E. E. MOYER, "Electronic Control of D–C Motors," *Electronics*, May 1943, p 98; June 1943, p 119; July 1943, p 119; September 1943, p 133.

HERBERT J. REICH, *Theory and Applications of Electron Tubes*, McGraw-Hill Book Co., New York, 1944, pp 543–53.

JACOB MILLMAN and SAMUEL SEELY, *Electronics*, McGraw-Hill Book Co., New York, 1941, pp 419–32.

Resistance Welding Manual, Resistance Welder Manufacturers' Association, Philadelphia, Pa., 1942.

Chapter 17

ELECTRONIC REGULATORS

One of the earliest attempts to introduce the new-born art of electronics into industrial fields was through the medium of electronic regulators. The fundamental advantages possessed by electronic tubes that can be so fittingly applied to regulation were manifest to design engineers many years ago. Their response is practically instantaneous, no parts have to move, and no electric contacts wear because of arcing. It was recognized too that new feats of regulation not possible by other means could be accomplished. For example, through the phototube, the position of printed lines can be made to appear at the desired location on a sheet or package, because the phototube can "see" the printers' ink and regulate its register accordingly. Thus regulation at high rates of speed is possible without any physical contact with the item regulated.

It is not surprising, then, that electronic regulators were first applied to photoelectric register control and to regulators of a-c and d-c generator voltage. Success did not come quickly, because the pliotrons of years ago could not control enough power. Practical and reliable electronic systems of regulation did not appear until the development of thyratrons of higher power ratings.

"Control" and "regulation" are not synonymous. The difference between the principles of these two systems is both real and important. When a system *controls*, the input to the control device is entirely independent of its output. As an example of control, Fig. 17.1, a phototube P, excited by the beam of light source L, is located before the threshold of a doorway, and a "signal" from P is connected to the input of a control. Any of the photoelectric relays of Chapter 16 serve this purpose. Output of the control device is fed into a mechanism M to open the door. When the light beam is interrupted, the door is caused to swing open. Input and output to the control system are entirely independent, because the functions of phototube P and mechanism M are not in any way related.

On the other hand, in any system of *regulation* input and output of the regulating system are definitely related, and whatever happens to one affects the other. A simple system to regulate direct voltage of a generator, Fig. 17.2, illustrates this. Let the regulating system be assigned the task of holding constant voltage at the input terminals A–B, and suppose this

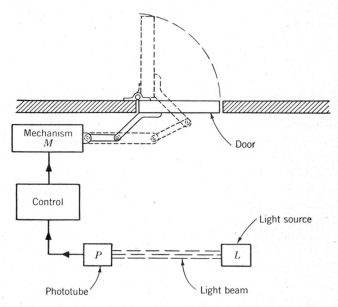

FIG. 17.1.   Illustrating the principles of *control*, a door is opened by interrupting a light beam.

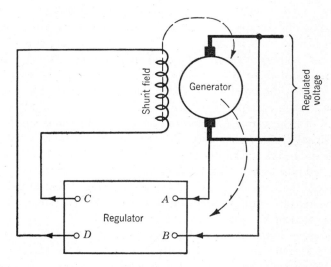

FIG. 17.2.   Illustrating the principles of *regulation*, the effects of input and output are interrelated by a closed circuit.

requirement is momentarily satisfied. If some external cause reduces the generator terminal voltage, a reduction to input A–B of the regulating system brings about an immediate increase of output C–D to increase the generator field excitation and, thereby, corrects the deficiency. However, the cycle becomes closed in the case of regulation, for an increase in output C–D is indicated by a rise in generator voltage, which continues on to affect input A–B. This interchange of action between input and output continues until a balance is obtained and the new conditions of the system are satisfied. Thus, in a system of regulation, input and output are dependent one upon the other, a feature that distinguishes regulation from control and makes the problems of the two vastly different.

Regulators are broadly divided into two classes, one called *static* and the other *astatic*. Static regulators are sometimes called "dead zone," because the regulator output does not change so long as the quantity being regulated remains within a narrow margin, that is, near the desired value. In other words, the regulated quantity must swing beyond a "zone of correctness" before a static regulator begins to make any change in its output. An approximate parallel occurs in the driving of an automobile. While the road is level, the driver makes no alteration of the throttle opening until coming to a grade, whereupon a changing speed makes evident that more power is required. Once the throttle is opened wider, to compensate for the new load conditions, the desired speed is maintained, and no further throttle adjustment is required.

On the other hand, such is seldom true in steering a vehicle for, although the experienced driver may not realize it, an automobile is held to a so-called straight course by small corrections of the wheel being made continually, first in one direction and then in the other. This is characteristic of regulators of the astatic type, which are, in effect, continually vibrating to make the average of the regulated quantity agree with the established operating level. The familiar Tirrill voltage regulator with its rapidly vibrating contacts represents this class. Although it may be difficult to conceive of an electronic circuit as "vibrating," the electrical significance agrees with this principle.

Static Regulators

A representative static regulator is the Westinghouse type-RR–6 photoelectric two-direction register regulator for the positioning of a reference mark with respect to the top (or bottom) of sheets cut from a continuous web. The equipment used for cutting machines, either to cut individual sheets of paper, or to cut them and fold into bags, is illustrated by Fig. 17.3. The operation of packaging machinery whereby the photoelectric equipment automatically registers the wrapper to the correct position on the package is similar.

An uncut roll of paper on which the design has been printed in sequence is mounted on bearings to the left. Coincident with the printing of each design is some reference mark, which may be a portion of the design itself, but is illustrated here by a mark along the right edge of the sheet. As the uncut paper moves from left to right by feed rolls, it is cut into sheets by a

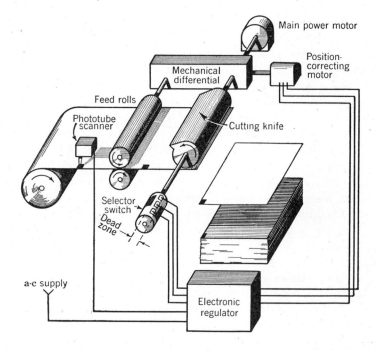

FIG. 17.3.   Schematic drawing of a static-type electronic register regulator used with a rotary cutter to cut lengths of paper from a continuous roll to individual sheets, positioning each cut through a suitable reference mark printed on the web.

rotary knife. Rotation of the knife continues at a constant speed represented by its direct connection to the main drive motor. The feed rolls are also driven from the main motor but through some variable-speed transmission typified by a mechanical differential gear. An auxiliary positioning motor is connected to the planetary differential gear such that when the positioning motor is at standstill, the feed rolls rotate in synchronism with the rotary cutting knife. But, when the positioning motor is rotated, say clockwise, rotation of the feed rolls becomes faster than that of the rotary knife, and the position of the printed design advanced relative to the blade of the cutting knife. Counterclockwise rotation of the positioning motor retards the position of the design with respect to the knife.

An electric selector switch is driven directly from the cutting-knife shaft. The selector switch has three stationary contacts or brushes. The rotating member of the switch carries two conducting segments arranged such that one segment closes the circuit between the center and right stationary brushes, while the other segment closes a circuit between the center and left brush. The two segments are displaced so that no electric connection is completed between stationary brushes throughout several degrees of rotation. This portion of the switch rotation represents a dead zone of the regulator operation.

FIG. 17.4. A phototube scanner for reflected light applications. (Left) Phototube, pliotron, and exciter lamp removed from the housing. (Right) Assembled scanner. The left unit is the light source. The phototube with its amplifier is enclosed in the right unit. (*Courtesy Westinghouse*)

A photoelectric scanner, consisting of a light source, a phototube, and an amplifier, is located along one edge of the paper sheet (see Fig. 17.4). The light beam cast onto the sheet by the exciter lamp and projecting lens is reflected from the sheet, collected by a receiving lens, focused onto the phototube cathode, and amplified by a pliotron included within the scanner housing. (If the material is transparent, such as Cellophane, the light beam is transmitted through the material and the phototube located on the opposite side of the sheet.)

When a reference mark passes under the scanning beam, the amplifier anode current is instantly affected. Output of the scanner is connected to a regulator cabinet, Fig. 17.5.

The equipment is aligned such that, when the knife is cutting the sheets in exactly the desired position, a reference mark intercepts the scanning beam in synchronism with the dead-zone position of the selector switch. The circuit to the stationary brushes of the selector switch is then open, and

FIG. 17.5.   Cabinet with thyratrons, relays, and equipment for static-type two-direction register regulator, such as shown in Fig. 17.3.

(Courtesy Westinghouse)

the impulse from the scanner terminates in the open position of the selector switch. The positioning motor remains idle. The feed rolls and cutting knife continue to rotate in direct speed relation. Should accumulative shrinkage of the sheet cause a reference mark to pass under the scanning beam somewhat earlier in the cutting cycle, a segment of the selector switch completes a circuit between the center and one stationary brush coincident with an impulse from the scanning amplifier. A thyratron within the regulator control then starts rotation of the positioning motor to drive the differential gearing in the correct direction to speed up the knife rotation with respect to the constant speed of the feed rolls. The positioning motor continues to rotate for a short interval of time controlled by a capacitor-discharge timing circuit within the regulator. Rotation of the positioning motor may continue for several timed intervals until the selector switch once more is matched to its dead-zone position coincident with the position of a reference mark under the scanning beam.

Should the accumulative error, resulting for example from expansion of the sheet, advance the cutting line in the opposite direction, the alternate circuit of the selector switch causes rotation of the positioning motor in the opposite direction. The knife speed is thus decreased with respect to the feed rolls and the reference mark position corrected in the opposite manner.

Regulators of this type are classified as *static* regulators, because the equipment remains inoperative as long as the result remains regulated close to the desired quantity. The closeness of this regulation is controlled by adjusting the width of the dead zone of the selector switch.

A schematic diagram, Fig. 17.6, illustrates the function of equipment. Phototube T_5, pentode T_3, and exciter lamp T_6 are remotely mounted in the scanner, Fig. 17.4. Thyratrons T_1 and T_2 are connected to a d-c source of anode voltage, consisting of Rectox rectifier 1 and filter capacitor C_5. A d-c source for amplifier T_3 and the grid circuit consists of Rectox rectifier 2, filter reactor L_1, and capacitors C_3 and C_4. Voltage-divider resistors R_4, R_5, R_6, and P_1 provide d-c potentials required for the circuits.

Thyratrons T_1 and T_2 are normally held nonconducting by the negative grid voltage across R_5 from the thyratron cathode terminal 21 to their grids through resistors R_7 and R_8. Phototube T_5 is impulse-coupled (see Chapter 15, page 360) to the pentode amplifier T_3.

The connection shown is for operation by a reference mark darker than the paper sheet. Illumination of T_5 by the relatively bright reflection of the sheet charges C_1 by the voltage drop across resistor R_1. Illumination is decreased by a dark reference mark passing at high speed under the scanner beam, rapidly discharging C_1 through R_2 suddenly making the grid of T_3 more negative, relative to its cathode connections. Bias for T_3 is adjusted by P_1. Resistor R_3 is the load resistor in the anode circuit of amplifier T_3. Normal adjustment of the circuit is such that the anode current of T_3 is large, making the voltage drop across R_3 large and negative at terminal 10. Negative potential, applied to the grid of T_3 by suddenly decreasing the phototube illumination, reduces anode current through R_3 making terminal 10 less negative, that is, more positive.

Thyratrons T_1 and T_2 are normally nonconducting by the bias voltage 21–2. As the selector switch rotates, first closing the circuit 10–9, the grid

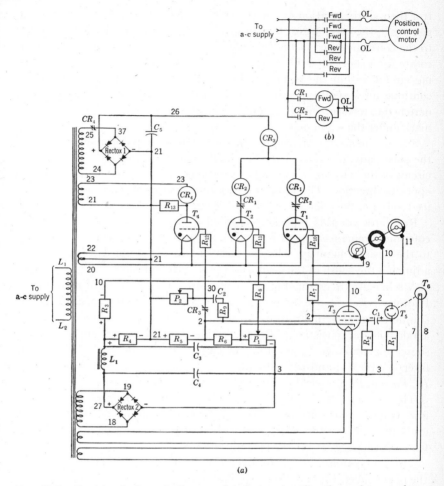

FIG. 17.6. Functional schematic diagram of static-type two-direction register regulator.

circuit of thyratron T_1 is returned to the cathode terminal 21 by way of resistor R_3 and voltage-divider resistor R_4. If the phototube illumination is decreased while circuit 10–9 of the selector switch is closed, the grid of thyratron T_1 is made positive by the decrease in voltage drop across R_3 at terminal 10. Thyratron T_1 immediately conducts to energize the coils of relays CR_1 and CR_3. Although the grid potential of T_1 is made positive for only a brief interval, thyratron T_1 remains conducting because of the d-c potential applied to its anode.

A contact of CR_1 closes to energize coil *Fwd* of a reversing contactor control, Fig. 17.6b whence the positioning motor immediately rotates in the clockwise direction. Timing thyratron T_4 is biased by the negative potential 21–2 and is nonconducting. Energizing the coil of CR_3 instantly opens contacts 2–30 in the grid circuit of T_4. Capacitor C_2 then begins to charge through resistor R_9 and potentiometer P_2 across the source of potential 21–2. Initially, the zero charge of capacitor C_2 makes the grid terminal 30 negative at the potential of 2 (the voltage across R_9 is negligible). As C_2 charges, the potential of terminal 30 becomes positive relative to terminal

Fig. 17.7. This packaging machine automatically wraps candy bars, electronically controlled by a single-direction register regulator. Reference marks printed at the left edge of the sheet are scanned by light source 1 and phototube-amplifier housing 2. The cycle is timed by selector switch 3 and the web position corrected by the two-speed gear unit 4.　　　　　　　　　　　　　　　*(Courtesy Package Machinery Company)*

Fig. 17.8. Electronically controlled automatic wrapper. Reference marks **2**, printed on the web, are scanned by scanner 1 (see Fig. 17.4) used with regulator 3. The cycle is timed by selector switch 4. Solenoid 5, energized by the electronic control, shifts the ratio of the two-speed V-belt drive 6 to control the sheet register.

(*Courtesy New England Confectionery Company*)

2, and at the end of the desired interval thyratron T_4 conducts to energize CR_4. The duration of this interval is adjusted by potentiometer P_2. Energizing CR_4 opens contact 25–37, causing the instant removal of the d-c anode potential to thyratrons T_1 and T_2. Relays CR_1 and CR_3 are de-energized, and contact 2–30 of CR_3 returns the negative bias of T_4 and rapidly discharges C_2 through R_9. The circuit is instantly reset.

The closing of selector-switch circuit 10–11 operates thyratron T_2, relays CR_2, CR_3, and main contactor Rev, Fig. 17.6b, for counterclockwise rotation of the positioning motor.

As long as the machine is cutting to exact register, impulses affecting the phototube cause positive peak potential at terminal 10 in synchronism with the open-circuit position of selector switch 9–10–11. Thus, the changing voltage across R_3 is not applied to the grid of either thyratron T_1 or T_2, and these tubes remain biased negatively through resistors R_7 and R_8. Thus, no control relays are energized, and the equipment remains static as long as the register is exactly as desired.

Photoelectric register regulators are also designed for correction or operation in a single direction, Fig. 17.7. Electronic equipment of this type is usually applied to machines for packaging and usually includes a thyratron-actuated control relay together with a capacitor-discharge thyratron timing circuit for holding the control relay closed for a predetermined interval. Numerous mechanical schemes are employed to control single-direction packaging machines. One type, Fig. 17.7, is designed with a mechanical drive to the feed rolls purposely adjusted to feed slightly lower than required to maintain a correct register between the cutting knife and design. Reference marks are scanned by light source 1 and phototube amplifier 2. A selector switch 3 continuously compares light impulses with the position of the cutting knife in a manner similar to that previously described. As the reference marks fall behind the required register (because of purposely underfeeding), the photoelectric equipment actuates a speed-changing gear unit 4 to increase the feed rate momentarily. The web is thereby brought back to the exact register position by the single-direction control.

Another type of packaging machine, Fig. 17.8, uses similar photoelectric equipment. In this, the mechanical feed is purposely adjusted somewhat faster than required to hold exact register. Operation of the equipment is similar to that previously described, except that the mechanical speed-changing device is a two-speed V-belt drive that reduces the feed rate by the photoelectric control so as to retard the web and hold the register in correct alignment.

Astatic Regulators

Astatic regulators, contrasted to those previously described, do not operate within a dead zone. Instead, the quantity being regulated is always either too great or too small. Hence, the regulating action is never static and can be thought of as continually vibrating. Indeed, the Tirrill voltage regulator is a familiar type, which exemplifies the operation of all astatic regulators and is one by which continual vibration is self-evident. Although electronic regulators give no visual indication of vibration, the action occurring within the electric circuits is similar.

A description of several types of astatic electronic regulators follows. Space permits mention of only a few* that typify the method of regulating different quantities.

FIG. 17.9.   A scanner, removed from its enclosure, for electronic edge control of slitting. A synchronous motor (top) rotates four small lenses (bottom) to project a rotating light beam.   Light reflected from the material scanned (not shown) is received by the photo-tube (bottom).   An amplifier tube is shielded within the can (upper left).

(*Courtesy Westinghouse*)

REGULATION OF POSITION — WESTINGHOUSE TYPE-*SC* SLITTER REGULATOR

The Westinghouse type-*SC* regulator is employed for the purpose of slitting material such as paper or Cellophane to a reference line printed continuously along the strip. The equipment operates equally as well if the edge of the material itself is used as the reference, although throughout this discussion only the use of a printed reference line is considered.

Heart of the control system is the scanning unit pictured by Fig. 17.9

*For a description of other electronic regulators see Gulliksen and Vedder, *Industrial Electronics*, pp 175–239.

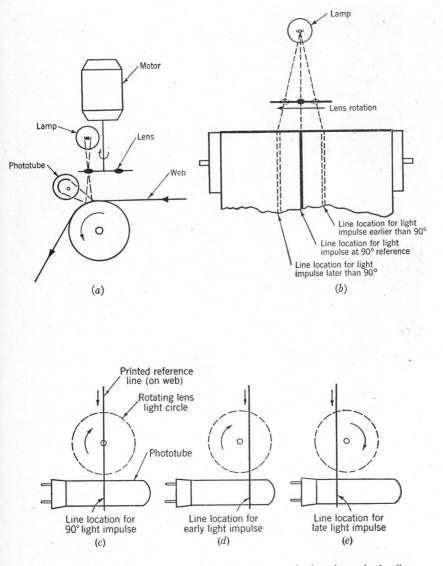

FIG. 17.10. (a) Schematic drawing of rotating scanner viewing the end of roll over which the web runs continuously. (b) The rotating beam crosses the reference line affording a variation in the cyclic reflected light impulses as the reference line moves either side of a central position. (c) (d) and (e) Plan view of reference line relative to the rotating light circle for three positions.

FIG. 17.11. Paper wrappers of roll 1 are slit into individual rolls (not visible) by this machine, using an electronic regulator to edge-control the slitting position. Phototube scanner 2 operates electronic control 3 to afford speed and direction of positioning control d-c motor 4. Mechanical screw 5 (driven by the motor) moves shaft 6 to the left or right as required to maintain the cutting line in register with the wrapper design.

(*Courtesy Nashua Gummed and Coated Paper Company*)

(removed from its case) and Fig. 17.12 (installed on a machine). The unit consists of four lenses equally spaced, mounted in a disk rotated 1800 rpm or synchronously with respect to the a-c power source feeding the equipment. An exciter lamp is mounted behind the rotating lens to project a rotating light circle toward the material scanned below. Light reflected from the material is collected by the phototube cathode and amplified by a pliotron mounted inside the housing.

Function of the scanner is shown by Fig. 17.10a. The four lenses rotate at synchronous speed to obtain a light impulse reflected from the material being scanned in exact synchronism with the sinusoidal voltage supplying the equipment. Because four lenses are rotated at 1800 rpm, one light impulse is obtained for each half-cycle of 60-cycle voltage. If the reference line lies directly below the exciter lamp, the reflected light impulse occurs exactly as one rotating lens passes the direct line between the lamp and reference mark, Fig. 17.10b. As will be explained, this position is referred to as a 90-degree reference position. Should the mark move toward the right, the reflected impulse occurs sooner in the rotating lens cycle. As the mark moves toward the left, the light impulse comes later. These conditions are further illustrated in Fig. 17.10c, d, and e.

Fig. 17.12. Close-up of rotating scanner. (See Fig. 17.9.) The reference line is visible near the left edge of the sheet.
(*Courtesy Nashua Gummed and Coated Paper Company*)

A typical installation is given by Fig. 17.11, 17.12 and 17.13. With reference to Fig. 17.11, the printed web 1 is slit into two separate rolls (not visible in the illustration) and is edge-controlled to cut with reference to the black line near the right edge of the web (more clearly seen to the left in Fig. 17.12). Scanner 2, as previously described and further illustrated by Fig. 17.12, controls the amplifier circuit within cabinet 3, and Fig. 17.13. These electronic units control the direction and speed of rotation of d-c motor 4 which chain-drives a nut-and-screw mechanical device 5. Rotation of the screw provides lateral movement of shaft 6, turning the roll 1 and also positioning the roll toward the left or right as required to hold the reference line on alignment with the photoelectric scanner and slitting knives.

The functional schematic diagram, Fig. 17.14, shows phototube P connected to amplifier T_1 by an impulse-coupling circuit C_1, R_3, R_4, such as described in Chapter 15, page 361. These devices are mounted remotely in the scanning head on the machine, Fig. 17.12. Amplifier T_1 is coupled to fire thyratron T_2 through a peaking transformer TR_2. As the intensity of light impulses picked up by the phototube suddenly changes, T_1 anode-current pulses flow in the primary winding of TR_2. These current pulses induce a voltage in TR_2 secondary sufficient to exceed grid bias E_{cc1} to fire

FIG. 17.13.   Electronic-control cabinet for slitter regulator.

(Courtesy Westinghouse)

thyratron T_2. These secondary voltage peaks, Fig. 17.15a, occur in exact relation with reflected light impulses on the phototube and thus translate the relative time cycle of light impulses to voltage peaks timed with reference to the alternating-voltage wave. If the reference mark is toward the right of the central position, Fig. 17.10b and d, thyratron T_2 is fired early in its conducting cycle as Fig. 17.15a shows. Conversely, if the reference mark is toward the left of center, firing of T_2 is delayed, Fig. 17.15b.

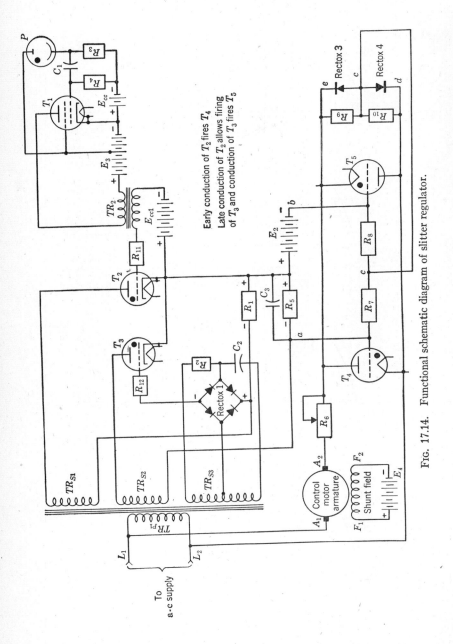

Early conduction of T_2 fires T_4
Late conduction of T_2 allows firing
of T_3 and conduction of T_3 fires T_5

FIG. 17.14. Functional schematic diagram of slitter regulator.

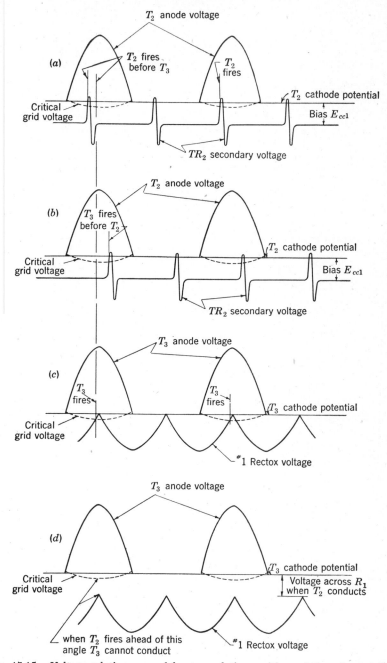

FIG. 17.15. Voltage relations caused by two relative positions of the reference line. (a) and (d) Light impulses are received before the 90-degree position. (b) and (c) Light impulses occur later than the 90-degree position.

Resistor R_1 connected in the cathode circuit of T_2 passes the load current of this tube. As long as T_2 remains nonconducting, voltage across R_1 is zero. As T_2 fires, voltage across R_1 assumes the polarity indicated in the figure. The grid voltage of thyratron T_3 has two components. One of these is the rectified but unfiltered output of Rectox 1, which is phase-shifted 90 degrees by means of transformer winding TR_{S3}, resistor R_2, and capacitor C_2. The phase-shifted Rectox voltage causes thyratron T_3 to fire at the 90-degree point of each anode-voltage cycle, as Fig. 17.15c shows. The voltage developed across R_1 while T_2 is conducting displaces the Rectox voltage component downward such that T_3 cannot conduct, Fig. 17.15d. To correlate the meaning of Fig. 17.15a, b, c, d, if a light impulse occurs *before* the 90 degrees point, thyratron T_2 conducts to displace T_3 grid voltage downward (d) before T_3 can be fired by the voltage of Rectox 1, and T_3 remains nonconducting. If a light impulse is received *after* the 90-degree point, thyratron T_3 has already been fired by the voltage of Rectox 1 (c), and the subsequent conduction of T_2 is unable to prevent further change in the already conducting state of T_3.

Motion to alter the slitting position of the machine is controlled by a shunt-wound d-c motor, pictured in Fig. 17.11 and diagrammed in Fig. 17.14, with constantly excited field F_1–F_2. Armature A_1–A_2 is energized by half-wave rectified current of thyratrons T_4 and T_5. These are connected inversely such that conduction of T_4 rotates the motor clockwise while conduction of T_5 reverses rotation. By the connection of Rectox rectifiers 3 and 4 with resistors R_9 and R_{10}, thyratron T_4 is fired by positive potential applied to its grid terminal a. Thyratron T_5 is fired by positive potential at b. Thus, T_4 or T_5 can be fired selectively by reversing the polarity of voltage a–b. The direction of rotation of the positioning-control motor is thereby reversed.

The function of resistors R_9 and R_{10}, together with that of Rectox rectifiers 3 and 4, may be understood if we note that, during the half-cycle that supply terminal L_1 is positive, current from e is down through R_9 and Rectox 4 to d. Because of the low conducting resistance of Rectox 4, terminal c is nearly the same potential as d. In this way, c is essentially "connected" to the cathode of tube T_4. As the a-c polarity reverses, voltage across Rectox 3 is small, and c is essentially "connected" to the cathode of tube T_5. Whatever the magnitude and polarity of the voltage between terminals a–b, it is divided by resistors R_7 and R_8. Furthermore, by the switching action of Rectox 3 and 4 with resistors R_9 and R_{10}, one half of the potential a–b is alternately applied to the grids of T_4 or T_5.

These functions are correlated by Fig. 17.16. Assume that the light impulses are early, and therefore T_3 cannot conduct. Potential E_2 appears between a and b without modification. This condition is manifest by Fig. 17.16a and b. With terminal L_1 of the a-c supply positive, positive

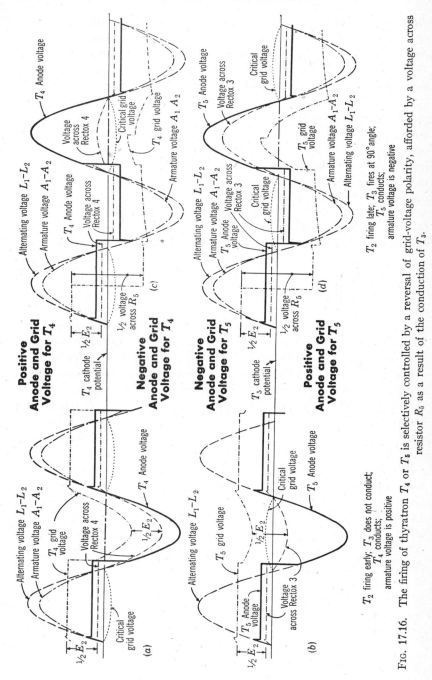

FIG. 17.16.   The firing of thyratron T_4 or T_5 is selectively controlled by a reversal of grid-voltage polarity, afforded by a voltage across resistor R_5 as a result of the conduction of T_3.

potential is applied to the anode of T_4 and the cathode of T_5. Thyratron T_5 is, therefore, not subject to conduction during this half-cycle. By the previously explained action of Rectox 4 and resistor R_9 approximately one half of E_2 is impressed from the cathode to grid of T_4 with the grid terminal positive. Thyratron T_4 fires early in the voltage cycle. Voltage across the tube elements drops to the arc voltage, leaving the remainder of the a-c source potential applied across the motor armature (except for the drop through adjusting resistor R_6). This is illustrated by Fig. 17.16a. During this same half-cycle the anode voltage of T_5 is negative, limited to the arc-drop voltage of T_4, and its grid potential is negative. Therefore, T_5 cannot conduct.

As the a-c supply reverses polarity L_2 is positive. The conduction of T_4 continues for a part of this half-cycle because of the circuit inductance and is then extinguished. Anode voltage of T_5 is now positive.† However, the switching action of Rectox 3 with R_{10} assures that nearly the full magnitude of $1/2E_2$ is applied to the grid of T_5, negative at the grid terminal, Fig. 17.16b. In this way the conduction of T_5 is blocked and motor-armature voltage is zero‡ for nearly the full half-cycle. Armature voltage of the positioning-control motor is, therefore, positive during the conduction of thyratron T_4.

Assume that the sequence of light impulses is delayed so as to render the conduction of T_3, accompanied by a large voltage across resistor R_5. Thyratron T_4 is conducting, Fig. 17.16c, as this first impulse occurs (because of the phase relations of the circuit), and its conduction is not altered by the change of grid polarity caused by the voltage across R_5.

As the a-c supply becomes positive at L_2, positive anode potential is applied to the anode of T_5, Fig. 17.16d. Because of the voltage partially retained across R_5 by capacitor C_3 after T_3 is extinguished, and with the aid of Rectox 3 and resistor R_{10}, a positive grid voltage is applied to T_5, as Fig. 17.16d shows. Thyratron T_5 fires immediately as soon as T_4 is extinguished, and the polarity of motor-armature voltage is reversed. As the a-c supply reverses to negative at L_2, the T_5 anode voltage is negative. Also the action of Rectox 3 with resistor R_{10} makes the grid voltage of T_5 strongly negative. Thus, T_5 is nonconducting. During this half-cycle the anode voltage of T_4 is positive although its grid voltage is negative, because of the action of Rectox 4, resistor R_9, and the slowly diminishing but sufficiently large voltage across R_5 (and C_3) as the right portion of Fig.

†In referring to Fig. 17.16 it should be noted that for (a) and (c) positive anode and grid voltage of T_4 is *above* the zero cathode potential while for (b) and (d) positive anode and grid voltage of T_5 is *below* the cathode zero potential.

‡In this discussion the consideration of the armature counter electromotive force is disregarded to avoid complications which do not influence a functional description of the basic operation.

17.16c shows. Thyratron T_4 is thereby held nonconducting. Because neither T_4 or T_5 conduct, the motor-armature current is zero.

If the sequence of light impulses continues to be delayed, T_3 conducts repeatedly, and capacitor C_3 is recharged at the half-cycle mid-point, as the right of Fig. 17.16c shows. In this way the grid voltage of T_4 is maintained sufficiently negative to prevent its conduction.

Armature voltage of the positioning-control motor is, therefore, negative during the conduction of T_5.

Regulators operating as described are used to control the slitting position within plus or minus 1/32 inch with average conditions while the material moves continually at approximately 600 fpm.

Astatic Voltage Regulators

Electronic voltage regulators for control of d-c and a-c generators were one of the first attempts of the industrial-control engineer to utilize electronic devices. Although the earliest designs were limited to a relatively small control of power, the advantage of marked sensitivity, rapid response and over-all performance led engineers to recognize the inherent advantages of the electronic regulator. Many systems have been devised to accomplish some specific results. Though details make these many types appear different, each is composed of three essential parts. These are: (1) a voltage-indicating circuit, (2) an amplifier or power circuit, and (3) an antihunting circuit. Without these components, the astatic voltage regulator is incomplete.

VOLTAGE-INDICATING CIRCUITS

The purpose of a voltage-indicating circuit is to sense a change in the magnitude of the regulated voltage, interpret the magnitude and direction of this change, and convert this to a signal voltage applied to the regulator input. The principles are illustrated by the block diagram, Fig. 17.17. A coupling unit is connected directly to the voltage-regulated bus. The coupling unit may consist of a simple voltage divider, or, if alternating voltage is to be regulated, the coupling unit may consist of a transformer and rectifier to obtain a direct voltage proportional to the alternating bus voltage. The reference voltage is a source of constant d-c potential and can be obtained in any one of several ways. The voltage output of the coupling unit is connected in series opposition with the constant reference voltage. Any change in the coupling-unit voltage is instantly detected as a difference between these two voltages and appears as the indicating-circuit output.

A simple voltage-indicating circuit, Fig. 17.18, consists of voltage-

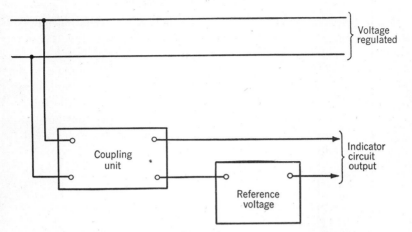

Fig. 17.17. Block diagram of a basic voltage-indicating circuit.

dividing resistors A and B, connected across a 250-volt d-c bus. The resistors are proportioned so that the 46-volt drop across resistor B is opposed against a constant 45-volt *reference potential* from a battery. The indicating-circuit output potential of 1.0 volt is the difference between the voltage

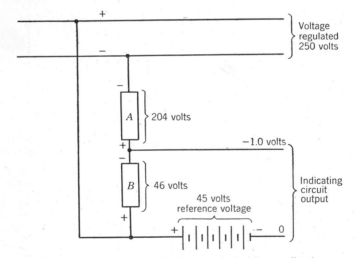

Fig. 17.18. A voltage-indicating circuit for d-c application.

across resistor B and the reference potential. If the bus voltage rises to 255 volts, the voltage across B is increased to 47 volts and the indicating-circuit output is doubled to -2.0 volt. Should the bus voltage drop to 245 volts, the indicating-circuit output becomes zero, and any further reduction in bus voltage changes the polarity of the indicating-circuit output. Thus, the indicating circuit is responsive to the magnitude and direction of bus-voltage change from its normal of 250 volts.

One type of voltage-indicating circuit for use with an a-c system, Fig. 17.19, uses a transformer, TR_1, a double kenotron T_1, and filter C_1, L_1, C_2 as the coupling unit. The direct-voltage output of the full-wave rectifier is smoothed by the filter and opposed by the constant-battery reference voltage. The indicating-circuit output is manifest by the difference between these potentials.

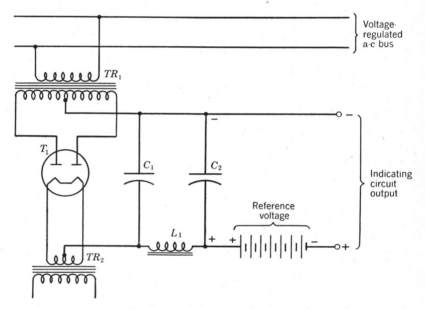

FIG. 17.19. A voltage-indicating circuit for a-c application, used when the a-c generator maintains a constant ratio of rms to average value of the voltage wave.

This type of voltage-indicating circuit is widely used for single-phase a-c systems. It is sometimes modified by the substitution of a three-phase transformer and rectifier of the coupling unit, such modification possessing the advantage that filter constants can be chosen to obtain a shorter time constant without detracting from the purity of rectified wave form.

The indicating circuit of Fig. 17.19 offers the practical advantage of simplicity. Also the circuit output voltage rapidly follows a fluctuation of a-c bus voltage. However, it has one disadvantage resulting from the fact that the rectified voltage becomes the *average value* of the a-c bus voltage, whereas the *rms* value is desired. The wave form of many a-c generators remains so nearly constant with variable-load conditions that in most cases the ratio of average-to-rms values remains fixed, and the circuit satisfies these requirements. Occasionally, electronic regulators are applied with an a-c generator whose wave form changes with variable-load conditions. Here, the ratio of average-to-rms values does not remain constant, and the indicating circuit is not found satisfactory.

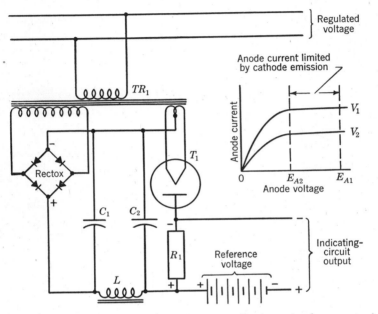

FIG. 17.20. A voltage-indicating circuit for a-c application. Anode current of the kenotron is a function of cathode-heating current and the circuit output responds to the rms value of regulated voltage.

A voltage-indicating circuit eliminating the previous objection is shown in Fig. 17.20. This circuit employs a kenotron T_1 of the direct-heated cathode type. Energy for the cathode heater is provided by a winding of TR_1, the primary circuit of which is connected to the a-c bus. Thus, the emission of T_1 is proportional to the rms a-c bus voltage. A source of d-c potential for the tube anode is obtained from a rectifier, shown as a copper-oxide bridge in the figure, and filtered by C_1, L, C_2. Although the rectified direct voltage changes in proportion to the a-c bus voltage, the effect is eliminated by operating kenotron T_1 throughout its saturated region, as between limits E_{A1} and E_{A2}, Fig. 17.20. In this way, anode current through T_1 responds only to a change in its cathode temperature and is essentially independent of the anode-voltage source. Anode current through a constant-load resistor R_1 manifests a voltage across this resistor proportional to the anode current through it. The output voltage of the coupling unit is then proportional to the rms value of bus voltage. This is opposed by the constant-reference potential, and the indicating-circuit output gives the desired results.

However, this circuit is not without some disadvantage. Although the cathode of kenotron T_1 is made of fine wire, its temperature, that is, emission, does not change instantly with a change in a-c bus voltage, and the indicating circuit lags a change in input voltage. This circuit is satisfactory when applied with loads changing slowly but is not adaptable to rapidly changing loads if close instantaneous voltage regulation is required.

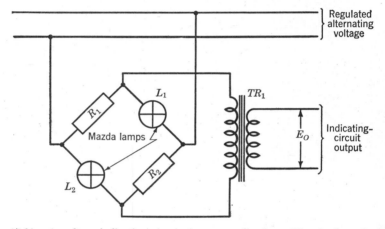

Fig. 17.21. A voltage-indicating circuit for a-c application. Magnitude and phase of the output voltage is affected by a change of regulated voltage.

A different type of voltage-indicating circuit, Fig. 17.21, connects a bridge circuit consisting of two Mazda lamps and resistors R_1, R_2 across the a-c bus voltage. Resistors R_1, R_2 are constructed of material having a low temperature-resistance coefficient, whereas the resistance of lamps L_1, L_2 changes appreciably with the current through them. Transformer primary winding TR_1 is connected across the bridge, and the indicating-circuit output voltage E_O is proportional to the transformer excitation.

The bridge is balanced, and E_O is zero for a definite value of a-c bus voltage. E_O is increased by either a rise or fall in a-c bus potential. A decrease of input voltage manifests a rise of output voltage in phase with the input voltage. If the input voltage exceeds the normal, rising output voltage is opposite in phase. Such an indicating circuit is sometimes useful where the magnitude and phase relation of an output voltage is required.§

§Other voltage-indicating circuits are given by Gulliksen and Vedder, *Industrial Electronics*, pp 179–85.

Antihunting Circuits

Regulating systems are commonly called *closed-loop* circuits. This name is derived from the relation tying together regulator input and output such that any change in one quantity affects the other. Because of this interrelation between input and output, regulating systems require that some means to prevent hunting be incorporated in the circuit. (Some regulating systems do not *apparently* include any antihunting component, although the characteristics to satisfy stability must be present and in some cases may be inherent within the component parts of the system). An analysis of the requirements to satisfy a stable regulating system frequently becomes complicated and is beyond the intended scope of this chapter.‖

One conception of the problems affecting the stability of a simple regulating system can be illustrated by a common analogy. Assume an automobile at standstill, and the driver is suddenly commissioned to proceed to some exact mark further down the street as rapidly as possible. The analogy may be similar to a requirement to increase the field current of a generator rapidly to satisfy an increased load demand. The driver accelerates the car quickly, although, in spite of a full throttle opening, some time delay is necessary to attain full speed. Should the driver continue at full speed until opposite the assigned new mark, obviously the vehicle would overshoot the destination, and it would be necessary to reverse to arrive at the mark. The method by which the new mark is reached most quickly and with the least disturbance is to decelerate before reaching the new destination. This is accomplished by applying a braking force which is *opposite to the original movement required to satisfy the condition*. This force in opposition to the original movement is akin to the antihunting force required to stabilize all regulating systems. It should be noted that, no matter how great the braking effort, a time delay must elapse before the speed change is affected. A skillful driver can best bring the vehicle to the new destination by a compromise in his ability to accelerate, traverse at high speed, and decelerate, allowing for the inherent time delays required to change the vehicle velocity. Likewise, the stability of regulating systems is attained by compromise of the electrical and mechanical components synonymous with those of the assumed analogy.

‖For further study of the stability of regulating systems, see:

Hanna, Oplinger, and Valentine, "Recent Developments in Generator Voltage Regulation," *AIEE Transactions*, Vol 58, 1939, pp 838–44.

Hanna, Oplinger, and Mikina, "Recent Developments in Speed Regulation," *AIEE Transactions*, Vol 59, 1940, pp 692–700.

Boice, Crary, Kron, and Thompson, "The Direct-Acting Generator Voltage Regulator," *AIEE Transactions*, Vol 59, March 1940, pp 149–57.

Mathematics of Modern Engineering.

One of the most common antihunting circuits used with electronic regulators is that of Fig. 17.22. The system illustrates regulation of a constant voltage across generator terminals A and B. Output of the voltage-indicating circuit passes through resistor R_2 to reach input terminal D of the electronic regulating system. Exciter field current is controlled by the regulator output E–F. Antihunt capacitor C_1 is charged, the polarity as indicated and the charge magnitude controlled by the slider position R_1. The antihunt

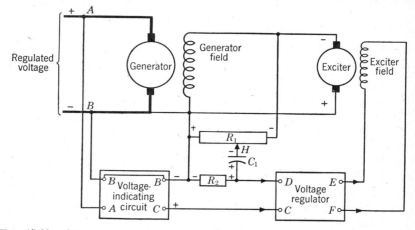

Fig. 17.22.   One type of antihunting circuit. Capacitor C_1 charging or discharging through resistor R_2 introduces a voltage to the regulator input in opposition to the change of indicating-circuit potential.

action is observed by assuming the regulated voltage to rise momentarily above the desired magnitude. The negative potential of terminal B is increased and is transferred appreciably unchanged through R_2 to D of the regulator. The larger negative signal received by the regulator input immediately decreases the exciter field current, causing decline in exciter voltage. Voltage B–H instantly decreases in proporton to the exciter voltage change, and capacitor C_1 discharges. Electron flow of the discharging capacitor through antihunt resistor R_2 causes a voltage drop through R_2 with the polarity indicated in the figure. The polarity at terminal D makes the input terminal, normally negative, more positive. This action of the antihunt circuit is in opposition to the influence present at generator terminals A–B. The action of the rapidly changing exciter voltage is thereby arrested, and the generator voltage decrease is checked before undershooting the reference level.

Reverse action of the antihunt circuit occurs when the voltage A–B drops below the desired level. In this case, rising exciter voltage increases potential B–H to charge capacitor C_1, making the voltage across resistor R_2

positive at B and negative at D. As before, the antihunt potential opposes the change $A-B$ to stabilize the regulator performance. The degree of capacitor charge or discharge and, hence, the antihunt voltage developed across R_2 depend upon the rapidity of changing exciter voltage. In this way, the antihunting force is made proportional to the magnitude of exciter-voltage *change*. This is one criterion for the prevention of hunting.

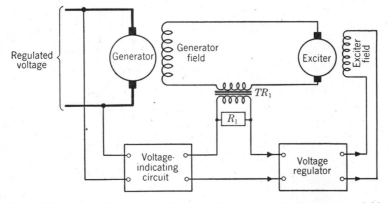

FIG. 17.23. An antihunting circuit responsive to current in the generator field.

One other antihunting circuit, Fig. 17.23, uses a specially designed transformer TR_1, connected between the voltage-indicating circuit and the regulator input. The primary of TR_1 completes the circuit between exciter armature and generator field and is affected directly by the generator shunt-field current rather than by the exciter armature voltage as for the previous circuit, Fig. 17.22. Secondary voltage of TR_1 responds in magnitude and polarity to the *changing* current of the generator field. This secondary voltage, developed across R_1, provides the antihunt potential with the action previously demonstrated with Fig. 17.22. Antihunt circuits of the type illustrated by Fig. 17.23 have an advantage that several transformers such as TR_1 can be used to summarize several time delays that may be present throughout the regulating system. By carefully co-ordinating the design of each transformer with the characteristic of the machine in which the transformer primary winding is connected, the antihunting components can be made to stabilize the entire system.

WESTINGHOUSE TYPE-DT–5 D–C VOLTAGE REGULATOR

The Westinghouse type-DT–5 regulator, Fig. 17.24, typifies the method by which the voltage of a d-c generator is controlled electronically. The equipment consists of a direct-voltage-indicating circuit, antihunting circuit, a pliotron amplifier, and a three-phase thyratron grid-controlled rectifier for controlled excitation of the exciter field. A functional schematic diagram, Fig. 17.25, illustrates operation of the circuit. Some details of the actual circuit have been omitted to minimize undue complication of the diagram. The principal omissions, which can be seen in Fig. 17.24, are the

FIG. 17.24. An electronic voltage regulator for application to d-c generators. Test jacks and built-in instrument provide for circuit testing with the regulator in normal operation. (*Courtesy Westinghouse*)

use of two pliotron amplifier tubes and test jacks for periodic testing of the regulator without requiring additional equipment. If two pliotron amplifiers are used connected in parallel, the failure of one tube does not noticeably affect operation of the equipment. Likewise, when a three-phase thyratron rectifier is employed, failure of one tube does not impair operation if the equipment is temporarily continued in service with only two thyratrons operating.

Reference to Fig. 17.25, shows a direct voltage $m-n$ obtained across coupling resistors P_1 and R_2 opposed by reference potential $n-p$ and connected $m-k$ to pliotron amplifier T_4. Antihunt resistor R_3, capacitor C_2, and adjusting potentiometer P_2 operate as previously explained in connection with Fig. 17.22. Secondary winding, T_{S3} of the transformer energizes

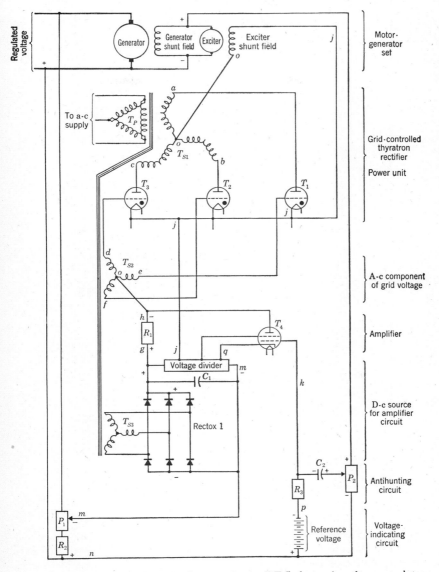

FIG. 17.25. Functional schematic diagram of type DT-5 electronic voltage regulator.

Rectox 1 to furnish the filtered source of d-c potential across the voltage divider. Resistor R_1 is the anode load resistor of amplifier T_4. In the normal operating condition, voltage $m–n$ is equally opposed by reference voltage $n–p$, virtually applying bias voltage $q–m$ to the grid terminal k of the amplifier. A nominal anode current flowing through R_1 develops a voltage

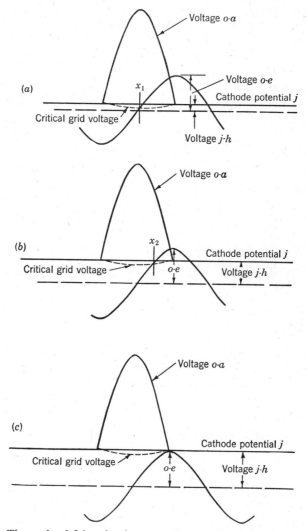

Fig. 17.26. The angle of firing the thyratrons is controlled by combining a constant a-c grid potential (*o-e*) with a variable d-c potential (*j-h*). When the d-c potential is small (*a*) the thyratron fires early. Conduction is delayed (*b*) or arrested (*c*) by a larger d-c component.

drop *g–h* across the anode resistor R_1. As the generator voltage drops below normal, voltage *m–n* decreases, and the grid voltage k of amplifier T_4 becomes more negative. This change reduces T_4 anode current. Voltage *g–h* across resistor R_1 is reduced. Likewise, a rise in generator voltage above normal increases voltage *g–h* across resistor R_1.

Secondary winding T_{S1} furnishes anode potential to thyratrons T_1, T_2, T_3, and the three-phase rectification produced by this circuit energizes the shunt field $o-j$ of the exciter.

Secondary winding T_{S2} furnishes an a-c component of grid voltage connected to thyratrons T_1, T_2, T_3. Note that, by the interconnection of secondary windings on successive transformer legs, the a-c component of grid voltage is made to lag the anode voltage by 90 degrees. For example,

FIG. 17.27. The voltage of a-c generators is regulated using a DT-5 regulator (top) with an a-c voltage-indicating unit (bottom). The a-c indicator shown is designed so as to be easily converted to either of the circuits typified by Fig. 17.19 or 17.20.

(Courtesy Westinghouse)

grid voltage $o-e$ applied to the grid of T_1 lags by 90 degrees, the anode voltage $o-a$ by correct proportion of windings on the three-phase transformer. In a similar manner, grid voltages $o-f$ or $o-d$ lags by 90 degrees the anode voltages $o-b$ and $o-c$.

If the cathode-to-grid circuit of any thyratron, as T_1, is traced, a d-c component of voltage $j-h$ is connected in series with an a-c component voltage $o-e$. The a-c component is constant in magnitude while the d-c component j–h varies, depending upon the voltage g–h across R_1, that is, the anode current of amplifier T_4. The grid control resulting from this variable d-c component of grid potential is best illustrated by the aid of Fig. 17.26. At (a) the a-c component o–e (for thyratron T_1) lags by 90 degrees the

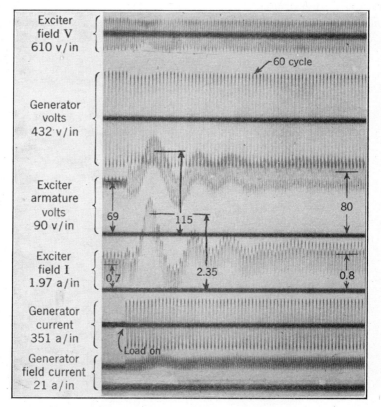

FIG. 17.28. (a) Performance of a voltage regulator of the type described showing the effects as load is suddenly applied. (*Courtesy Westinghouse*)

corresponding anode voltage o–a. The a-c component is displaced negatively below cathode potential j by an amount j–h corresponding to a relatively small voltage drop across R_1. Such a condition would result from a generator voltage below normal, making the grid of amplifier T_4 strongly negative, decreasing the anode current through it. The instantaneous grid potential, j–e (of thyratron T_1) crosses the critical grid voltage, causing the thyratron to fire at x_1 of its cycle. In a similar manner, thyratrons T_2 and T_3 are made to fire at this same relative point of their respective anode-voltage cycles. The three-phase thyratron rectifier thereby excites the generator field winding by maximum current denoted by firing point x_1

occurring relatively early throughout each thyratron conducting cycle. ¶

As the generator voltage rises, the T_4 grid potential becomes less negative, and the increasing anode current also increases voltage g–h to make h
more negative. This is illustrated by Fig. 17.26b, wherein potential j–h

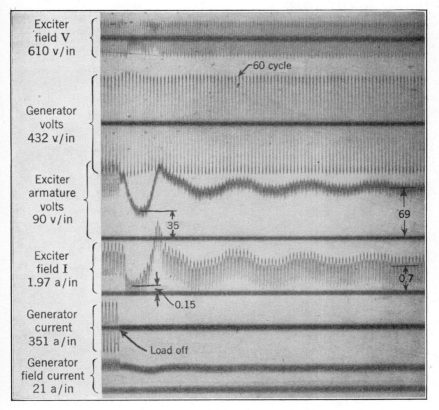

FIG. 17.28. (b) Same as (a) as generator load is removed.

(Courtesy Westinghouse)

displaces the a-c component of grid voltage further downward. Intersection
x_2 between the grid potential and critical grid voltage then occurs later in
the thyratron conducting cycle. Rectified current through the exciter field
winding is reduced to check the rising generator output voltage.

Should the generator potential rise considerably above its normal magnitude, the d-c component voltage j–h becomes large enough to displace the

¶Because of the large inductance common to generator shunt-field windings, conduction is delayed; in this instance it is assumed that 90 degree is the most forward firing
angle required for the inductive load.

a-c component downward far enough that grid potential does not intercept the critical grid voltage. This is shown in Fig. 17.26c. In this case, the thyratrons do not conduct, and the exciter field current becomes zero.

In this way, a small change in potential applied to grid terminal k of the amplifier tube is made to shift the firing angle of thyratrons T_1, T_2, T_3 so as to control effectively the magnitude of exciter field current. The value of voltage to which the electronic equipment regulates the generator output is adjusted by setting the slider of potentiometer, P_1. Hence, the voltage across the generator terminals required to develop a constant voltage m–n across the coupling resistors can be conveniently varied.

The type-DT–5 voltage regulator, previously described, although in itself designed for use with d-c generators, is readily adapted to the regulation of a-c machines by the use of an alternating-voltage-indicating unit, such as Fig. 17.27. This unit incorporates a rectifier and filter system and operates as described in connection with Fig. 17.19, page 466.

Operation of the regulator is illustrated by the oscillograms, Fig. 17.28. Approximately full load of the a-c generator is suddenly applied with the results shown by the first figure. Before the load is connected, the no-load exciter field current is 0.70 ampere and its armature voltage is 69 volts. As load is applied the generator a-c terminal voltage drops. The regulator immediately starts to increase the exciter field current, and within 6 cycles field current increases to 2.35 amperes, and exciter armature voltage rises to 115 volts. Although the alternating voltage is below normal, the antihunting action forces the exciter field current to be reduced. Further action of the antihunting influence is evident until the end of approximately 30 cycles when the excitation required for the new load condition reaches a steady state. The exciter field current rises to 0.80 ampere and its armature voltage to 80 volts.

As the generator load is suddenly removed, Fig. 17.28b, the exciter field current decreases very rapidly to 0.15 ampere. The antihunting action then forces the exciter field current to increase although the generator alternating voltage is above normal. Further antihunting action is evident in the figure. Although the alternating voltage is essentially restored to normal within 30 cycles, the steady-state conditions for the reduced load are not reached until the end of approximately 75 cycles.

ELECTRONIC SPEED REGULATORS

Electronic regulators for maintaining a constant operating speed have been applied to various types of machines. Some of the earliest were installed about 1930. The original equipments are operating successfully, and the experience gained by these installations has long since proved the adaptability of electronic equipment for reliable continuous service and extreme sensitivity. Many of these units are applied to single-motor variable-speed paper-machine drives, a service demanding absolute reliability for long-continued periods of operation. A typical installation, Fig. 17.29, shows the electronic regulator located at the right of the control panel. The motor–generator set for supplying d-c power to the motor driving the paper machine can be seen in the background although the motor itself is not included in the figure.

FIG. 17.29. A typical control for a paper-machine lineshaft drive using an electronic regulator, at right of panel, for constant-speed regulation of the driving motor.
(*Courtesy Westinghouse*)

The speed-regulating system, Fig. 17.30, employs a standard direct voltage regulator such as previously described in connection with a d-c tachometer generator coupled to the shaft of the machine whose speed is to be regulated.

The tachometer generator, sometimes called a pilot generator, is a special design of d-c machine with constant field excitation and characteristics such that the armature voltage is exactiy proportional to its speed of rotation. The tachometer-generator armature is connected to a direct-voltage regulator through coupling resistors R_1 and P_1. Operating speed is adjusted by P_1, and the equipment operates as previously described for the Westinghouse type-DT–5 regulator. The current controlled by the

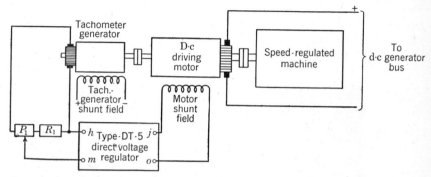

FIG. 17.30. Block diagram of a speed-regulating system. The tachometer generator converts motor speed to a proportional direct voltage. With this transition, the system operates as for direct voltage regulation.

regulator excites the shunt field of the motor driving the machine. In this way the operating speed of the motor is governed by the electronic regulator. Installations such as shown in Fig. 17.29 and diagrammed in Fig. 17.30 will maintain the motor speed constant within 0.5 percent except for momentary fluctuations occasioned by suddenly applied or removed motor loads.

ELECTRONIC TEMPERATURE REGULATION

Electronic equipment is well adapted to the accurate regulation of furnace temperature. The extreme sensitivity and stepless control afforded by electronic circuits contribute to the steadily increasing popularity of electronics as a means of executing precise regulation of operating temperature. Although the most usual application of such systems is toward the regulation of electric-furnace temperature, the principle is equally well adapted to any type of unit requiring the maintenance of constant temperature.

One method by which the temperature of an electrically heated furnace is regulated is by the Westinghouse Furnatron. A typical installation, Fig. 17.31, shows a four-section panel with pyrometers toward the top and electronic equipment near the bottom of each panel. Such an installation is applied to a single furnace having four separate heating zones or is used to control four furnaces independently.

A single-phase block diagram, Fig. 17.32a, shows a saturable reactor

FIG. 17.31. An electronic-furnace temperature-control panel for controlling four zones. The indicating instruments are (top) recording pyrometer, (center) control pushbuttons, and (bottom) electronic equipment. (*Courtesy Westinghouse*)

connected in series with the electrical-resistance heating element and the a-c supply. Furnace temperature is recorded by a standard pyrometer by using a thermocouple located as desired in the furnace zone. The pyrometer incorporates a motor-driven slide-wire potentiometer a–c whose contact arm b rests in the center position if the temperature exactly corresponds to the level to which the pyrometer is adjusted. Variance of the temperature above the desired level moves the potentiometer arm toward the top terminal a and conversely traverses the arm toward the bottom terminal c as the operating temperature drops below normal. An electronic regulating equipment responds to position of the potentiometer located within the pyrometer instrument and controls the direct current flowing through the saturating winding n–q of the saturable reactor. In this way, current through the resistance heating element is controlled, and temperature is closely regulated to any desired level.

A three-phase installation employs heating elements connected in wye, Fig. 17.32b, or the heaters can be connected in delta if preferred. Each phase requires a separate saturable reactor, although the d-c saturating coils are connected in series to a common electronic regulator. The similarity between the single-phase system, Fig. 17.32a, and the three-phase system, Fig. 17.32b is obvious. Hence, description of the equipment is confined to the more simple single-phase system.

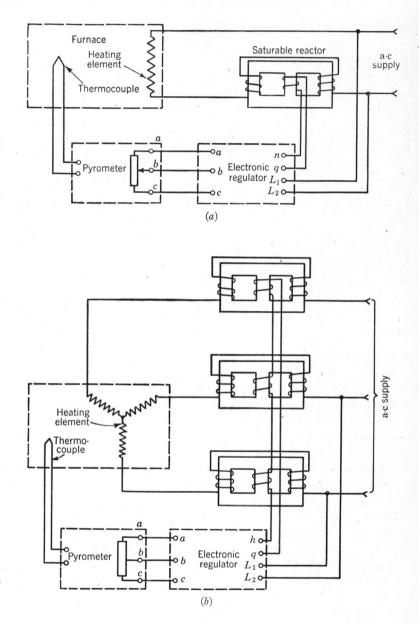

Fig. 17.32. Block diagram of a (*a*) single-phase resistance–furnace temperature-control system. (*b*) A three-phase system is similar with the d-c coils of the saturating reactors series connected to a single electronic regulator.

A functional schematic diagram, Fig. 17.33, shows potentiometer P_3, with its arm position b connected in a bridge circuit with potentiometers P_1 and P_2 and transformer secondary winding T_{S1}. A portion of the unbalanced bridge voltage $b-e$ is connected to the grid of T_1 through grid transformer TR_2. Triode T_1 functions as the automatic-amplifier-control tube in a manner described later. Coarse adjustment of the operating temperature is made, such that slider b is near its mid-position at the regulated temperature. A fine adjustment of temperature is then made by the manually adjusted potentiometer P_1. During normal operation, the bridge operates slightly unbalanced such that a negative (out-of-phase) component of voltage $b-d$ appears across the sensitivity adjustment potentiometer P_2. A portion of this voltage, $b-e$ is fed to the grid of triode T_1 through transformer TR_2. If the temperature rises above the regulated level, slider b moves toward terminal H, increasing the negative component of grid voltage to T_1, and reducing its anode current. A drop of furnace temperature moves slider b toward terminal L, which reduces the negative component of T_1 grid voltage, or, if the slider is moved sufficiently toward terminal L, the T_1 grid voltage is phase-shifted and becomes relatively positive. In this way T_1 anode current is reduced by excessive temperature or increased by a temperature below the regulated normal.

Current through the resistance heating element is controlled by the effective impedance of the a-c windings $r-s$ of the saturable reactor. When current through the d-c winding $n-q$ is zero, impedance of the saturable reactor is large, and current through the heating element is small. Sufficient current flowing through d-c winding $n-q$ decreases the reactor impedance, and current through the heating element becomes a maximum.

The direct current to excite winding $n-q$ is derived from thyratron T_4 and transformer secondary winding T_{S7} operating as a half-wave rectifier. The magnitude of the saturating direct current is varied by the firing angle of thyratron T_4, controlled by grid voltage $n-j$. Current flow of the half-wave rectifier circuit is made continuous by phanotron T_5 and resistor R_5 connected across the high inductance of d-c winding $n-q$.

The voltage $j-n$ connected to the grid of thyratron T_4 is the instantaneous sum of a constant a-c potential and variable d-c component. The constant a-c potential is phase-shifted by a circuit comprising transformer secondary winding T_{S4}, capacitor C_1, and resistor R_1 (see Chapter 15, page 367). The variable d-c component consists of the summation of voltage drops across resistors R_2, R_3, and R_4. For the present, the voltage across R_2 can be considered constant in magnitude and is neglected throughout the following description.

Kenotron T_2 is employed as a half-wave rectifier for the purpose of obtaining an adjustable voltage drop across its load resistor R_3, smoothed

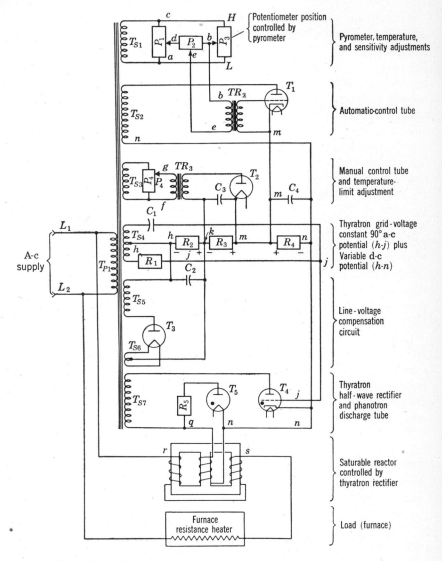

FIG. 17.33. Functional schematic diagram of temperature regulator.

to a reasonably ripple-free potential by capacitor C_3. The voltage across R_3 is adjusted by potentiometer P_4, which adjusts the anode voltage applied to T_2.

Voltage across R_4 depends upon the anode current of the automatic-control tube T_1, the function of which has been described previously.

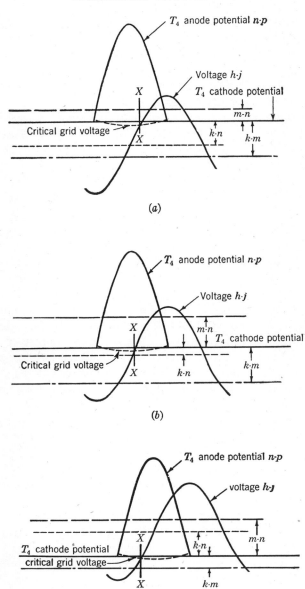

FIG. 17.34. Thyratron conduction is controlled by a constant alternating voltage (h–j) combined with a summation of two variable d-c potentials (k–m and m–n). These combine to a variable direct voltage (k–n) capable of shifting the firing point X–X from a late (a) firing angle to an early (c) angle.

With reference to Fig. 17.34a, the grid voltage to thyratron T_4 becomes the phase-shifted a-c potential h–j, which is displaced either above or below the cathode potential of thyratron T_4, depending upon the relative magnitude of voltage across resistors R_3 and R_4. Assume the operating conditions to be such that the current through T_2 causes voltage drop k–m across R_3. The polarity of this voltage is such that terminal k toward the grid of thyratron T_4, is negative and is, therefore, represented below the T_4 cathode potential in Fig. 17.34a. Voltage across R_4, resulting from anode current of T_1 is of opposite polarity, as m–n of the figure. The summation of these two voltages, k–n, displaces the a-c component h–j below the T_4 cathode potential. Intersection of the instantaneous grid voltage with the critical grid voltage of the thyratron occurs at X–X, firing the thyratron relatively late in the cycle. This represents a relatively small direct current through the reactor saturating winding, and the current flowing through the furnace heating element, is small. Should the furnace temperature drop below the regulated normal, current through T_1 increases to raise the voltage m–n across resistor R_4. Let Fig. 17.34b represent the maximum voltage that can be obtained across R_4 by the maximum current of automatic control tube T_1. Summing up the voltages across R_3 and R_4 changes the instantaneous grid voltage to the new position shown by the figure. Firing of the thyratron T_4 is advanced to the new intersection X–X with the critical grid voltage. Average current flow through the saturating winding is thereby increased, and current through the furnace heating element is increased to the maximum limits obtainable for that particular adjustment of the control.

If the temperature-limit adjustment P_4 is reduced by moving slider g toward f, voltage R_3 is decreased, Fig. 17.34c. If the same maximum current is used through the automatic-control tube T_1 as in the previous example, voltage across R_4 is now greater than the voltage across R_3, and the instantaneous thyratron grid voltage assumes the new position illustrated by the figure. Conduction of thyratron T_4 now advances to an earlier angle X–X, and current through the furnace heating element is now limited to a greater value than previously. In this way, potentiometer P_4 serves as a maximum temperature limit control.

Sensitivity of the automatic regulation is adjusted by potentiometer P_2, which determines that portion of the unbalanced bridge voltage b–d fed to the grid of tube T_1. If slider e is moved all the way to terminal b of P_2, the grid of T_1 receives no control from the pyrometer, and temperature of the furnace is then controlled only by the manual-adjustment potentiometer P_4, which then functions as a manual temperature-limit control.

The regulating circuit is adversely affected by a change in the a-c supply voltage unless some means is used to compensate for a variation of line voltage. Heating by the furnace resistance element is proportional to the square of the current through it. Current through the load circuit is increased or reduced more than directly proportional to a change in supply voltage, because, without compensation, direct current through the saturating winding of the reactor also varies in proportion to a change in line voltage. These two effects are cumulative, and together they would impair close regulation of temperature if allowed to function without compensation.

An effective method of compensating for a change in supply voltage employs a special type of kenotron T_3, together with anode-voltage winding T_{S5}, cathode-heater winding T_{S6}, and anode load resistor R_2. Kenotron rectifier T_3 is operated throughout its saturated region; that is, anode voltage T_{S5} is sufficient to draw all electrons emitted by the cathode to the anode. Anode current is then emission-limited, and anode current depends upon cathode temperature and not upon anode voltage. In this way, the anode current and, hence, the voltage across resistor R_2, manifests a large change in relation to a variation of supply voltage. The polarity of voltage across R_2 is such as to displace the a-c component of thyratron T_4 grid voltage below its cathode potential. The effect is the same as increasing voltage $k-m$ across R_3, as illustrated by Fig. 17.34. In this way, a rising supply voltage retards the firing angle of thyratron T_4 to reduce the average current through the saturating winding of the reactor. Effective impedance of the saturable reactor is increased by an amount sufficient to compensate for the rise in supply voltage. Should the line voltage drop below normal, compensation acts in the opposite manner to decrease the effective impedance of the saturable reactor.

The previous circuit description refers specifically to a single-phase system using one saturable reactor and furnace heating element. Operation for either wye- or delta-connected three-phase systems is the same as described except that the saturating winding of all reactors are connected in series as suggested by Fig. 17.32b. All reactors are simultaneously controlled by the thyratron rectifier within the electronic-control cabinet.

SUMMARY

Systems of control or regulation differ in these respects:

(*a*) When a system *controls*, the input to the control device is entirely independent of its output.

(*b*) When a system *regulates*, input and output of the regulating system are definitely related. Any increase or decrease of one affects the other.

Static regulators are characterized by their "dead-zone" action, because the regulator output does not change so long as the quantity being regulated remains within a narrow margin near the desired value.

Photoelectric register regulators used either for the longitudinal cutting of a web to a reference line on the web or for the exact alignment of colors printed by a multicolor press typify the application of static-type electronic regulators.

Two-direction register regulators afford correction of the position regulated either forward or backward as required to satisfy the desired register.

Single-direction register regulators afford correction of the position regulated by a corrective action in one direction only. This may be either to lengthen or to shorten the sheet cut by the machine, as indicated by the machine design.

A scanner, consisting of a light source (lamp and lens assembly), a phototube (with its light receiving lens), and usually one amplifier tube are used for photoelectric register applications.

Astatic regulators are characterized by their continually "vibrating" action. The quantity regulated is always slightly greater or less than the desired amount. There is no "dead zone" within which the regulator output remains static.

A slitter regulator, of the photoelectric astatic type, edge-controls a web position to affect the slitting line, holding this in register with a reference mark printed on the web.

Astatic electronic voltage regulators have three essential components:

    (*a*) A voltage-indicating circuit.

    (*b*) An amplifier or power circuit.

    (*c*) An antihunting circuit.

The purpose of the *voltage-indicating circuit* is to sense a change in the magnitude of the regulated voltage, interpret the *magnitude and direction* of this change, and convert this to a signal voltage applied to the regulator input.

The amplifier or power circuit amplifies the signal of the voltage-indicating circuit to the point where excitation of the generator (or its exciter) is direct by the electronic equipment.

The antihunting circuit derives a signal voltage which is connected to the regulator input in such a way that a *changing* signal of the voltage-indicating circuit gives to the regulator input a signal of *opposite* polarity, the *magnitude* of which is *proportional to the rate of change* (of the voltage-indicator signal).

Electronic speed regulators function according to the principles of voltage regulation. A tachometer generator, connected by a suitable drive to the machine being regulated, provides a voltage proportional to speed which is used to govern the voltage-regulating circuit.

Electronic regulation of temperature affords stepless control of heater current from minimum to maximum. The system combines a furnace pyrometer with electronic control of a saturable reactor to affect the current through a resistance-type heater.

REFERENCES

F. H. GULLIKSEN and E. H. VEDDER, *Industrial Electronics*, John Wiley & Sons, New York, 1935, pp 175–239.

C. R. HANNA, K. A. OPLINGER and C. E. VALENTINE, "Recent Developments in Generator Voltage Regulation," *AIEE Transactions*, Vol 58, 1939, pp 838–44.

C. R. HANNA, K. A. OPLINGER and S. J. MIKINA, "Recent Developments in Speed Regulation, *AIEE Transactions*, Vol 59, 1940, pp 692–700.

W. K. BOICE, S. B. CRARY, G. KRON and L. W. THOMPSON, "The Direct-Acting-Generator Voltage Regulator," *AIEE Transactions*, Vol 59, 1940, pp 149–57.

APPENDIX

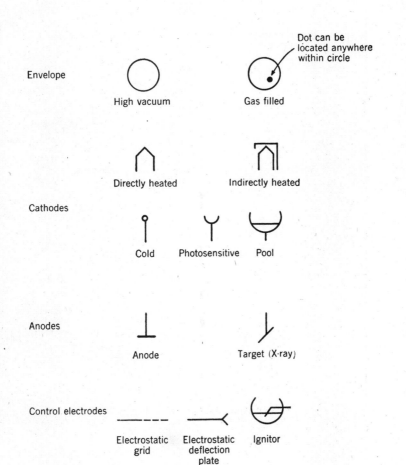

Envelope

High vacuum Gas filled

Dot can be located anywhere within circle

Cathodes

Directly heated Indirectly heated

Cold Photosensitive Pool

Anodes

Anode Target (X-ray)

Control electrodes

Electrostatic grid Electrostatic deflection plate Ignitor

Symbols for Tube Elements.

Kenotrons

Directly heated
cathode

Indirectly heated
cathode

Two elements in
single envelope

Pliotrons

Triode

Shield
grid

Control
grid

Tetrode

Suppressor
grid

Shield
grid

Control
grid

Pentode

Phototubes

Vacuum phototube

Multiplier phototube

Cathode ray

Electrostatic control

Magnetic coils
added as
required

Magnetic control

Symbols for High-Vaccum Tubes.

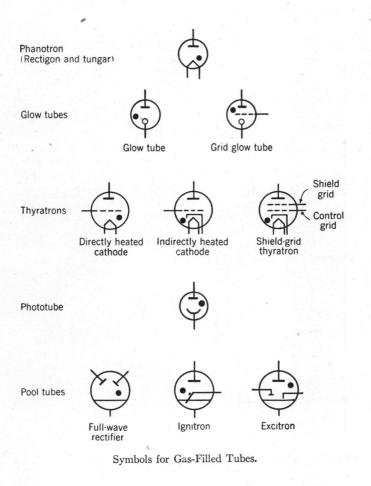

Symbols for Gas-Filled Tubes.

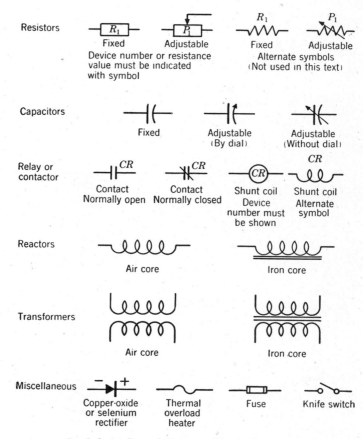

Symbols for Several Common Circuit Components.

E is the rms value of
an alternating voltage

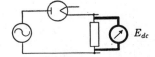

E_{dc} is the average value of a
rectifier load voltage

E_{bb} is the anode voltage
supply

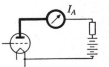

I_A is the average value of anode current
i_A is the instantaneous value
of a varying anode current
I_{A0} is the constant anode current when
the grid signal voltage is zero

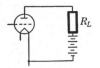

R_L is the tube load resistor

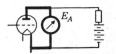

E_A is the constant or average anode voltage
e_A is the instantaneous value
of a varying anode voltage
E_{A0} is the constant anode voltage when
the grid signal voltage is zero

E_S is the screen voltage

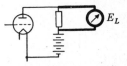

E_L is the constant or average voltage
drop across the load
e_L is the instantaneous value of
voltage drop across the load
E_{L0} is the constant voltage drop across the
load when the grid signal voltage is zero

Several Circuit Components and the Value Assigned to Anode Current
or Load Voltage.

E_{cc} is the grid bias
voltage supply

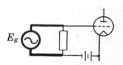

E_g is the rms value of the
grid signal voltage

R_g is the grid resistor

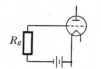

E_c is the average grid voltage
e_c is the instantaneous value
of a varying grid voltage
E_{c0} is the constant grid voltage
when the signal voltage is zero

C_g is the grid capacitor

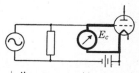

I_c is the average grid current
(positive toward the grid)
i_c is the instantaneous value of
a varying grid current
I_{c0} is the constant grid current when
the signal voltage is zero

R_K is the cathode resistor

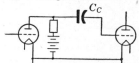

C_C is the coupling capacitor connecting
one stage of amplification to another

Several Circuit Components and the Value Assigned to Grid Voltage
or Current.

INDEX